MW00650554

Ginger,
I know your successful career has echoes throughout this book.
Happy Birthday!
Ravee

Being a Woman Surgeon
Sixty Women Share Their Stories

Best Wishes!
Preeti R. John

Notable Gordian Knot Books

Reflections on Medicine: Essays by Robert U. Massey, MD,
edited by Martin Duke, MD

Doctor, Why Does My Face Still Ache? Getting Relief from Persistent
Jaw, Ear, Tooth, and Headache Pain,
by Donald R. Tanenbaum, DDS, and S. L. Roistacher, DDS

Contemplative Aging: A Way of Being in Later Life,
by Edmund Sherman, PhD

Where Are We Going? by Miriam Finder Tasini, MD

Identifying and Recovering from Psychological Trauma: A Psychiatrist's
Guide for Victims of Childhood Abuse, Spousal Battery, and Political
Terrorism, by Brian Trappler, MD

Watching Walter Cronkite: Reflections on Growing Up in the 1950s and
1960s, by Austin Ken Kutscher, MD

It's Good to Know a Miracle: Dani's Story: One Family's Struggle with
Leukemia, by Jay Shotel, PhD, and Sue Shotel

Putting Universal Human Rights to Work: Policy Actions in the Struggle
for Social Justice, by Archibald Stuart, PhD

Seminal Sociological Writings: From Auguste Comte to Max Weber: An
Anthology of Groundbreaking Works that Created the Science of
Sociology, edited by Richard Altschuler, PhD

Seminal Sociological Writings, Volume. 2: From Harriet Martineau to
W. E. B. Du Bois: An Anthology of Groundbreaking Works that
Created the Science of Sociology, edited by Richard Altschuler, PhD

Women, Marriage, and Wealth: The Impact of Marital Status on the
Economic Well-Being of Women through the Life Course,
by Joyce A. Joyce, PhD

Dancing on the Tails of the Bell Curve: Readings on the Joy and Power
of Statistics, edited by Richard Altschuler, PhD

Being a Woman Surgeon
Sixty Women Share Their Stories

Edited by
Dr. Preeti R. John

Gordian Knot Books

An Imprint of Richard Altschuler & Associates, Inc.

Los Angeles
Distributed by Ingram

Being a Woman Surgeon: Sixty Women Share Their Stories. Copyright © 2015 by Preeti R. John. For information or special orders contact the publisher, Gordian Knot Books, at 10390 Wilshire Boulevard, Suite 414, Los Angeles, CA 90024, (424) 279-9118, or send an email to Richard.Altschuler@gmail.com.

Library of Congress Control Number: 2015931888
CIP data for this book are available from the Library of Congress

ISBN-13: 978-1-884092-63-3

Gordian Knot Books is an imprint of
Richard Altschuler & Associates, Inc.

Cover Design: Josh Garfield

Front Cover Group Photograph: Jordan Denner

Back Cover Editor Photograph: Tom Jemski

Printed in the United States of America

Distributed by Ingram

DEDICATION

To women and children around the world who do not have access to education . . . and to my parents, who provided for my education.

CONTENTS

"Medicine is so broad a field, so closely interwoven with general interests, dealing as it does with all ages, sexes and classes, and yet of so personal a character, in its individual appreciations, that it must be regarded as one of those great departments of work in which the co-operation of men and women is needed to fulfill all its requirements." — Elizabeth Blackwell, the first openly identified woman to receive a medical degree in the United States.

EDITOR'S INTRODUCTION

About the Book

Being a Woman Surgeon is a compilation of essays, poems and interviews that captures the essence of being a woman in a demanding medical field. It is the first anthology of its kind, which consists of contributions by a multidisciplinary group of female surgeons. Surgery blends science, art and craft, and these narratives of determination, enchantment, frustration and fulfillment offer a vivid portrayal of the culture of surgery from a woman's perspective.

About the Authors

We are a group of women surgeons living in the United States and Canada, who, despite differences in age, background, personal lives and race, have some things in common—we have persevered to become trained in this demanding profession and are passionate about what we do: making a difference in other people's lives.

The following are among the trailblazers who have contributed to this anthology: the first woman president of the American College of Surgeons (ACS); the first woman to head an academic Department of Surgery in Canada; the first woman to head the Department of Surgery at The Johns Hopkins Hospital in Baltimore, and the first to do so at Walter Reed Army Medical Center in Washington, D. C.; the founder of the Association of Women Surgeons and second president of the ACS; and a former Ship's Surgeon on board the United States Navy-commissioned aircraft carrier "USS Carl Vinson." These and other remarkable contributors have provided candid accounts of their lives and experiences.

The ages of the contributing authors range from the twenties to the seventies. Some are general surgery residents, others are fellows undergoing specialized surgical training. The majority of the authors are fully-trained surgeons in the following specialties: General Surgery; Trauma/Critical Care; Surgical Oncology; Urology; Neurosurgery; Vascular; Transplant; Breast; Colon and Rectal; Minimally Invasive; Hepato-biliary and Pancreatic; Obstetrics and Gynecology; Orthopedic; Cardio-thoracic; Pediatric; Plastic and Reconstructive Surgery and Otorhinolaryngology.

Sadly, the work of one author is published posthumously: Kimberly Ephgrave passed away a short time after submitting her essay.

What Inspired This Book

Professional women in fields where they have traditionally been under-represented have unique career paths: They must overcome challenges, defy stereotypes and find a way to balance the competing demands of work and personal life. I compiled this collection to document the powerful variety of experiences encountered by women surgeons.

My own exposure to surgical training stimulated thoughts about the challenges of working in this field. Like my colleagues, I was motivated, had a sense of purpose and found most experiences exhilarating. However, there were occasions when I felt disheartened and disillusioned. Had I known that others shared these instances of self-questioning, they would have been easier for me to endure.

Surgical residency training programs have no personal support system that I am aware of. Having traveled here for the first time from another continent soon after completing medical training, and being somewhat of an introvert, I turned to books for solace during difficult times. I hoped to read about others who had undergone similar experiences. As one of the contributors in this anthology points out, when you are at your most vulnerable, it is comforting to share stories with people you have something in common with—in my case, women. When I searched for books describing surgical residency training, I found only a handful authored by women. Most books were by women who trained in an earlier era, when female trainees were a minority and gender discrimination was rampant and customary. What I read was far from inspiring.

After completing residency and fellowship training, my need for camaraderie with other women who had undergone similar experiences in the world of surgery persisted. I wanted to create a source of inspiration and guidance that would help others face tough decisions and guide them through difficult periods of self-doubt (*"Why on earth did I sign up for this?!"*) and frustration. I was further motivated by questions from medical students contemplating a career in surgery. I kept reading accounts of women in other fields, such as business, finance, politics and journalism, who were overcoming challenges and succeeding in their careers, and wanted to add to this rich conversation by sharing our stories as women surgeons.

As an attending surgeon, my urge to compile an anthology increased. I reached out to a virtual stranger in the mid-west, Dr. Carol Scott-Conner, whose surgical text-books I had read during training, and was encouraged by the fact that she did not disparage the idea. She agreed that there was a need for such a book, submitted an essay (my first contribution) and promised to support me in my endeavors. I then proceeded to reach out to other women in surgery. Several contributors responded to on-line announcements on surgical websites. I also contacted people by e-mail, requested contributions in the form of essays, poems or written interviews, and gave each contributor the option of submitting an inspiring quote by a female. Most women I contacted graciously responded to my persistent requests. This anthology was eventually compiled over a period of two years.

My Goal

I am honored that fifty-nine women have graciously shared their stories, opinions, and memories with me. I wish to share these narratives with the general public and hope to provide a source of inspiration for young physicians. As is evident in many of these essays, training in surgical specialties is challenging regardless of one's gender. In addition to physical stamina, it requires strength of character, balance, careful planning and a firm commitment to what is important. I hope that medical students across the globe, and anyone contemplating a career in medicine, will be encouraged and enthused by reading this book.

Overt discrimination is no longer tolerated in this field. Opinions vary as to whether unconscious biases and more subtle forms of gender discrimination persist. It is my hope that this anthology will represent a tool for dialogue and insight for those who study social behavior, for those not in the medical field and for women interested in embarking upon careers where they have traditionally been under-represented.

Women have been performing surgical procedures for thousands of years. This book is a celebration of the role that women have played in the field of Surgery. It is also a testimonial to the many remarkable men and women who have paved the way and helped us achieve our goals.

Preeti R. John,
Baltimore, Maryland.

FOREWORD

The Practice of Surgery is All-Consuming

This is a fascinating set of stories by a remarkable group of women. All survived a daunting set of obstacles to realize their dream. Almost all endured the rigors of surgical training; a few are still facing these trials. These women share a number of characteristics. Most important, perhaps, is a passion for surgery, a passion that carried them through the challenges of training and the demands of a profession that pays little attention to clock or calendar: No matter what the time of day, day of the week, holiday, or family celebration, the surgeon on call comes in and operates. And no matter how long a procedure takes, with nurses replaced when their shift is over, a surgeon keeps going until the patient is closed. This takes both physical and emotional strength. As one contributor observes, "Being strong is one of the most important qualities for a career in surgery. You need to be physically strong and have a strong ego and a strong work ethic, just to keep going and show up every day without fail, even if the patient is not doing well, even if you don't feel well, if you made a mistake, if you don't get the promotion you want." This strength is illustrated in these stories.

We encounter the women in their ninth month of pregnancy who managed to get close enough to the table to operate; the woman who operated with the flu while the nurses started an IV to hydrate her; and the woman who took a shorter period of time to return to work after the birth of each child—three weeks for the first, two weeks for the second, less than a week for the third and a few days for the fourth! A woman surgeon must not only be strong, but tough. Not in the negative sense of being "overly aggressive, brutal or rough," but "strong but pliant . . . will bend, twist . . . without tearing or breaking."[1] The surgeon who held a bake sale outside the office of the dean who refused to pay for pelvic teaching models exemplifies this ability to bend without breaking, as does the woman who waded through months of overwhelming red tape to make sure that Hawaii had a transplant program. As one contributor notes: "The practice of surgery is all-consuming, it becomes your identity."

Many of these surgeons were trained before the eighty-hour workweek was instituted (if not always obeyed) and overt sexism was proscribed (if not always avoided). There are fewer horror stories today. No residency programs announce "Women may not apply," no lawyers must be consulted to enable a woman to complete a training program, no attending surgeons are permitted to stand outside the OR screaming "Anybody but the girl! Anybody but the girl! Give me a trained monkey—I'd rather have anybody but the girl!"[ii]

Nevertheless, even today, surgical training is difficult for women. Some of these difficulties are mentioned by the contributors. Surgical training is grueling and residency and fellowships occur during a woman's peak childbearing years. A woman must decide whether and when to become pregnant. She must weigh, as one contributor notes, the effect of the pregnancy on the residency and the effect of the residency on the pregnancy. Some programs and chiefs are sympathetic; others feel pregnancy itself indicates an unacceptable sign of weakness. Contributors chose various solutions. One woman managed to have a full-time career and six children! A few had four. A number decided to remain childless, and one woman relates a heartbreaking story, shared by colleagues in her demanding sub-specialty, of numerous unsuccessful attempts to become pregnant once she felt professionally ready to do so.

Nurses play, perhaps, a more crucial role in surgery than other medical specialties, and they can be helpful or obstructive. As these stories indicate, some women seem instinctively to know how to mobilize their support. Others, however, have found nurses antagonistic and challenging. Some nurses apply a double standard: Behavior that is tolerated from a male surgeon is deemed unacceptable from a female. A woman must learn to lead and command in a way that does not alienate nurses and junior residents. This can generate a double bind: "You're either a bitch or a patsy," declared one woman I studied, discussing her behavior in the OR— and others agreed. A senior woman confided to me that as she climbed the career ladder, the rank of the nurses who undercut her rose correspondingly; and when she reached the top, it was the Director of Nurses who gave her a hard time.[ii]

Other obstacles are influenced not by gender *per se* but by what sociologist Rosabeth Moss Kanter calls "structural factors."[iii] Analyzing corporate leadership, Kanter shows how the possession of power (defined as the ability to get things done[iv]) or, alternatively, its lack, affects behavior.[v] Leaders in positions with accountability but little power tend to be rigid, controlling, overly rules-minded and territorial: characteristics frequently attributed to women. She examines the behavior of "tokens," noting that "If one sees nine Xs and one O, the O will stand out:

X X x x X X O X x X

This high visibility generates a set of pressures for the 'token.'"[vi] Appearance is noted and commented on, with technical abilities eclipsed by physical appearance. Kanter observes, "The token does not have to work hard to have her presence noticed, but she does have to work hard to have her achievements noticed."[vii]

One way organizations deal with a small number of women is to create a "woman's slot." This position frequently has less prestige and opportunity for advancement. Think of the acting head of the breast service at a celebrated university hospital who, when she demanded a salary equal to that of men with similar training, was told "But it's just titty surgery!"[ii]

Token women may be constrained by a set of informal stereotyped roles: *mother*, *seductress*, *pet*, and *iron maiden*, while structural circumstances and pressures from the majority may cause *two* tokens to compete rather than join forces.[viii] Kanter concludes that "People's treatment . . . is not automatically fixed by inflexible characteristics but depends on their numbers in a particular situation."[ix] In other words, when there are sufficient Os, the game changes.

More women are entering surgery, which means that there are fewer situations where they feel the pressures experienced by tokens. Nevertheless, the problems have not disappeared.[x] Since the publication of my book on women surgeons,[xiii] several women have contacted me describing either why, after years of struggle, a woman is leaving surgery or why members of a particular sub-specialty are finding their academic positions painfully inhospitable to women. In each case, it would seem that the women have found themselves in token situations: in a practice group, where the men allocate the cushy schedules and interesting patients to their male colleagues, or in a subspecialty with so few women that each woman is an O among Xs in her department.

In addition, I wonder whether the current sovereignty of "evidence-based medicine" does not reflect a kind of dualism with an implicit masculine bias. In evidence-based medicine, the results of scientific, large, prospective, randomized, double-blind clinical trials are opposed to unscientific, anecdotal, intuition-based and emotion-permeated treatment. We have here a set of oppositions: hard versus soft, scientific versus touchy-feely, rational versus emotional. The oppositions, based on the Logical Positivist distinction between facts and values[xi] are presented as mutually exclusive: not facts *and* values but facts *or* values, rational *or* emotional. These oppositions emerge in medicine, science, and social science, with more prestige always allotted to the first term. Surgery is hard, psychiatry is soft.[xii] It's a small step to map these dualisms onto gender: men are hard, women are soft. Naturally, women can and do practice evidence-based medicine and conduct "hard" science. The dualism, however, has not disappeared, it has just gone underground[xiii]. The "soft" emotions are still attributed to women, who are expected—by others and often by themselves—to be caring, compassionate, empathetic.

Why are there so few women in top positions in surgery? "Intrinsic aptitude," the Larry Sommers of the world might contend—even if they've learned to keep these attitudes under wraps.[xiii] Many of the contributors to this volume are familiar with the ferocious opposition generated by the appointment of a woman to a top position in surgery; some may well have experienced this in person.

Despite advances, then, the playing field for women in surgery is still not level. A few years ago, I heard a senior man direct a barbed compliment at one of the contributors to this volume; he smilingly described this beautiful, talented, successful woman as "a piece of work." An ambitious, forceful woman is "a piece of work," whereas an ambitious, forceful man is "a formidable surgeon." Perhaps we will know that women have made it in surgery when a woman no longer has to be remarkable to succeed: being intelligent, talented, hard-working and passionate about surgery will be sufficient.

-**Joan Cassell**, Ph.D. Anthropologist, author of *The Woman in the Surgeon's Body*, *Life and Death in Intensive Care* and *Expected Miracles— Surgeons at Work*.

References:

[i] Webster's New Twentieth Century Dictionary of the English Language, p. 1929.

[ii] The Woman in the Surgeon's Body, Cambridge MA, Harvard University Press, 1998 (Cassell)

[iii] *Men and Women of the Corporation*, New York, Basic Books, Inc. 1977 (Kanter)

[iv] The complete definition of 'power' is: "the ability to get things done; to mobilize resources, to get and use whatever it is that a person needs for the goals he or she is attempting to meet (Kanter p. 166)

[v] Kanter studied a corporation but her findings apply to a large number of organizations including hospitals and medical schools.

vi Although Kanter analyzes this in terms of women, the token can be any O in a field of Xs: a blind person, a member of a minority, or although she doesn't mention it, an overtly gay person.

vii Kanter p. 216

viii Kanter pp. 238-240

ix Kanter p. 241

x Allocation of office space (who gets the big corner office and who is assigned to the closet-sized cubicle) is a visible sign of who has prestige and power, as is delegation of on-call duties during holidays. Salary inequality is less public but just as painful. A woman who suffers any or all of these insults knows she's valued less highly than her male colleagues. Rationalizations, such as "You don't have children, so the holidays are not as important to you" or "Your husband earns a good living, so you don't need as much money as a man who has to support a family" are unconvincing.

xi The Logical Positivists, in the first half of the 20th century, used a strict principle of *verifiability* to reject as meaningless the non-empirical statements of metaphysics, theology, and ethics. Philosopher Rudolph Carnap went so far as to label all statements to do with metaphysics, ethics, and epistemology "nonsense" since they are unverifiable and hence "logically invalid." (*Logische Syntax der Sprache*, 1934 English translation, *The Logical Syntax of Language*. Kegan Paul, 1937.) Although few philosophers today adhere to this distinction between facts and values, positivist thinking lingers in medicine, the sciences and social sciences.

xii In an attempt to be "harder" many psychiatrists have disavowed psychoanalysis, shifting to the administration of drugs (*Of Two Minds: The Growing Disorder in American Psychiatry*, T.M. Luhrman, Alfred A. Knopf, 2000.)

xiii Today, it may be politically incorrect to voice them, witness the uproar when in 2005, Laurence Summers, then President of Harvard, suggested that one reason there are relatively few women in top positions in science and engineering may be issues of intrinsic aptitude at the high end. The fact that voicing this view publicly is frowned upon does not mean that the conviction that science is "hard" and women are "soft" has vanished.

SECTION 1—SPECIALTY SURGEONS AND THEIR STORIES

Sarah N. Cross, MD
Obstetrician-Gynecologist

In Birth and In Death

My sixth-grade teacher had us make "time capsules" on parent-teacher day. With my mother's help, I sealed up a shoebox that I faithfully stored until graduation from high school. One of its contents was a questionnaire which included the question "When I grow up I want to be . . ." In my twelve-year-old handwriting, I had written "physician." Using a combination of memory and imagination, my motivations at that time mostly stemmed from my family. The physicians in my family were scientists, healers and international travelers. And importantly, they were women. My grandmother's grandmother graduated from the Women's Medical College of Pennsylvania in the late 1800s.

Of course life happens—and the motivations I brought with me when I actually applied to medical school and those that I think of every day have evolved. And despite my early desire to become a physician, it took me a little bit of time to get to medical school. The summer I graduated from college, my mother died suddenly from sepsis, after what was thought to have been a viral upper-respiratory illness. She spent five days in the intensive care unit on maximum support surrounded by her family, which included three physicians. At the age of twenty-one, I was alone with her when she died, each machine sounding off her increasingly abnormal vital signs, until all that remained was the din of what had been. In that moment I understood that medicine is a human endeavor besieged with the limitations of humanity. There was no error in her care, and despite the truest efforts of the intensivists at this academic medical center, my healthy, relatively young mother could not be saved. The doctors taking care of my mother, in addition to being scientists and healers, were human beings. They had come up against the limitations of their science and, when my mother died, they cried.

I entered medical school at the age of twenty-four—twice as old as I'd been when I first made my intention so clear. It had taken me four years to imagine being able to learn in a hospital, to possibly work in an intensive care unit. In addition to all the things I'd wanted before and everything I had learned about medicine through my mother's death, I knew I wanted to make my mother proud. I wanted to do work that was worthy of her, and I wanted to be as good a doctor as she had been a judge (my mother was a New York City Supreme Court Judge at the time of her death). She approached her job with an intellectual ferociousness. When I asked her how she could work in a system that seemed so flawed, her response was, "The only way to make something better is to get inside of it." She created, in NYC, one of the first specialized courts to hear domestic violence cases. I thought perhaps medicine was not so different from law, perhaps there was something I could try to make better.

Having been a psychology graduate in college, I had fully intended to pursue psychiatry. In my third year of medical school, I started out with psychiatry, which was then eclipsed by my obstetrics and gynecology rotation. When I set foot inside the operating room, I knew I had to be there. It was bright, mysterious and magical. After recovering from a vaso-vagal episode during my first cesarean—the metallic smell of all that blood—I fell in love. Surgeons were purposeful explorers of the body, physical healers of the sick. Working with the obstetric-gynecologic surgeons in medical school was like helping an elite athlete play a technically difficult game. It was beautiful.

I remember my first glimpses into the pale, pink cavern of the pelvis on laparoscopy, the first time I held an ovary in my hand and felt the thick placenta inside the uterus. The task of learning surgery and becoming worthy of operating on another human being was awe-inspiring to me. In medical school, I considered pretty much every specialty, but obstetrics-gynecology became an ever increasingly clear choice; I saw myself as a physician for women, and the field offered to me its incredible breadth of primary care, preventative medicine, radiology, surgery and science. I was yet another physician in my family, but the first surgeon and the first physician for women.

What also drew me to obstetrics-gynecology and then to further specialize in perinatology (also known as maternal-fetal medicine, or "high risk" obstetrics) is its rich history, its unique meeting of medicine with the natural. I found myself asking questions that many others have asked: How did birth become so "medicalized?" Are we doing the right thing? How do you know how much intervention is necessary to keep women and their babies safe? How much is too much? What is the difference in outcome

4

now compared to when women labored at home with midwives or were unattended at the time of birth? What progress have we made? And what are the consequences of this progress? This was, perhaps, the thing I could help make better. And it does not escape me that I chose the only field in medicine where all my patients are mothers.

The surgery I perform most often is a cesarean delivery—the most common surgery performed in the United States. With our cesarean delivery rate around 30 percent,[1] many women will end up birthing in the operating room. And certainly the availability of the operating room means fewer obstetric fistulas and stillbirths from obstructed labor, and fewer women dying of conditions such as placenta previa. But the staggering number of cesareans performed in our country and the rising rate of certain associated complications, such as placenta accreta, has many of us asking: How many is too many?

This is an important and difficult question to answer on a population level and on an individual level. It is a focus of research for me and something I think about and discuss every day at work. These questions are magnified in my field. I deliver the smallest babies, take care of the sickest mothers. The cesarean delivery rate in my patient population is even higher than the national average, due to a multitude of maternal, fetal and pregnancy complications. But even in my "high risk" patients I am always asking whether an intervention is necessary, whether I am unnecessarily "medicalizing" something that is natural and safe.

When I have decided that a cesarean is advisable, my next step is a conversation with my patient. I have to make sure she understands my reasoning, my recommendations as well as the risks. What is hard to explain about cesarean is that there are more than just the immediate risks of the surgery. People don't get appendicitis again but they do get pregnant again, and my recommendation to perform a cesarean in a given situation in a given pregnancy will have ramifications for future pregnancies, even if the woman does not have a future cesarean. Asking women to consider the future when I am making recommendations about the present is an insurmountable task. I take this conversation regarding cesarean very seriously. It is my job to make a recommendation based on my medical expertise, but I also handle a range of emotions, including disappointment, relief, guilt and fear.

In the operating room (or the delivery room, for that matter) it is hard for me to imagine my life having any other purpose. I am honored to be witness to birth, this universal truth, over and over. I am buoyed by humanity. I sometimes think of my mother—how we have already been together in birth and in death. I remember what she taught me: that the only way to improve a system is to become a part of it. I often think of my patients and their babies and how to keep them safe in birth, when to intervene, when to let nature take its course and how to figure out how to continue to make our practice of obstetrics better.

[1] www.cdc.gov/nchs/fastats/delivery.htm

Inspiring Quote:
"The only way to make something better is to get inside of it."
— Margaret Lee Cross

Barbara E. Lazio, MD, FAANS
Neurosurgeon

"My Mom Touches Brains All Day"

Part of being a good parent is paying attention to the latest dogma about the diet, technology, and discipline that will generate a brilliant, talented, and well-adjusted child. This includes telling my daughters that too much TV will rot their brains. I should know, because, as one of them wrote in the First Grade Mother's Day Anthology, "My mom touches brains all day at work."

So it came as a big surprise to my girls that one eureka moment in my decision to become a neurosurgeon came while watching a made-for-TV movie starring an ex-Charlie's Angel. I had mentioned in third grade that I wanted to be a neurosurgeon, but had been met with kind suggestions that I should consider a more appropriate career such as scrub nurse. Imagine how awesome it was when I saw this (fictional) woman on TV who was not only a neurosurgeon but also a widowed mother of a six-year-old girl. What was more, her mentor was a crusty, seasoned, older neurosurgeon who was also a woman! She told her daughter, "Neurosurgery is what makes me tick." It is amazing and somewhat embarrassing to me that I cannot remember the names of the teachers I had in school that year, but remember that dialogue in a long forgotten movie. However, this was the first time it was suggested to me that this was a career path that was available to someone like me.

I abandoned the thought again for several years, but my attraction to biological science and medicine kept resurfacing. When I did my neurosurgery month in the third year of medical school, I was thinking this was my last opportunity to see brain surgery. After that, I never looked back. I found myself more exhausted on the so-called less rigorous rotations in medical school, like pediatrics and psychiatry, because they did not hold my interest. I would escape to the neurosurgery operating room after psychiatry rounds or pediatric afternoon checkout and watch the team clip an aneurysm or remove a tumor in the depths of one's soul. Ultimately, I decided that whatever specialty I chose in medicine, I was going to work hard. It would be more exhausting to work fewer hours doing something that bored me than to work long hours doing something that "made me tick." The operating room was, and has since been, my home base, my comfort zone, my happy place.

Fast-forwarding to real-life, since residency I have realized some unique challenges in doing this job with two X chromosomes. The first is the inconvenient clash in timing of the completion of residency with the "advanced maternal age" for having a family. During residency I was too busy and was not sure I even wanted to have kids. My husband and I had a good rhythm—working, advancing our careers, and having a social life every other day when I was not on call. It became evident, however, that all around us our friends were growing up, buying houses, and having families, while we were in this prolonged state of adolescence.

Feeling some self-imposed pressure to get the show on road, we got a puppy and built a house. I had two babies and a miscarriage in eighteen months. I dutifully carried the breast pump and accouterments around the hospital between cases, so as not to be caught giving my child formula by the breast-feeding extremists. I was hungry, skinny and exhausted! I had clearly not paid enough attention to what my siblings and friends were doing raising their kids while I was in training. I had no idea what to do with these little creatures. My coffee table was littered with baby user-guides and continuing medical education materials. Unfortunately, my eyelids did not always cooperate with my nighttime reading ambitions.

My desk at work accumulated piles of half-done projects: case reports, board review materials, Institutional Review Board applications for studies I wanted to do. My desk at home had an equally intimidating pile of to-dos. When I went to national neurosurgery meetings, I saw that some of my contemporaries were now moderating sessions, doing platform presentations, teaching courses. I would feel a little guilty that I was not more driven to pursue these things. Some of them were women, too. At the end of the day, though, whom was I trying to impress? My colleagues? The neurosurgery societies?

The second unique challenge has been gracefully dealing with the lack of respect or understanding shown to me as an attending neurosurgeon. It comes from all directions. There was the patient of my junior colleague who thought I was his nurse after I had introduced myself, examined her, and went over all her discharge information. There was the office manager who assumed I was working part time. There was the neurosurgeon from another group who would only address my male colleagues with questions. There are the people who meet my husband and me at functions and ask if he is the neurosurgeon. "Yes, I am the one who does the surgery." "Yes, that was the doctor who just talked to you for thirty minutes." "Thank you for thinking I look too young or small to be a neurosurgeon, but I have been doing this for quite a while now!"

On the flip side, there is an ever-growing group of patients who love lady doctors! And why not? We can often relate to female patients or the male patients' significant others, who often influence their decisions. There are also many more primary providers who are also women and find it easy to work with us.

I always enjoyed endurance sports like cross-country running, skiing, and cycling. There is always a painful first two miles or so no matter what shape I am in, then I will hit my stride and can go forever. Over a decade into this career, I think I have finally hit my stride. The painful two miles of residency and early motherhood have passed. I have switched gears to impress the most important persons: my family, my patients, myself. I moved from a job at a tertiary center, with busy call and high acuity patients, to one that is perhaps a bit less exciting, but has lowered the stress in our collective family life significantly.

One thing that spending more time with my kids has done is give me a great appreciation for stay-at-home parents! It is hard work to raise girls. My girls are fabulous, spirited creatures who love sports and dirt and crafts and movies. They wrestle and argue and challenge. They are surprising and unpredictable. They rarely get tired and, like most kids, have not much sympathy for a tired parent. Their names are "Yeah-but" and "But-I." Not really, but at least they understand sarcasm.

Keeping track of homework, sports schedules and music practice while making sure there is a minimum of brain-rotting influence around is a monumental task without two full time jobs. Sometimes by the end of a weekend my husband and I get a TGIM (Thank God It's Monday) feeling. At least at work I feel in control!

Where I can, I have cleared away the clutter of things that generate stress. I found that an academic career path just did not work for my family and me. We never lived close enough to extended family to get consistent kid help. My husband has done double duty, working full time as a software engineer and taking on a lot of the home tasks. He does sometimes complain that he needs some sports time after braiding hair and helping with earrings. To hold up my end, I say no to committees and meetings sometimes. I make time to go to as many of my kids' school performances and sporting events as I can. I feel lucky that at this stage in my life I have some control over my schedule.

And best of all, I get to touch brains all day at work!

Inspiring Quote:
"Stand for something or you will fall for anything. Today's mighty oak is yesterday's nut that held its ground." — Rosa Parks

Imani Rosario Jackson, MD
Urologist

A Certain Type of Woman

There is a certain type of woman who becomes a surgeon. And this particular breed of woman is simply not your average woman.

Like all doctors, we are fascinated by biology and all of the natural sciences. We excelled as kids in math, physics, and chemistry. We were over-achievers at best and nerds or social misfits at worst. We spent high-school weekends reading entire books in one sitting. During summers we took college prep courses. We went to science camp.

We were all future doctors. We were pretty much the same. Until we first stepped into the operating room as third year medical students. At that very moment, the surgeons are separated from what (in my arrogant surgeon speak) I call the "non-surgeon" students.

For the future surgeon, scrubbing into that first surgery is a rush like no other. There is a tension in the air as the patient is prepped and the instruments are counted that makes you stand up straighter. When you stand at the sink scrubbing with the resident and almighty attending surgeon, you feel like you are being initiated into some super exclusive, super important club. And you are so lucky for it. The ritual of standing before the scrub nurse as she dresses you in the sterile gown and covers your hands in the sterile gloves, with a second nurse standing behind you tying the gown closed, feels like a baptism of sorts. To this day, I find scrubbing in and gowning extremely relaxing, almost like a meditation, prior to starting a complicated case.

And then there is the first cut. The vast majority of normal human beings find the sight of a sharp instrument cutting into human flesh extremely unnerving. But for the surgeon, it is a thrill: the first step in the process of improving a life, relieving pain, curing cancer. At this moment, for a certain type of woman, everything will shift. She finds that she is holding her breath. The world outside that operating room will cease to exist. And she knows she is a surgeon.

I've heard many other doctors say that they didn't choose their specialty. Instead, their specialty chose them. Surgery is especially good at choosing its children. It is even better at trying to weed them out. This is

11

especially true of its "daughters." It has an agonizing yet thrilling way of taunting you with a series of challenges during your training, to figure out if you have what it takes.

As a student, can you stand in one position holding a retractor for eight hours without moving? And if your arm goes numb, can you remain in that position so as not to incur the wrath of the attending physician, who would have you believe that the slightest shift in the position of that very retractor will kill the patient? Can you stay up all night on call in the hospital, then go "ace" a career-determining exam?

As a resident, how long can you go without food, without urinating? How many hours can you go without sleeping? Can you work with the flu? No, not really? OK, how about if you hook yourself up to an intra-venous (IV) line and infuse two liters of saline to manage the dehydration? You can make rounds by scooting around in a chair with wheels on it, IV pole in your left hand, and the patient's chart in the other. Oh, you didn't know about the hooking yourself up to an IV thing? You'd better be tough enough for this, girl, or there is no hope for you. And by the way, how many months without seeing your family and how many years without so much as a pap smear?

During my training I've been spat upon, had my nipple twisted, been threatened with bodily harm, and missed countless family functions. I've spent more than one Christmas alone in a dark, cold call room. I've gotten my period in the middle of a case and stood there with blood running down my legs because there was no way in hell I would scrub out. I've left a case unable to walk because my back was so stiff from standing in the same position for twelve hours. I've removed my scrubs after surgery only to discover that clotted blood from an HIV-infected patient I operated on had soaked through to my underwear. I've accidentally taken a shower with my bra on because, with the exception of a slight feeling that something wasn't quite right, I was too tired to realize I wasn't naked.

I've gotten sick and holed up in the call room until my next shift forty-eight hours later, because I was too weak to drive home and afraid I wouldn't make it back in. My parents' house burned to the ground during my intern year, with all of my belongings in it, and I never had the opportunity to sift through the ashes to see if any of my most important possessions had survived. My grandmother died in another hospital while I was taking care of someone else's grandmother in my hospital. I've tolerated flagrant, egregious sexually inappropriate behavior, because I wanted to be seen as a team player—someone who was tough and could take a sexist, misogynistic joke despite being a woman. And to this day, though I wouldn't recommend my course of action to someone else, I am sure that I did the right thing. For me. At that time.

As I said, it takes a special kind woman to be a surgeon.

I chose Urology as a subspecialty for so many reasons. Urologists cure cancer, fix babies born with devastating, congenital defects, and relieve the horrible pain of kidney stones. We can reattach a severed penis. We can build a bladder-cancer patient a new bladder from his intestines. It is an amazing field. Also, very important in my decision was the fact that I knew I wanted a life outside the hospital; Urology has a reputation for being one of the "cushier" fields within surgery. But most important, there are just so many wonderful, intellectually and technically challenging aspects of the field that I find fascinating.

For the sake of full disclosure, I must also admit that part of the reason I went into Urology is the fact that I have an unusual obsession with elderly men. I'm convinced it has a lot to do with growing up without a grandfather on either side. I just love their stories, their perspective on life. I love taking care of them. And they get such a kick having "such a cute young girl" as their doctor. As a woman of a certain age, how do you not love that? This obsession also manifests itself outside of the operating room. Regrettably, I have been known to point out an adorable, little, old guy in the street and say to my husband, "Honey look at that one, isn't he the cutest?" Most recently, I begged the elderly, toothless father of the owner of a fantastic little restaurant on the Italian island of Lipari to take a picture with me. In the photo, I am smiling ferociously. He is not.

But just as it takes a certain type of woman to be a surgeon, it most certainly takes a certain type of woman to be a Urologist. First and foremost, you must be able to deal with the ever present and ever problematic genital organ: the penis. The penis is sometimes brought to see you because its owner has been suffering from erectile dysfunction. This is often an odd complaint, because when the penis in question is revealed for an examination, it is more erect than the empire state building. Sometimes the penis is absolutely normal but its owner makes up false complaints just to get you to touch it. Sometimes penises become cancerous and must be removed, altering a man's life in a devastating, catastrophic, cataclysmic way—a way that most women cannot understand; a way that, as a woman urologist, you *must* understand.

There is another way in which women urologists are much different from most women. We can't have babies. Of course, like many career women who have deferred child-bearing until the late thirties in order to further our careers, women urologists have a harder time conceiving than other women. This is simply because by waiting until residency is complete, we have waited too long. But the "women in urology" sisterhood is a small one. There aren't very many of us, so we all tend to know each other to some degree. And of all the women urologists I know, there is only one who was able to conceive her children naturally. And one of her pregnancies was so complicated that she almost died in the delivery room. I'm not sure whether it's from stress, long hours, or all of the radiation exposure (women urologists in general are exposed to more fluoroscopy than those in other surgical fields); but almost every woman urologist I know has had to resort to in-vitro fertilization.

Nothing in my life, in my training, or even in my imagination has prepared me for the emotional roller coaster that is infertility. Before my husband and I even started trying, I was aware that at age 36 I was well past my peak fertility years. I knew the biology. But still. I knew my egg quality was declining by the minute. I knew that when and *if* I was able to conceive, I would be of advanced maternal age and, therefore, at high risk for complications and birth defects. I knew that it would take a while. I knew that I would probably need some "help." But still.

Nothing prepared me for the dozens of vaginal ultrasounds during the heaviest, most uncomfortable days of my cycle. The hundreds of injections. The painful tests without anesthesia; the painful tests with anesthesia. The sticking of needles into ovaries to suck out eggs. The holding of breath, waiting to see if my eggs are any good. Then if they are any good, the holding of breath waiting to see if they would fertilize with my husband's sperm. Then if they fertilized, the holding of breath to see if they would grow. If they grew, hopes dashed with each call from the embryologists, informing you of how many of the previously growing embryos had, inexplicably, stopped growing overnight. And if any of them made it to day five—the point at which they could be placed into your uterus and hopefully turn into a baby—the agonizing, gut twisting, heart squeezing, two week wait. Each time, I felt like I was holding my breath the entire two weeks. Two entire horrible weeks at the end of which you are told everything you went through was for nothing. Sorry, your pregnancy test was negative. Or even worse, sorry, your pregnancy test is positive, but your hormone levels are too low. In effect, yes, you are pregnant right now, but in a few days you will start bleeding and you won't be.

So many times I found myself crouching in the tiny space beneath the desk in my office sobbing. Then my pager would go off and I would run to the OR, turning off my pain as if there was a switch in my heart, to make someone better. And yet there was absolutely nothing that could make *me* better. My two best friends, exactly the same age as I was, got pregnant one after the other. Women who didn't want to be pregnant were abandoning babies at the bus stop in front of the hospital. Every Friday, in the operating room right next door to mine, gynecologists aborted unwanted babies by the dozen. I am staunchly pro-choice, but it's hard as hell to want a baby more than anything and know that they are being sucked out of wombs ten feet away from you. Especially when you know the biology. Especially when you are a surgeon.

Throughout my journey, I have missed out on many things. I have sacrificed many more things. I can live with these losses because, in exchange, I have been blessed with the opportunity to become a healer. I have been able to improve life, to restore a life that is pain free, to restore a life without cancer. But so far I have not been able to create a life. I am an author. I am a teacher. I am a healer. I am a doctor. I am a surgeon. One might even say I am somewhat of a feminist. But in the part of me that is simply a wife, simply a woman, I feel I am nothing if not a mother.

Inspiring Quote:
"Courage is the most important of the virtues because without courage, you cannot practice any other virtue consistently." — Maya Angelou

Editor's note: Dr. Jackson Rosario gave birth to twins—Jackson Alexi Rosario and Addison Maddalena Rosario—in September 2014.

Nia D. Banks, MD, PhD, FACS
Plastic Surgeon

Missing Images

I'm shifting in my seat and rewrapping the scarf around my neck, again. "Why is it always so cold in these conference rooms?" I take copious notes to take my mind off of the cold. "Jeez, is that another before-and-after slide of a Caucasian woman? Do black women not get breast cancer at his hospital?" I have seen this particular surgeon present many times about breast reconstruction. I have met him a few times and highly respect his talent and experience. A year ago, I would have thought nothing of it.

After practicing for a year and performing breast reconstruction for an overwhelmingly African American population, I remember how hard it was to find before-and-after images of black women going through breast reconstruction. Now, two years later, I have plenty of images of my own patients; but early on, it was difficult to manage expectations. (Patients like to see "before-and-after" photographs when consulting a plastic surgeon, to give them an idea of the quality of the surgeon's work). Also, women need to see images like themselves, to know that the end result is attainable for them, too, not just Caucasian women.

It does help immensely that I can speak to patients frankly, as a woman, about their breasts and their goals for their breasts. But women need to have a realistic expectation of breast reconstruction, its complexities and what to expect at each stage. It's a long process and it can be daunting. The federal mandate that insurance carriers cover breast reconstruction is still fresh—and many women are still concerned about what insurance will cover and what it will not.

So rather than let it go, this time I asked the presenter why he did not include images of black women. I asked because I wanted to know the answer, and because I wanted him to consider my question from his perspective, as a colleague and as a Caucasian male. I asked the same question of the representative from the company sponsoring the conference, regarding the lack of diversity of images in their breast reconstruction patient-education materials. I had known the representative since my surgical residency at Johns Hopkins, when the hospital was part of her territory; and I considered her a colleague and an ally.

To my surprise, the presenter was not taken aback or offended. Maybe he had been asked before. His simple answer was that the scars didn't show up as easily in photos of Caucasian patients. So true! In fact, if I had to present to a room full of plastic surgeons as an expert about breast reconstruction, I would choose what I thought were my best photos, too. All plastic surgeons are salesmen and scars are scary.

The company representative responded that their patient materials were recently changed to include Latina women, and she acknowledged that they neglected to include images of black women. She understood that, just like young people choosing careers, it really helps to see images that look like you.

So imagine a time when you are at your most vulnerable—when you are sick or injured. How comforting would it be to see someone who looks like you? Someone you share some common ground with, no matter how narrow that commonality may be? As physicians, as surgeons, we are the ultimate professionals. We take care of people to the best of our ability, regardless of their backgrounds. Our medical schools and residency programs have trained us for this. We talk about ethics and cultural competency and are graded on it. We may leave our biases at the door, or try to, but you can believe that the patient has not made the same resolution. If anything, when you are vulnerable, hurt, scared, your fall back on your defense mechanisms. Racism, sexism, paranoia, ageism, classism, xenophobia, east versus west, north versus south, it all comes out.

As a surgical resident, you are taught to keep your head down, toe the line, get it done. Don't make waves, don't complain (whine), just *get it done!* When my assertiveness (read "assertive" if you are talking about a male, read "aggressive" if you are talking about a female) failed to get things done, I would gently remind the consultant/nurse/radiology technician, "You are not doing it for *me*, you're doing it for the *patient*." No one cares what biases you have to navigate when you're a surgical resident—just *get it done!*

I could understand the patients' biases. I was young, black, female, and wore my hair in a large Afro. Needless to say, I found it necessary to deal with biases head on! I could sympathize with vulnerability and the resultant defense mechanisms. The patients were easy: They would get the care that I would have wanted. They would get the time I would have wanted from my doctor when I had questions. They would get the reassurance I would have wanted from my doctor when I was scared. They would get the forgiveness I would have wanted when I lashed out as a result of fear or pain. They would get my very best in the operating room where they have given their ultimate trust. It was, and is, a privilege to be a surgeon.

When I chose my fellowship, I chose an international fellowship. I wanted to get away from traditional Halstedian surgical training programs, and I needed to reinvent myself. I did a cranio-facial fellowship in Paris with a surgeon largely influenced by Paul Tessier, the legendary French surgeon who revolutionized plastic surgery with his innovations. It was a very desirable fellowship for plastic surgeons and, for me, it meant being in a place where the fact that I was not French overshadowed the fact that I was black or female. People were curious and wanted to make a connection with you. They wanted to talk about training in the United States; and, at the time (it was 2008), they wanted to talk about the presidential campaign of Barack Obama. It was a great time for me. My energy and enthusiasm for my chosen profession were restored.

The city of Paris, where good food and fashion are seen as not frivolous but essential to daily life, was also critical to my personal rein-vention. It was okay again to value vanity and leisure. From Paris, I traveled to Spain, North Africa, London, Italy, Prague, and Germany. I found common ground in each place and I rediscovered myself. I remembered the pleasure I got from meeting new people and good conversation, which was part of why I chose medicine over a career in engineering. I fed my love of art and architecture, which had led me to plastic surgery in the first place. I mimicked the delicate balance between being feminine and being strong that French women seem to fall into so easily. Taking time to enjoy myself made me a better surgeon.

Inspiring Quote:
"Greatness is not measured by what a man or woman accomplishes, but by the opposition he or she has overcome to reach his goals."
— Dorothy I. Height

Christina (Tina) L. Cervieri, MD
Orthopedic Surgeon

Suddenly

I first noticed I was a girl (and I suppose not a typical girl) circa 1976, when I went to the first day of Little League Baseball tryouts in third grade. "Try-outs" is a bit of a misnomer because every kid was going to make a team, but the team assignments had not yet been made. So there were a gazillion kids enthusiastically swarming the cluster of town athletic fields, in the warm spring sun, ready for play—all boys except me. I don't know what made me anxious exactly. Everyone was happy. It was warm. I knew one of the coaches. I just felt like I didn't belong there, that I had been dropped off in the wrong place. No one looked like me. When I left that day, I never went back. I didn't join a team; I didn't play baseball.

The next year was fourth grade, a change of school buildings, new activities and growing up. Music class was based around learning an instrument. Not just the recorder for everyone any more. We could choose—saxophone, flute, clarinet, whatever. There were so many choices. I don't remember why exactly, but I chose drums. That seemed really fun. I couldn't wait. Until I got to the drum class and my heart sank: it was me . . . and all boys. Although I loved my little snare sticks—how they were held, how they rat-a-tat-tatted against the table and bounced about—I quit after just a few classes. I cherished what I had learned (and remember to this day), but I somehow felt like I didn't belong in drum class. There was no one who looked like me. I didn't play drums. I went back to the recorder, which I didn't give a hoot about.

The road to Orthopedics has been long, in the sense that the journey through life, its twists and turns, ups and downs, has been long. Many decades long. By the time I was accepted to an Orthopedic Residency Program in 1999, I was no longer surprised to find myself the only female person in the room. Even as a licensed physician, though, I remained anxious about my gender, thinking about proper "female but not feminine" business attire, what I said and how I reacted to what was said, how bodies touched at an OR table, how orders were given and received. Every professional woman probably has thought at some point about that "fine" line of being assertive while being accepted. In the "boys club," all of those considerations were

19

heightened; I was surrounded by the club all day, every day, for six years; and every intuitive fiber of me tingled to advise me on the best behavior to stay in the club, in the game, in my chosen profession. It was stressful.

But I did not quit. I became the third woman to graduate from my Orthopedic Residency Program (in its thirty-plus-year history), but not happily. My enthusiasm for Orthopedics had become tainted by the obvious and unconscious personal sacrifices I had made to that point in my career. My male colleagues were married, starting families, enjoying the collegiality of their Orthopedic "buddies;" I was not. I did not have study buddies, attendings did not take me under their wings, and I felt increasingly alone in my chosen place of work. That feeling did not change during Fellowship. I was hardened. I was saddened. But I kept on. I did not walk away. I did not want that taken from me also. The goal and pursuit of being an Orthopedic Surgeon had become stronger than my insecurities.

It is sort of hard to explain how even though an "opportunity" exists there is no equality of experience. I miss female companionship and camaraderie. Only four percent of Orthopedic Surgeons are women[1]; and—no surprise—I do not work with any of them. We are dispersed through hospitals and clinics across the country, one here, one there, each making a way for ourselves individually, without that mirror of reassurance that Orthopedics is who we are too. It makes it harder to find my place in the world, my family, my relationships, my work. Academic feminism gives some tools to confront the world, some intellectual confidence at demanding my fair share, but it does not translate to the day-to-day texture of life per se, or replace a relaxed feeling of belonging and being where one is supposed to be.

And on that note, excuse me from my ramblings and remembrances, because I need to assess a wrist fracture.

Reference:
[1] 'The uneven distribution of women in Orthopaedic surgery resident training programs in the United States' *J Bone Joint Surg Am.* 2012 Jan 18;94(2):e9; Van Heest AE, Agel J http://www.ncbi.nlm.nih.gov/pubmed/22258016

Inspiring Quote:
"One's prime is elusive. You little girls, when you grow up, must be on the alert to recognize your prime at whatever time of your life it may occur."
— Muriel Spark, Novelist

Jeannie Chun, MD
Pediatric Surgeon

Reflections of a Pediatric Surgeon

I love what I do. Pediatric surgery is the *best*. The degree of satisfaction from witnessing parents travel from terror to laughter is immense. I create or recreate things so that babies can eat, poop, and grow. I follow these babies until they go to their senior prom. I also meet funny four-year-olds that make me laugh, and beautiful teenagers just starting to become independent. The older children usually come in and out of my life, needing me for just a brief time. The variety in my practice keeps me challenged, and I cannot imagine doing anything else.

That being said, getting here was *hard*. I never thought about surgery as a specialty until my third-year clerkship in medical school. I did it first "to get it out of the way." I let all the gunners (hyper-competitive students) do the great cases and operate with the bigwigs because I wasn't trying to impress anybody. But the culture started to seep into my skin. Getting up so early became less onerous because I was excited about the day. I loved the directed, focused thinking: Something is wrong, identify what it is, find a way to fix it, then fix it. I started to wonder, "Could I be a surgeon?"

There were two female residents who had a profound influence. The first was a senior plastic surgery resident. Her father was a surgeon and she grew up playing with sutures and needle drivers. She treated me like an apprentice, sharing her thoughts and teaching with patience. She let me place my first stitch reattaching a man's thumb. How cool is that? The second resident was a general surgery chief resident who was widely recognized as the best. Attendings would ask her opinion on cases at morbidity and mortality conferences. My junior resident called her to help him when he had trouble getting a bedside central line. Of course she got it in one stick. As she was getting gowned and gloved, she turned to me and demanded: "Tell me ten complications of a central line." She was a bad-ass. I wanted to be like these two women—smart, competent, and slightly terrifying.

I decided to do a trauma sub-internship to get the surgery bug out of my system. I remember watching the chief resident run the level I traumas like an orchestra. Trauma operations, in particular, are thrilling: people are running, blood is spilling and it feels as if we are in the midst of a battle. The surgeon is the general, directing the action, often elbows-deep in the patient. Ultimately, I decided I loved the operating room and could not give it up. I scrambled to get surgery letters of recommendation and was fortunate to match at a great, female-friendly program.

Surgery training is rigorous, no question. The demands and stakes are daunting. Lives are literally on the line. In retrospect, the years are a blur, but one early experience has remained with me. The first case I performed skin-to-skin was an open appendectomy. The on-call chief resident saw me hanging around the consult resident and offered to take me through the case. He asked the attending (who obligingly stayed seated in the corner) and then patiently directed me step-by-step. We finished at 2 a.m. Afterwards, I felt like I was walking on air.

The next morning I told the chief resident on my service that I almost called her, I was so excited. She said, "You should have!" I said, "It was amazing! It was . . ." "Better than a first kiss!" she finished the sentence for me. She knew exactly what I meant. I often think of that morning, when I feel the first stirring of irritation when a resident is struggling through a procedure. Surgery is an art and it has been a privilege to learn and hopefully teach well.

During my early residency my only focus was training. My future husband was also in surgery training, and it took some time for us to realize our relationship needed the same degree of attention as our careers. Fortunately, we eventually figured it out and married, and six years later we have two beautiful children. Now that I'm an attending I realize the value of having interests outside surgery, because surgery is hard. Patients will have complications. They will die. You will make mistakes. If there is nothing else in your life to bring you joy, you will burn out.

I hope this anthology will demonstrate to future surgeons why we are here. We represent a vast array of experiences and, hopefully, female surgeons are no longer a rarity wherever they currently are. If you feel the passion for surgery, do not dismiss those feelings. Recently I had two different mothers give me hugs as they stated, "Thank you for saving my baby's life."

As I shared before, pediatric surgery is the *best*.

SECTION 2—THE PRIVILEGE OF BEING A SURGEON

Kate Khalifeh, MD
Colon & Rectal Surgeon

One Day at a Time

In my first life I was a nurse. I worked in the cardiac surgery ICU for ten years before starting surgical residency training. I watched a lot of different people rotate through the ICU, and I truly appreciated the impact being a doctor had on them and their lives. I saw the evolution of interns to residents and residents to attendings. I watched some grow while others crumbled under the stress; one even committed suicide while on our unit. When I got into medical school, the resident on the unit told me to keep the admission letter close to my heart, and to remember how great today felt, because there would be days ahead where I would undoubtedly regret the decision!

I applied to medical school almost on a lark. I was already in a Masters program, but I was getting a lot of encouragement from those around me to apply. I thought, "Why not?" figuring I would apply and thus never have to think, "Oh, I wish I had . . ." down the road. I never imagined that I would actually get in.

As it turns out, I was accepted into not just one program but had multiple offers. How could I turn this down? The first two years of class were a struggle. I was conditioned to being physically active and thinking critically at work; simply sitting for hours on end, memorizing and paying attention was a challenge. I continued to work through medical school. My plan was to become an anesthesia /critical care physician like those who had mentored me. Working afforded me a social outlet and desperately needed stress release. It also helped me keep my eye on the prize as I suffered through long lectures.

Surgery turned out to be my very first hospital rotation. This was fine by me. If I knew one thing, it was that I was *never* going to be a surgeon. I didn't particularly care if I looked a bit clueless. The only problem was that I ended up liking it—*a lot!*

My chief resident was one of the few women in the program at that time and she remains my role model to date. Not only is she a great surgeon but she was and still is a class act and truly cares about her patients. Every evening, no matter how late we rounded, she would show up on the floor in a dress and heels. She would sit down on the end of a patient's bed, carefully tucking her skirt beneath her, and talk to the patient as if he/she were a person, eye to eye. She might not spend a long time but she would spend *enough* time, and it made each patient feel valued and cared for. She was the epitome of "do unto others" and I was in awe.

At the end of my surgical rotation, I thought, "This must have been a fluke," so I went back for more. The next rotation was trauma, the most hated rotation by the residents: long, unforgiving hours; late night cases; thankless patients. I can vividly remember my first incision and drainage procedure, so basic and rote now, but at the time I was actually cutting into someone and fixing something. During my first chest-tube insertion, you could hear the guy yelling two units away. I couldn't stop talking about it for a week. But what now, I wondered? I had to think long and hard. This isn't the specialty I had envisioned. The lifestyle, residency, and job itself were all very different from anesthesia and critical care, and watching all those residents over the years now gave me pause. What about kids? I wasn't married or even dating anyone at the time. Did this mean I would be a spinster?

I decided I would go for it, but I also made a very conscious choice: I would not allow myself to be eaten alive by surgery. I would try, diligently, to be very aware of myself during training. I understood there would be ups and downs, sleep deprivation, and stressor upon stressor, but I would make it a priority to maintain relationships with friends and family, and would craft a life outside of surgery. To me, having a life had to be something to which I made a commitment, just like with my job. It was my choice to go into surgery and I did not want my friends and family to feel second best. I went to a lot of events dog tired, more than a little late; and some I swear I can't even remember, but it was important to make the effort—and people appreciated that. Like working through medical school, it helped my keep my eye on that prize.

I met my eventual husband while I was in medical school. He was a resident, graduating just as I was beginning. He still claims he did the longest residency on record, between his six years and mine. We lived in different cities for much of our courtship, dating for six years before getting married, in the midst of my fourth year of residency. We got married over a holiday weekend and were both back to work on Monday. (I'm still waiting for that honeymoon!) We were in the same place just long enough to get pregnant. My first reaction when I found out was to cry: How was I going to do this all? In a program whose motto for women was "Pregnancy is what the labs years are for," having a pregnant chief was not popular. I choose to think that I did it with grace. I never turned down an operative case, never missed a call, and did a Whipple procedure the Friday before I was induced two weeks after my due date.

I was fortunate to have had an easy pregnancy. The first few months post-birth, however, were not as graceful. I literally had myself discharged for the hospital post C-section in time to keep the one and only fellowship interview that ensured my husband and I would live in the same city. I was so goofy, my dad had to drive me to the interview and I have no idea what I said, but they gave me the job. Six weeks later, I returned to residency, struggling from sleep deprivation in a way that my years of medical training had not prepared me for. I was almost hallucinating. My husband still lived in another city, the baby didn't sleep at night, and I would operate on people, unable to recall what I'd done to them the next morning on rounds. Mommy guilt ate at me daily, and I was so maxed out I didn't even lactate. I thought about taking a year off before fellowship, but I was given great advice that I appreciate immensely in hindsight: power through, as it will only be harder after a year off.

I chose colorectal surgery as my specialty. Unsurprisingly, everyone asks, "Wait . . . you're a butt doctor?? Why?!" I tell anyone considering surgery to look closely at colorectal surgery. It is a great specialty! I do big abdominal cases, laparoscopic and open, J-pouches and cancer resections. I also do colonoscopies and ano-rectal cases which, while often lower stress, can still be challenging. The outpatient cases afford me a day of control, one that is predictable and gets me home for dinner. My anal fissure patients are often my happiest patients. The cases are rarely middle of the night, the patients are educated about their diseases—participating in their healthcare by having their scopes—and sometimes I can even cure some cancers with surgery.

I joined a big, busy, private practice of seven colorectal surgeons. We work hard, absolutely, but at the end of the day we all have our protected family time as well. I can't say that I love my job every day. I struggle with my confidence when patients don't do well or have complications. Sometimes when I spend too much time at work or get called in at night, I wonder if this was the right choice for my family. I focus on making my home time count and feel confident that my girls know I love them. Overall, I feel privileged to do what I do and hope that I am a good role model to my children and residents, helping them see that you *can* have it all. It isn't always elegant, or tidy, or on time, but I wouldn't trade it in for anything.

Inspiring Quote:
"True happiness is to learn how to live beyond the imperfections."
— Rita Maatta

Minerva Romero Arenas, MD, MPH
General Surgery Resident

Impressions: The Art and Culture of Surgery

The decision to choose a career in surgery was one of the biggest in my life. I thought a lot about the sacrifices I would be making: time for my family, time for myself, and all the other experiences that would be put on hold. I also thought about the sacrifices I would be asking others to make. No longer would I be able to support my brother at every basketball game. I could not go shopping with my mom on a weekend, nor could I celebrate birthdays and share holidays in the way I always did. Instead of being deterred by these considerations, I use them every day as motivators to work harder for my patients, for my family, for myself. It would be an intense five-to-ten-year path through residency, and possibly fellowship, but I knew I would not be satisfied if I pursued any other field. I knew I would miss the OR, the sense of healing that is almost immediate, the intensity of surgical work, the opportunity to treat patients at critical points in their lives.

When I told friends and classmates I would be applying to residency programs in general surgery, the almost universal response was "You are too nice to be a surgeon!" I was not surprised, since this was my impression when I entered surgery clerkship. My experience altered this impression. I was inspired by the surgeons and residents, from whom I learned to love the art of surgery. They were kind and committed to excellence. They were extremely bright, had tremendous compassion, and were actually very down-to-earth. They were frank about the stresses a career in surgery placed on their personal lives. Attending surgeons shared their wisdom about how to cope and continue to grow. They were enthusiastic about sharing their knowledge and skill with the next generation. Most important, they were the one group of people who never discouraged me from pursuing medicine, and especially about pursuing surgery. So long as I was sure I wanted it, and worked hard, it would be within reach.

Despite being enamored of the field, surgery is a whole different animal. Culture shock was eye-opening. Although residency hours have improved dramatically, the eighty-hour week is still an overwhelming adjustment for a new resident, as is dealing with the educational demands outside of work hours, being away from home, and adapting to a new life. One of the biggest stressors is fitting into the culture of a new institution. Having to submit to unquestioned authority was a learning experience. I do not have a background in police or military structure. I had learned to ask questions in order to better understand a process or plan of care; now my questions were perceived as a breach of authority. Nonetheless, I learned to see the value this provides in making sound and firm decisions about patient care. As I have progressed in my training, I have also seen different styles of leadership, and have found that the best surgeons and educators actually welcome questions and help you find the answers.

Coming from a family of strong women, being in a male-dominated field has definitely been challenging. I have always strived to be seen as equal to my male colleagues (the way I see myself). I never thought that my strength, which had always opened doors for me and helped me achieve my goals, could actually feel like a burden. I found myself facing interesting behavior from some colleagues and superiors, as if these strong and intelligent men could actually be threatened by me merely because of my gender. Occasionally, I found myself having to work harder, having to justify my decisions and thoughts and prove that I was worthy of being here. While I always expected to face these demands in my career, it was hard not to notice that my male colleagues did not face the same demands. This behavior came not just from surgeons. There was also a struggle with nursing and mid-level providers and non-clinical staff. Rather than fighting small battles every day, I chose to win the war with kindness and let my work speak for me.

As for my female colleagues, I noticed an interesting trend. Nobody wanted to be identified as feminine, or simply not "one of the boys." Nobody wanted to be labeled as an emotional woman, nobody wanted to be seen as weak, nobody wanted to face hardship for being identified as a woman. It is the traits that are culturally attributed to women that everyone seemed to want to shake off. One of them told me, "I want to be treated like a male."

That is not what I want. What I want is to be treated like a woman who is just as brilliant and resilient as a man. What I want is to be able to wear heels to clinic, be able to take pride in my appearance, without worrying about having my skills doubted because I'm "too girly." We praise males for wearing suits and ties, but a woman in a colorful blouse can be deemed too flashy. In my culture, one is expected to be presentable out of respect for oneself and others. How can I expect patients to take my recommendations seriously if I cannot pull myself together?

I can surely appreciate the strides we have made in the field. I know the women who came before me had it much harder. Being the first and only women to train in surgical residency, they opened the door for the rest of us. While the overt discrimination toward women has disappeared, there are many subtleties that maintain a wide wage and achievement gap between male and female surgeons—and, unofficially, a difference in satisfaction/personal happiness.

Take, for instance, starting a family. It is always women who are accused of having a "ticking clock" when it comes to having children. Yet starting a family is a very different choice for male as opposed to female residents. While many male residents I know have strategically planned to have children during lighter duty years, female residents have different considerations. You have to consider the stress of pregnancy on the resident and the stress of residency on the pregnancy. Doctors have poor outcomes for pregnancy, and surgeons fare the worst. Even if you get through the pregnancy, you must consider the cost of child care (which can be nearly impossible on a resident's salary), and the stress of not sharing the very special first moments of your child's life. I know many bright medical students who would never consider surgery because of these demands. I know residents who have quit because of difficulty juggling both. I am awed by the "super moms" I have come to know. These female residents, fellows, and young attending surgeons have had the strength to start or grow their family under the magnifying glass of a surgery department.

I chose my career being well aware of these sacrifices, although this was one of the toughest pills to swallow. Yet I am in a group of women proud to have escaped the traditional role of housewife, young mother, or the person whose career is less important. Coming from a Latino/Hispanic background, this alone can be seen as an achievement. I look up to the many women who have shown me it is possible to have a wonderful career without children. In the end, it will be my decision and one I am thankful to be able to make.

I would be wrong to focus only on these distractions. The truth is that I still wake up content every day. It is small victories that give you a sense of accomplishment: finding that the margins on a frozen section are free of malignant cells; performing lifesaving surgery on a trauma victim; seeing a patient's blood sugar normalize after bariatric surgery; receiving a smile and a "high five" from the child after you perform an appendectomy; successfully advocating for your patient's plan of care to an insurance officer, to cover a benefit such has rehabilitation services after a life-changing amputation. When there is chaos, we as surgeons are the ones who take charge and get things done.

Most important, it has been the "female trait" of sensitivity that has paid off more times than I can count, such as the times I have provided comfort and connected with patients in a way that other members of my team have been unable to do (in addition to providing excellent medical and surgical care!). One call night, when making nighttime rounds, I visited a patient being treated for breast cancer. My patient had cerebral palsy, was in her thirties, and her mom was by her side every minute. That day we had been given less than encouraging news about my patient's diagnosis. When I asked Mom how she was going, she opened up about how heartbroken she was about having to face the thought of losing her daughter. She sobbed, she lamented, she grieved. It was instinctive to reach out and embrace her in a hug to let her know I understood her pain. She thanked me for providing support and showing how much we surgeons cared about her daughter. When I later mentioned this encounter to a group of male colleagues, it struck me that they were not only surprised but would never have considered embracing a patient or family member.

I am thankful for the support and courage the important people in my life have given me to pursue this career, which is one of the biggest challenges I have ever undertaken: my family, for supporting my every dream' my significant other, for unconditional love and support throughout this journey; my friends, for not giving up on our friendship and giving more than I can offer in return.

I am fortunate to be working with a brilliant group of people, my co-residents and faculty, who inspire me every day. They inspire me to learn the best way to treat patients. They inspire me to think about the ways we can make strides in our field through research. Above all, I must thank the surgeons I've worked with, who have served as excellent mentors—most of whom happen to be male. It is because of these individuals that I know I will fulfill my potential. They push me to be better. They listen to my concerns, my fears, and my dreams. They help me find solutions to problems and find a way to make things happen. They offer advice on which books to read, which loupes to buy, which atlas to use. They critique my every move during surgery, so that I may refine my technique into a well-tuned symphony of cutting and suturing. And yes, occasionally they make fun of my high heels!

Inspiring Quote:

"It is fatal to be a man or woman pure and simple; one must be a woman manly, or a man womanly." — Virginia Woolf

Anees B. Chagpar, MD, MPH, FRCS (C), FACS
Breast Surgical Oncologist

On Being a Surgeon

I always wanted to be a surgeon. I'm not sure how exactly I knew, but I did. No one in my family is a doctor, much less a surgeon—yet somehow I just knew. Maybe it was the fact that in grade four I was completely fascinated by dissecting frogs in the biology laboratory, while the rest of my classmates were looking queasy at the amphibian insides. But it was my interaction with the surgeons early on in medical school that cemented my passion for the field. These early mentors were typically male, and seemed to always know what to do, especially during an emergency; they were confident and took charge, and somehow everything was fine. Their presence was reassuring in a moment of crisis. They were brilliant—but not in the internal medicine kind of way; they didn't necessarily have encyclopedic knowledge of every rare syndrome, but used common-sense to figure out the solutions to the most complex problems. They thought on their feet as they worked with their hands. Watching them operate was a like a symphony: Every element of the team worked in harmony. And as I watched the anatomy unfold, pathologic processes (like cancer) be removed, and everything be put back together with cosmetic precision, I fell in love. There was something magical about being able to see the problem, fix it, and move on to the next problem.

I suppose I've always been one for immediate gratification. I remember my first appendicitis patient. He presented with a board-like, rigid abdomen, in severe pain; but within a couple of hours, we had his appendix out, and he was thanking us in the recovery room! It was a beautiful experience.

I got drawn to breast surgical oncology for a few reasons. First off, I love the patient-physician relationship. You meet patients at a time when their lives have been turned upside-down by a diagnosis that they dread, and are able to get them through that—both from a physical and emotional point of view. You're able to remove the vast majority of breast cancers with curative intent; patients do incredibly well, and they are very grateful. The procedures themselves pull together oncologic principles with attention

34

to cosmetic outcomes; they are clean, meticulous and simply beautiful. I love working with a team—and in breast cancer surgery, you're an integral part of a team both in and outside of the OR, working closely with radiologists, pathologists, medical oncologists, radiation oncologists, plastic surgeons, nurses, nutritionists, physical therapists, social workers and others. And I love the research, which is fast-paced, meaningful, and relatively well-funded. Teams of people work on fundamental questions, spanning from the bench to the bedside, from personalized medicine at a genomic level to epidemiologic research on a population-wide basis.

Truthfully, I love everything about surgery: the satisfaction of using your hands, the relationship you have with your patients, the ability to really make a difference. Now I get to talk to medical students about their career paths. I try not to influence them unduly (even though I firmly believe that there is no greater profession than surgery) and tell them to follow their passion. Too many people are influenced by stereotypes. So allow me to clarify: *yes*, you can have a life and be a surgeon; *yes*, you can be married, have two or three kids, a dog, and a house with a white-picket fence and be a surgeon; *yes*, you can have a lab and a vibrant academic life and be a surgeon; and *yes*, you can be a girl and be a surgeon.

There is only one requirement to be a truly great surgeon—*passion*. You have to love it with your heart and soul. There is no doubt that surgical training is hard work. There will be times when you feel completely spent— but if you love it, the endorphins recharge your battery automatically. There is no question that it may be difficult at times to balance work and personal life, but if you set your priorities well and have reasonable time-management skills, you can be a mom/researcher/administrator and a surgeon at the same time—and there are plenty of role models to demonstrate this fact.

For me, my passion is in leadership and academic medicine. So I fill my days (and nights and weekends) doing what I love: I see patients and operate; I teach and mentor students, residents, fellows, and junior faculty; and I do research (both collaborating on translational projects and doing meaningful outcome studies and leading clinical trials). I am passionate about my administrative role at the Breast Center at Smilow Cancer Hospital, where we are constantly striving to achieve ever-increasing levels of excellence; and I am thrilled to be able to have administrative roles that are important to me, including being the Assistant Director for Diversity and Health Equity at Yale and serving on the Executive Committee for the Cancer Center. I love the work that I do with the Admissions Committee at Yale's School of Medicine and leading our Interdisciplinary Breast Fellowship. I enjoy meeting new people and expanding my horizons by co-hosting a radio show called *Yale Cancer Center Answers* that airs weekly on WNPR. And I really love being a student. Not just learning from everyday experiences that we all have, but also by doing an MBA for Executives: Leadership in Healthcare at Yale's School of Management. So, while I am not married with two or three kids and a house with a white picket fence, I am doing exactly what I love. My life is full of the things that make me happy.

I have never once regretted becoming a surgeon. It is by far the most fun, rewarding, and all-around amazing career that you can have. It really is like they say—do what you love and you'll never work a day in your life!

Inspiring Quote:
"There are two kinds of people, those who do the work and those who take the credit. Try to be in the first group; there is less competition there."
— Indira Gandhi

Gianna Scannell, MD, FACS
General Surgeon

Dissecting the Soul of a Woman Surgeon

Why did I leave my beautiful country, Italy, to cross the ocean and start over like the pioneers of the Mayflower, many years ago? I admit, the trip was not as treacherous, and the accommodation not as Spartan, but it was, nevertheless, the biggest adventure. The reason was, quite simply, because I wanted to know more. I wanted to learn how to care for sick patients, something that was just beginning to be understood in my country. And learn I did. As a trauma surgeon, I took care of hundreds of men, women and children at the doorstep of death. Because of what I learned, I could manage to pull a few back. For many, it was either too late, or their injury was well beyond my help. It was a draining experience. It made me understand how fleeting life really is. Step off the curb during a jog, sweat blinding your sight, and wham—you're dead. In the end, the most valuable lesson was to enjoy my life, and to tell the people I love that I do, every day. This anthology, too, celebrates life, lived in many different ways, by women who share a passion. Enjoy it.

Perhaps I'm a surgeon because I'm an introvert. I cherish the quiet isolation of the operating room. I also enjoy driving to work every morning. I get up when it's still dark and, half-asleep, I climb on board my faithful Jeep Liberty (wonderful name) and drive down the hill to reach my hospital. Thirty minutes of priceless, complete introspection. Besides, who wouldn't like a commute where frequently there is no other human-being on the road? I joked one day that I commonly shared my commute to work with five kinds of living creatures—deer, rabbits, quails, mice and the occasional wild turkey.

I live in rural Washington, but I wasn't raised here. In fact, I wasn't even born here. I'm here because, after a lifetime of schooling, residency, fellowships and seriously intense work, here is where I belong. When I was a young child in Italy, five European countries vowed to never attack each other again. Treaties and free trade agreements were signed that contained the seed of what is today a united Europe. The leaders of those countries promised justice, equality, and opportunity for all the people of this new world. Enthusiasm for this new state of affairs trickled down from

37

governments to communities, and all the way to families. I grew up in this special time in history, when women experienced an independence they had never enjoyed before. I was lucky. To my parents, education came first, and they demanded that I do well in school. When time came to choose my future, I was allowed to go to medical school. Yes, *allowed*. My parents fully expected that, in the end, I would marry and stay home to raise children. But, partly because of their insistence, my grades were excellent, so they couldn't refuse.

A few months after college was over, I found myself attending the second oldest University in the world, the University of Padova, founded in 1222.

My first anatomy lesson took place in the same room where, centuries ago, Leonardo da Vinci and Andreas Vesalius dissected cadavers to learn how muscles attached to bones and shape an arm, a leg, or an entire body. We filed in front of the professor and took the stairs leading to row after row of circular benches that stacked on top of each other, all the way to the ceiling of the twenty-foot-tall room. There were no seats. Everyone stood. All three hundred of us!

Though in Leonardo da Vinci's time each of the students carried a lit candle, today a few powerful reflectors illuminated the table that stood in the center. On it was laid a young woman, her body covered with a powder-blue blanket. I remember the color vividly because it was the first time I had seen a corpse. At first I thought she was asleep but then I stared at her ashen face. "She's gray," I thought, "and strangely still. Good Lord, we're here for an anatomy lesson. She *is* the lesson!" A wave of nausea overcame me.

"How many of you have never seen a dead body?" The professor asked. He wore an immaculate white gown over his hunchback body, but the gown did little to hide his figure. A few of us timidly raised our hand.

"Move closer to the stairs," he commanded, "so you won't disturb the lesson if you get sick." Some people reshuffled.

Then the lesson began. The professor's hands danced over the flesh, swiftly and accurately placing the knife over the cadaver to begin the incision. In seconds the familiar Y-shaped cut revealed the mystery within, and I no longer worried that this body had once belonged to a living, breathing woman like me. Instead, I found myself engrossed in a scene few are privileged to see—the amazingly complex and superbly engineered insides of a human body.

When the lesson ended, I descended to the ground floor and approached the dissection table. I wondered if the old mechanism that allowed the table to flip over was still working. Could it provide the sudden appearance of a dead bovine in place of the human body (the reason my school had earned the name of "*Il Bo*," or "The Bull")? I imagined a scene out of medieval times.

*****

It was Christmas Day, and outside a dense, cold fog enveloped the city. The air was freezing in the anatomical theater, where the body of a criminal was being dissected under the suffuse light of candles. The men were quiet, as if they stood in a crypt. The knife cut through the skin and exposed the vessels of the neck. Then the base of the cranium came to light. The dissection of the nerves exiting the base of the skull was almost complete, when a loud knock disturbed the performance.

"Quick! Flip the table!" the dissector whispered through a porthole in the ground he had hastily slid open.

"This is the Inquisition!" a loud voice called from behind the locked door. "By order of the Pope, let us in!"

The table disappeared under the floor and within seconds returned with the body of a cow securely strapped to it. The scientists rushed to open the door.

"The Pope has no jurisdiction over Padova, my Lord," Andreas Vesalius said. "We belong to Venice, and as such we are a free republic. Besides, we are only dissecting a bull!" Venice was then a wealthy, independent city focused on expansion, where freedom to broaden one's views was cherished.

*****

I feel kinship with the people who assembled in that room over centuries, obsessed with learning, risking their lives to discover the inner workings of the body. When medical school was over, I started my residency in surgery at the same university, but soon realized that I needed to know more.

The care of the sick surgical patient was in its infancy at the time, and in Italy the anesthesiologists were in charge of small, open rooms, where twelve patients lay crammed next to one another, some connected to a breathing machine. Though sterility in the operating field was mandatory, there was no appreciation for antisepsis, and people moved from patient to patient without changing gloves. Actually, frequently they did not wear gloves at all. Surgeons looked at me flabbergasted when I suggested that one of us remain in the intensive care unit, on call with the anesthesiologist, so we could learn. All they wanted to do was to operate, and working on a patient *after* surgery wasn't considered part of their job. I knew that there were places where I could learn more, but I had to leave my country and learn a new language. I had to start over.

The first six months in the United States a recurring dream plagued my mind. I was attending a party in which about five dozen people spoke at once. I timidly stood in a corner of the large room, besieged by the buzz of overlapping conversations. I stared in dismay at moving mouths, gesturing hands and drinks spilling over, but understood little of what was being said. I felt as if I had suddenly gone deaf. Yet my ears were open and sounds vibrated through my cochleas. There was only one problem: All these people spoke a language completely foreign to me. It didn't last long. One day every word became miraculously clear, as if someone had turned on an electronic translator in my ears.

My (second) surgical residency was a blast. I met other women, surgical residents like me, and we became friends. Once it was over, I started a fellowship in Critical Care and finally learned how to properly treat sick surgical patients *after* the operation was completed. The surgeons who taught me were fantastic. I learned and researched, and it was heaven. I saw the sickest people on the planet, their bodies bloated and disfigured by the enormous amount of fluids they retained, and their skins oily and dirty, because any movement to be washed could trigger cardiac arrest. They were found in a hospital's Intensive Care Unit. I stood by their bedsides for hours, along with their nurse, in a second-by-second battle to keep them alive, until reinforcements came to relieve us. In my mind, hospitals exist to save lives, whatever the cost.

There are many women who have succeeded in academic surgery, such as doctors Olga Jonasson and Kathryn Anderson. These are no ordinary women. They are pioneers, the Andreas Vesalius of our time. Surgery requires team work, dexterity, a plan, and flawless execution—all talents a man acquires in childhood by playing games with his friends. Women are seldom part of those games and, therefore, men feel uncomfortable having women in their team, playing their same game.

In 1978, Dr. Jonasson explained to the *New York Times* that "The decisions of the surgeon as team leader are final, and men have simply been unwilling to accept women in that role of the all-powerful decision maker." It is not acceptable today to openly express those feelings without being accused of discrimination, but they still linger, and not only amongst male colleagues. Nurses, a profession made up mostly of women, sometimes endorse them too.

There are some centers where leadership is solid, roles well understood, transparency reigns, and support is strong and reliable. The focus then becomes not oneself, but the results. Thus, patient care improves, and not just today but also in the years to come. Unfortunately, this clear, unwavering commitment to quality—passionately shared throughout an organization—is rare. For things to change, this type of leadership must become the norm rather than the exception. In my view, women surgeons are primed for such leadership. We are born with an innate and deep desire to nurture the people in our care. It could start with us, the women surgeons. Why not? In 1222, Andreas Vesalius challenged the rules of the Inquisition. The culture of freedom prevailed in Padova and, as a result, the University prospered.

Inspiring Quote:
"I hope you find whatever balance you seek with your eyes wide open. And I hope that you—yes, you—have the ambition to lean in to your career and run the world. Because the world needs you to change it. Women around the world are counting on you." — Sheryl Sandberg

Fatima Garuba Wilder, MD
General Surgery Resident

Becoming a Surgeon

"You sure you want to become a surgeon?"

"You'll never see your kids."

"Your husband will leave you."

These are only a few of the rather surprising statements that I heard as a third and fourth year medical student when I shared my chosen career in life with them. The comments primarily came from those within medicine, those with and without surgical residency experience. There were many looks of concern and many attempts to dissuade me from committing to a life as a surgeon. But as I shared in my personal statement (see below) for residency application, I don't believe I chose surgery as much as I often believe it chose me.

It was my very first time ever stepping into the operating room. Between donning the green scrubs and watching the attending put on his gown and gloves with great ease and skill, I was simultaneously overwhelmed and excited. It took the first fifteen minutes of the case to strike a balance between getting a good enough view of the field and not contaminating it. As I stood there, I watched in awe and was grateful for the mask that covered my mouth, which remained open due to sheer joy. I was a first-year medical student witnessing a partial bowel resection on a young female patient. The procedure was indicated for her uniquely advanced case of Crohn's disease.

As I watched the attending and senior resident resect, retract, and recreate this young woman's bowel, I felt a tear—well, more like several tears—rolling down my face. They were tears of joy and gratitude, but in the moment, they terrified me. I quickly turned around out of fear that the attending would kick me out for being too "soft" in the presence of a surgeon. I managed to dry my eyes and avoid any more tear storms before I had to leave for class. As I walked to my car, I was on cloud nine. The thought that one could be given such a gift, a talent, an ability to drastically and tangibly affect someone else's life in a positive way, simply blew my mind. The thought that I could work towards one day being able to do the

42

same was not just a thought for long, but soon became what I knew was my calling in life. I made every attempt to fall in love with another specialty, but it was to no avail. I was committed. But even today, ten months into my internship (first year of General Surgery training), I do not regret my choice.

Yes, there are many days when I am up at two a.m. responding to a pager, which has become the bane of my existence. But those moments are outweighed by the many times when I feel that there is nowhere else I would rather be. Nowhere else that provides the same feeling or sense of purpose, as being in the operating room or listening to the moving life story of my patient who has endured unimaginable challenges and still manages to keep a smile on his face.

In my mind, the surgeon is the complete physician. Good surgeons are knowledgeable about the body as a whole and the disease processes that will affect their patient before and after surgery. They are strong, hard-working, good communicators, compassionate healers, avid listeners, good team managers, critical thinkers and people who will not settle for "good enough." Good surgeons need to have a certain level of self-confidence without sacrificing necessary humility. While surgery has historically been a male-dominated career, I believe women are especially equipped with all these qualities, in addition to a special God-given talent to connect with their patients in a necessary way.

At times, it is still scary when I think about other aspects of life that I always dreamed of experiencing—like weekend getaways on a whim or having a big family—and wonder if this will be possible. I have seen so many women who have achieved their goals in life without sacrificing their career as a surgeon, and this is reassuring.

I have received interesting, but primarily supportive, responses from those in and out of medicine, when they discover that I am a budding surgeon. While some seem unable to grasp the concept of a young, female surgeon, many are extremely supportive with comments like "Wow, that's awesome!", "You go, girl!" and "You must be so strong" from family, friends, and patients alike. All of the support is welcome and very much appreciated. I believe that the work-hour changes and an environment more welcoming to the career woman have certainly placed a relatively "normal" life more within reach. While many would argue that working even an eighty-hour week is far from normal, it is undoubtedly a worthwhile sacrifice to be able to fulfill what I believe is my calling as a woman in surgery.

Inspiring Zen Teaching:

"An oak tree is brought into creation by two forces at the same time . . . the acorn from which it all begins, the seed which holds all the promise and potential, which grows into the tree. Everybody can see that. But only a few can recognize that there is another force here as well—the future tree itself, which wants so badly to exist that it pulls the acorn into being, drawing the seedling forth with longing out of the void, guiding the evolution from nothingness to maturity. In this respect, it is the oak tree that creates the very acorn from which it was born." — Elizabeth Gilbert

SECTION 3—REFLECTIONS: LIFE IN SURGERY

Susan E. Pories, MD, FACS
Breast Surgeon, Surgical Oncologist

Life Is What Happens When You're Busy
Making Other Plans . . .*

First I planned to be a teacher, then an obstetrician, then a general surgeon, then a trauma surgeon, then a colorectal surgeon, and finally I found my place as a breast surgeon, a writer and medical educator! I remember going to a lecture entitled Female, Flexible and Fearless; this really resonated with me, and it is important to remember that as you grow and change your goals will too.

I fell in love with Vermont when visiting friends in college, and then transferred to University of Vermont (UVM) as a junior. At the time, I was planning to be a high school art and English teacher. I taught reading to migrant workers in New York, but the job market for teachers was very competitive at the time, and it was common for 200 people to apply for a teacher's aide job position. I noticed that teaching jobs were often victim to town budget woes and decided to change directions.

I wanted to be a doctor but was convinced I probably wasn't smart enough to handle the required science. But to explore this further I took a job as a medical assistant in an obstetrics and gynecology office. I weighed patients, took hematocrits, measured vital signs, washed instruments, filed charts and cleaned exam rooms.

At night I worked in the Burlington Free Clinic, where lay people were trained to follow short protocols for the care of common problems, mostly sexually transmitted diseases. We performed throat and vaginal cultures. We learned to do procedures by practicing on each other. I was a nervous wreck the first time I did a vaginal exam, but my co-worker and friend Joannie put me at ease, saying, "I've had two kids, Susan. I have a big, baggy vagina. You can't hurt me!" I relaxed and all went well.

Most of the clinic volunteers were interested in applying to medical school and did so successfully. One day Gary Z. came to the obstetrics and gynecology office where I was working to shadow one of the doctors. As a medical student, he was treated like royalty. The doctors showed Gary interesting findings under the microscope, took him in to examine patients, and spent time talking with him about physical findings. Since I knew Gary from the clinic, I knew that I was his equal; and it was on that day that I made the decision to go to medical school. My plan at that time was to be an obstetrician, just like the doctors I worked for. I had no money from my family at that point, since they had made a decision not to pay for graduate education. No matter. I quit my job, took out loans and signed up for pre-med classes, calculus, physics, chemistry, biochemistry and biology. When I finished the courses and took the MCAT exams, I applied to medical school and took a job in a research lab at UVM. We were studying the actions of prostaglandin in monkey ovaries.

UVM was my first choice for medical school because I loved Vermont, was a state resident and qualified for more reasonable tuition. In addition, I met my husband in Vermont and his family was in the area. He didn't really want to go to another state. The interview at UVM was weighted heavily, and I was very anxious about this. I was interviewed by a fourth-year medical student and a primary care doctor, Mildred Reardon. I have forgotten most of the details, but do remember that they asked me what my strengths were. I answered that my strength is that I'm strong, meaning that I always show up and get the job done. I berated myself after the interview for giving a dumb answer: My strength is that I'm strong. What a stupid thing to say! But, as it turns out, Dr. Reardon gave me a "thumbs up" and I was accepted.

Actually, being "strong" is one of the most important qualities for a career in surgery. You do need to be physically strong and have a strong ego and a strong work ethic, just to keep going and show up every day without fail—even if the patient is not doing well, even if you don't feel well, even if you made a mistake, even if you don't get the promotion you want. . . . No matter what happens, being a surgeon is a responsibility that is with you twenty-four hours a day, seven days a week. Once you take responsibility for a patient, then you have to do your best for them and be there for them.

I was very lucky to be accepted at UVM, a very clinically oriented medical school where the culture has always been that the patient comes first. And UVM was one of the first departments of surgery to accept and graduate women surgeons. The Chairman of Surgery at the time was Dr. John Davis. Dr. Davis was one of the first surgical leaders to actively and consistently mentor and support women in surgery. At a time when most programs refused to consider women for surgical residency, John Davis not only accepted women residents but made sure that women were treated fairly. As chairman, he supported women in surgery and treated them as equals. Unfortunately, in 1986 Dr. Davis was stricken with viral transverse myelitis, which left him paralyzed from the chest down. He was forced to step down from his position as chair of the department. Although officially retired, he remained an active educator for many years. With a sharp wit and intellect and a ready sense of humor, he was a role model for many surgeons. In 1991, the American College of Surgeons bestowed on Dr. Davis their highest honor, the Distinguished Service Award.

Surgical training was tough by any standards. There were no work-hour restrictions in place at the time, and programs were traditionally pyramidal, meaning that more people were hired at a junior level than could graduate. This meant that at least one person had to be "cut" every year. This had the effect of discouraging complaining and pushing everyone to do their best, but also took a toll on relationships between residents. Pyramidal programs have been discontinued, and now residents who are "categorical" are guaranteed to finish their training, provided that they meet all the requirements of training. Work-hour restrictions have also improved the quality of life for residents today. However, when I was a resident, any discussion of an easier schedule implied you were weak—and nobody wanted to be perceived that way. In fact, the "best" programs were every other night call, because call every third night meant you were missing too many good cases.

The program in Vermont was very strong in trauma training, because Dr. Davis was a MASH surgeon in the Korean War, and was internationally recognized as an expert in trauma care. Several other surgeons in the department served in Vietnam as well. Trauma cases came to UVM hospital from all over Vermont as well as parts of New Hampshire, New York, and Canada. Naturally, I wanted to be a trauma surgeon in the beginning. Over time I became more interested in cancer surgery, and after residency I moved to Boston for a surgical oncology fellowship. This was focused on colon cancer research and I was hoping to be a colorectal surgeon. However, at the same time, I had my son and that really changed my perspective. A colorectal fellowship would have required moving and more time away from my family, so after the oncology research fellowship I went into practice. At first I did all kinds of general surgery cases, but over time my focus became breast cancer, both clinically and from a research perspective. Now I can't imagine doing anything else, and feel that I have been very lucky to have great mentors and opportunities along the way in my career. One of the keys to success in surgery or any other field is to be flexible and resilient. Remember not to give up when things don't happen the way you first imagined.

*Title of this essay from John Lennon song: "Beautiful Boy (Darling Boy)"

Inspiring Quote:
"The future belongs to those who believe in the beauty of their dreams."
— Eleanor Roosevelt

Helen Cappuccino, MD, FACS
Surgical Oncologist

Surgical Residency In the 1980s

Reflecting back on my residency training, I felt my program was somewhat enlightened for the time. I remember being grateful for the pioneer female surgeons (like Patricia Numann, Dorothy Lavinia Brown, Jennie Robertson, and Eleanor Davies-Colley) before me, who had blazed trails while enduring real discrimination. Every so often though, someone along the way, almost always a man, was open-minded and forward-thinking enough to give a woman an opportunity based on her merits and not her gender. So it was for me that the first person to encourage me to pursue a career in surgery was a man—one of my teaching surgeons in Buffalo, New York, Dr. Ralph Doerr. He saw how my eyes lit up in the operating room, saw my enthusiasm no matter the hour; for at that time, we medical students worked alongside the residents during the night they were on call. There were no work hour restrictions.

It was back in the day when Lou Flint, who chaired our surgery program, was rumored to have said, "If I had my choice between sex and surgery, I'd be the first on the way to the scrub sink." It was when revered surgical programs touted their 100 percent rate in chief residents of both divorce and peptic ulcer disease, and wasn't long after only rare marriages were "allowed" for surgical residents. While I couldn't imagine forgoing my family, or my husband, or my health for surgery, I was certainly excited by it. Ralph Doerr saw to that. My husband and I already had one child. He aspired to an orthopedics career, and I had been entertaining the thought of a stable, elective radiology career, as a fun and livable complement to my husband's career choice, when I began to want surgery. Choosing it as a career was a titillating but daunting possibility for me.

I finally committed (sort of). When Andy and I did the couple's match, I ranked all my surgical choices with him high, and left some radiology pairings low on the list. I figured fate would decide for me. Although I longed to stay near my home (to make child care and rearing easier), we had some great alternatives out of town. One particularly exciting possibility was a small program in New Jersey's Monmouth Medical Center. Andy and

I had a great interview day there. Their visionary Surgery Department Chair, Cyril Arvanitis, was a bright, distinguished gentleman, enlightened and modern in his thinking. I would later see he was also a most elegant surgeon. (He would always tell me, "There is no wasted motion in surgery, everything you do has to be for a reason;" "palms should always be facing down;" "always have an instrument in each hand." The way he used Metzenbaum's scissors was beautiful, never a wasted snip!) We hit it off immediately. I think he liked being around women, not because of their gender, but because of his perception of a woman's attention to aesthetics and detail. I think he also rightly perceived that women quietly worked twice as hard for half the recognition in that time, and expected no additional praise. During my husband's interview in Orthopedics, Cyril interrupted his meeting with their program chair, Bob Grossman, and said, "You should take him, we want his wife here." Andy, himself, was already warming up to the program and Bob's fun leadership style. Bob remains a dear friend to this day. Not surprisingly, on Match Day we opened envelopes to reveal our next home to be in Monmouth County, NJ. I was admittedly a little intimidated about leaving my hometown and extended family for the first time in my life, vulnerable as a young family. Not only did we have one child born, but another on the way. I chose not to divulge my pregnancy during my residency interviews, as I was afraid it would impact on my viability in their eyes. Thus, I didn't feel it appropriate to take maternity time off at the beginning of residency. So our son Mac was born June 18, and we started our residency on June 28. I was young, naïve, full of energy and excitement. I was sad to leave my son and our daughter so soon after giving birth. I would miss them during my long days and nights of work, but I was ready to be a surgeon.

For the most part, I found residency was gender blind. I worked really hard to distinguish myself. I was first to arrive, last to leave, knew my patients' charts inside and out. I was prepared for every operation after carefully studying *Zollinger's Atlas of Surgical Operations* before each case. I was rewarded by being given big cases to do at an early stage—inguinal hernias and appendixes during the first year; colon resections, thyroids and vascular procedures during the second year of residency. I did whatever I could to gain valuable experience, since my plan was to be a solo practice surgeon in my small hometown. I wanted to see and do everything I could, so I could be the best surgeon possible for my patients.

When my attending surgeons (all male, except for one trauma surgeon) saw my effort, they let me do the cases. They weren't afraid to be direct with us, though. Dr. Frank Frasco, one of my favorite supervising surgeons, would jokingly query me if I were taking too long on a case: "Dr. Cappuccino, you stand accused of savoring this case. How do you plead?!" I was usually guilty. I earned a very solid reputation among my attendings there. They started requesting me for cases.

Along the way, there were "hiccups." For example, I remember a thoracic surgeon who was arrogant and full of himself. He was clearly a chauvinist. Once during a case, he was palpating the patient's lung oddly. He then said, in the middle of a case, for everyone to hear, "Ah, if only women's breasts felt like the lung." You could have knocked me over with a feather! Another time, a surgeon said during surgery, "Give me a resident with big tits who knows how to keep them out of my way." Those two comments were the worst of it.

There was a lot of joking, but it was equal opportunity. One surgeon, who would caution female residents not to go into "labial fibrillation," mercilessly harassed the male residents too. If he saw me heading towards him with another female resident, he would say, "Here comes the Kotex commando!" It was meant in jest, and that's the way I took it. But there were a few other incidents that were unpleasant. Another surgeon, whom I liked to work with, once placed his hands on my hips from behind and pulled me towards him "as a joke." I backed off and told him firmly that he had crossed a line, and to his credit it never happened again, and it never interfered with the rest of our professional relationship. He knew he was wrong.

I was always very careful to be professional beyond reproach. I never sent out mixed signals. I never wanted my gender to be a crutch or an excuse. Some of the other female residents weren't so scrupulous— delivering poorly on their performance, exaggerating their credentials and experience, abusing time off, and then suing for discrimination. I hated them for it, since then all the women surgeons got painted with the same brush. Another female resident seduced an attending, broke up a marriage, confirming another bad stereotype. These women made it harder for me than any of my male colleagues.

The only real difficulty I experienced during residency because of my gender had to do with my pregnancies. I had two children during residency, admittedly a bit closer to each other than ideally I would have liked. One was born in my third year, the other my chief (fifth) year. I never took any time off other than my four weeks of vacation. I didn't take any maternity leave, and I took all my scheduled on-call duties. Despite that, when I told my new chair about my second pregnancy during my fourth year of residency, he went into an hour-long diatribe about what a terrible example I was for my peers, how I lacked seriousness, and that I was a disappointment. (This was the same man mentioned earlier who had caressed the patient's lung). I casually mentioned this to one of my colleagues, who reported back to the hospital's education director. There was quite a fuss. I pled for no action, preferring to prove myself through my actions, but the program saw that what he had done was a real deviation from acceptable. He was admonished, put through sensitivity training, and went on in his own little world. I stayed away from him as much as possible.

I think back on what was memorable from residency—it is all about the patients and the cases. In the time leading up to our fourth child's delivery in my chief year, one of the attendings booked an adrenalectomy. It was five months before residency ended, and I hadn't done one yet! I was so excited. It was booked for one week before my due date. I had never made it to my due date—always a week or two early. I panicked. My fourth-year resident was salivating at the prospect of an early labor for me so he could do the case. The day of the case arrived, and aside from Braxton-Hicks, there were no contractions on the horizon. Unfortunately for me, the patient had never received the pre-op alpha blockers ordered, and the case was postponed for a week. I was fit to be tied! I walked around carefully for the coming days. At the time of the original scheduled date I was already dilated to 4 cm. It was precarious but I made it until the next week, did the case, walked upstairs to the labor room and delivered a healthy baby boy.

As a woman trying to have a normal life during an extraordinarily challenging two-career training time, I remember reaching over a big gravid belly to do cases. I remember waddling down the halls. I remember talking to patients about who I was—not just as a doctor but as a human. I remember wearing nursing pads in my bra so no one would notice how much I was leaking during my first aneurysm repair. I remember being at the mercy of every disastrous baby-sitting nightmare imaginable. I remember bringing my kids with me on weekend rounds, and how wonderful and indispensable the nurses were in helping me get through those rounds when I had my kids. In many ways it was a different time with more latitude. These wonderful experiences made residency memorable, not only for me but for our kids too. They learned an appreciation for the commitment we made to our vocation—one that inspired exactly zero of our six children to go into a medical career!

It saddens me a little that so far (I haven't given up hope) none of our children aspire to medicine. I think it is the noblest of careers. Fortunately for us, it has enabled us to provide for our children in a way that allows them to choose to pursue whatever they like. It gives us a venue to do real charitable deeds that are life-changing for patients. Whether we travel to Third World areas or bring patients in need to us, I like my kids to see that this is a priority for us—giving back meaningfully with our medical skills.

Inspiring Quote:
"Life is not a journey to the grave with the intention of arriving safely in a pretty and well preserved body, but, rather, to skid broadside, thoroughly used up, totally worn out, and loudly proclaiming: wow, what a ride!"
— Erma Bombeck

Sharona Ross, MD, FACS
Hepatobiliary, Foregut and Minimally Invasive Surgeon

My Journey

Sometimes I can't believe it took fifteen years to get here. To say it was easy would be a stretch, but it was absolutely worth it. My journey has been truly amazing.

I was born and raised in the state of Israel and came to the United States with my husband, Jack, an American I'd met while he was working near my hometown of Ashdod. Ashdod is just south of Tel Aviv on the Mediterranean coast. I spent four years at American University (AU) in Washington, DC, as an Honors undergraduate. My first challenge was mastering command of the English language. I knew very little English when we moved to the US, and I was self-taught through recording and interpretation of lectures.

Nonetheless, I graduated summa cum laude from AU and spent the next four years at George Washington University School of Medicine and Health Sciences (GW). I then completed five years of surgical residency at the University of South Florida (USF) College of Medicine in Tampa. I was fortunate to be awarded an Advanced GI Surgical Fellowship and Gastrointestinal Endoscopy Fellowship at USF.

At the same time I was chasing my dream of being a surgeon, I was also raising a family. My two oldest kids, Eran who is seventeen and his sixteen-year-old sister, Nicole, were born during my undergraduate degree at AU. When I started medical school, Eran was a year and five months, and Nicole was two-months old. Our third child, Stephanie, who's now eleven, came during my last year as a GW medical student. Justin, my youngest child, who is now seven, was born during my Chief Resident year at USF.

During this time, Jack earned his Masters and graduated from the American University Washington College of Law.

To say the least, we were busy. When I see pictures from that time, I realize how desperately exhausted I was. I looked horrible! I never cared about myself during that time; the focus was family and school. The goal was to study, study, and then study some more. My haggard look was not without reason.

I wouldn't have changed a thing; I never wanted it any other way, and I'm not complaining now. In fact, it's just the opposite. I'm grateful, so absolutely grateful. I am fortunate to have been able to follow my dreams. Few people have had the opportunities I have been given.

It was always my intent to get married, have four kids and become a surgeon. I never thought I should have to give up one of those goals to accomplish the others. From the time I was a child growing up in Israel, I wanted it all; I wanted everything. No matter how many times others suggested that my goals were a little too lofty, or said such a life was nearly impossible to achieve, I believed I could do it; I could have it all, and I would.

Needless to say, there were a couple of breaks that went our way; these "breaks" were essential to achieving the goals Jack and I had laid out for ourselves. Both of our families were wonderful. When I was pregnant with Eran, my mother came from Israel and stayed with us to help; she did the same with the three children that followed. Jack's family was emotionally, physically and financially supportive. Whatever we needed, they were there for us; we couldn't have done it without them.

In the end, this is a story about how one individual had to adjust, persevere, sacrifice and overcome if she was going to succeed.

I was a woman who wanted to break into a world dominated by men, and all challenges aside, it fell solely on my shoulders to make it or not. Becoming a surgeon while being a mother and wife at the same time may have seemed insurmountable to others, but to me it was always within reach. It always struck me as ludicrous that women couldn't have the things that could fulfill their lives simply because society perceived it to be too difficult to achieve. To accept this notion was unacceptable!

It required two things: a support system, which I had, and a plan for life, which I developed, albeit, sometimes day to day. There were always backups on standby—Plans B, C, and D. All plans were geared towards success in each of the three realms in which I lived: student (later doctor), mother and wife.

The plan started with having children. Men in a similar situation would have the luxury of finishing their training and then starting to think about a family. Because I not only wanted one child, but rather four children, I had to plan from the beginning. My son Eran was actually a surprise, but as it turned out, the timing was perfect. I was twenty-five years old and we'd been married for three years. Focused on my grades, learning English, and the new American way of life, I was not focused on having children just yet. Fortunately, I never had to decide if it was the right time. Though I wanted children, I had a fear of balancing my schooling and medical career with family. Getting pregnant with Eran eliminated those fears. There were too many questions about motherhood and marriage I could not answer; I no longer had to worry about what it would be like. I committed at that moment to have it all, for myself and my family. After he was born, I realized I was mature enough, my marriage was secure enough, and my education was pushing nicely along—even my English at that point was great!

We decided to try and conceive another child six months after Eran was born. We thought this would provide him with a playmate, and this would allow me more time with my studies. Eran was still in diapers and we were already sleep deprived, so bringing another baby into the family didn't seem to be too much of a big deal. Our daughter Nicole was born nine months later.

Because I'd excelled in the honors program at AU, I didn't find the academics in medical school to be too much of a challenge. In fact, I liked it more because everything was interesting; I no longer had to take those pesky little undergraduate requirement courses.

We decided to have our third child, Stephanie, during my last year at GW. This enabled me to have her weaned off breastfeeding, and I would physically be back in shape to start my residency interviews. I didn't want anyone asking me if I had kids or if I had just delivered. I think I was paranoid for a good reason; I think that some people could have held it against me. Though the interviewers are not supposed to ask questions pertaining to kids, I had heard stories of the questions being asked. Some can be pretty blunt, for example, "Why should we spend the money on you? Why should we invest in you when you're probably not going to finish and may wind up going home to be a mother?"

I didn't want to deal with any of that, so we had Stephanie at the right time; I got in shape and went on the interviews.

Tampa, where my practice is today, was fourteenth on my residency wish list. I almost didn't go to the interview that day, but Jack encouraged me to go. He wanted to live in a warm climate, and Tampa offered a nice, family-oriented community. In the end, I discovered that Tampa had a really great program. As the saying goes, I saved the best for last. In addition, some of Jack's family lived in Florida, and they would be able to help support us, as we continued our family and work goals. Moving the lowest ranked interview on my list up to my first preference worked out perfectly on Match Day.

Once I got through the interview process and was accepted, I went to work in the residency rotation. If anyone asked me about my kids and my family, I was always happy to talk about it, but I never volunteered the information. If I didn't talk about it, people didn't focus on the fact that I had kids. What helped me as I moved through my residency was that I never used my family or my kids as an excuse. I never said that I couldn't show up to something because I had to take someone to the doctor or stay home because someone was sick. I always had a plan; I never made that into an excuse.

In the middle of my residency training, the resident's work week was capped at eighty hours. This enabled me to pick up my kids once in a while from school. In one instance, when I tried to pick up my daughter Stephanie, who was three at the time, from school, the teachers wouldn't let her come with me; they were used to seeing Jack or my mother. They reviewed my driver's license, but it was not until a neighbor of ours came in and authorized me as her mom, that they allowed me to take her home. This was a realization of how much I had sacrificed.

One of my last cases as a Chief Resident came when I was nine months pregnant with Justin. I'd felt nauseated and a little tired during the pregnancy, but I had been taking meds prescribed by my obstetrician. This had enabled me to work throughout the pregnancy without any issues. On the night of that last case, a man came in with a laceration to his neck that was bleeding profusely. I immediately jumped onto the gurney and applied pressure to the wound as the staff wheeled us both to the operating room. Some picture that would have made! When we got to the suite, I lay down on a stretcher to rest for a few minutes while they prepped him; I then did the operation. The patient was doing okay when we reported to the next shift, but I never found out what happened to him. Justin was born the next day, and he was a healthy, beautiful little boy.

During my residency and my two fellowships I became interested in laparoscopic and minimally invasive surgery. It was neat, even elegant. Although I had to get used to the lack of tactile sensation felt during an open operation, I quickly fell in love with laparoscopic surgery. Actually, I love both: open and minimally invasive surgery. Using a laparoscopic technique is easier on my arms, neck and shoulders, as there are no retractors. In addition, the patient's recovery is better; there is less pain, less chance of infection, and a quicker return to daily activities.

Working with the laparoscope is beautiful; everything is seen in high definition. The technology is constantly evolving, and it has proven to be a very exciting direction for my career.

My kids are all well-adjusted and growing up. My mother has returned to Israel. We do have a housekeeper to help, but the girls in particular have gotten used to doing things on their own. They are living healthy, independent lives. The boys are great as well; Jack is happy in his career and continues to be immensely supportive—a great partner in our marriage.

I'm pretty successful at compartmentalizing my life. It used to bother me more that I couldn't always be there for everything with my kids, but I've learned to live with it; they have as well. We have all grown to appreciate the time we get to spend together. A surgeon's life is not eight to five, and they know that. When I'm with them, we focus on spending quality time.

I have it all. I'm grateful and never take it for granted. I know how fortunate I am. I was blessed with the perfect husband, terrific kids, a great family on both sides and a career that I always wanted. I have a life that surpasses my wildest dreams.

Inspiring Quote:
"Trust yourself. Create the kind of self that you will be happy to live with all your life. Make the most of yourself by fanning the tiny, inner sparks of possibility into flames of achievement." — Golda Meir

Patricia E. May, MD, FACS
General Surgeon, Surgical Oncologist

It's All About Relationships

I worked at the VA for fifteen years and was amazed by patients' stories of bravery, suffering and endurance. We become the people we are as a result of our experiences with others. It's all about relationships. I recently operated on a ninety-one-year-old man who was accompanied to the hospital by many generations of family members. He was the beloved patriarch, and he had to make it through to the following year, when he would celebrate his seventieth wedding anniversary and his daughter's fiftieth. His attitude was extraordinary. He was quick to get up and walk after major surgery and required only five days of hospitalization. He trusted others and had confidence in our abilities. Near the end, you truly reap the benefits of a life well lived: you exhibit grace under stress, and have people who love you and will care for you.

I had the privilege of working with a pioneer woman surgeon at the end of her career. She had been at our VA more than forty years, and was quick to relate her many career accomplishments. She became ill at work one day, and we all tried to visit her when she remained hospitalized for the last few months of her life. She had never married or had children (she loved to see mine). Initially, I was sad that she had no immediate family to sit at her bedside. But I came to realize that she had lived her life on her own terms and was with her work family until the end.

It's important to cultivate relationships in the midst of a busy surgical career. I feel blessed to have a wonderful husband and three splendid young children. It's hard though: I connect with my patients so strongly that I often find it difficult to pull myself away from the hospital. There is always more to do! In the words of my colleagues, *sometimes you just have to leave*. I recently asked a friend to spend the night when my husband was out of town with our daughter on a field trip. I was on call and needed her backup. Sure enough, shortly after we got the kids to bed, I was called in and spent most of the evening working. I came home briefly, around one a.m. She was up and we shared girl talk until I was called in again. This was so much more vital than paying a nanny or babysitter to watch the kids. Obviously, you can't do this all the time, but calling on friends in need strengthens the friendship bond. We had so much fun!

I have known my best friend, Misti, since my freshman year of college. She attended my residency graduation dinner and was amusingly insightful about the differences between surgical and corporate culture. Through the years, she has supported me, prayed for me, and put up with long silences due to my surgical schedule. We have become more than friends, we are also sisters (sisters-in-law to be specific) for the last fifteen years. I met my husband, Jeff, at her wedding to his brother, Randy. Jeff and I walked down the aisle together in Laguna Beach, California, as attendants at their wedding, and they did the same for us five months later in Reno.

I want to say a few words about my research study nurse, who is also a Nurse Practitioner, and about the many nurses I've worked with over the years. They are some of my closest friends. I have been over-fed, prayed over, guided out the door home to my family, cleaned up, hydrated, nursed, and generally cared for over the years in ways that go far beyond their job *and* friendship descriptions. I think of the time when I was the only one on call, and operating, with the flu; the nurses started an IV and hydrated me. I made it through and the patients did well! They welcomed me to town with presents, birthday remembrances, Christmas gifts; and hosted a wedding shower, then baby showers. They brought my family food after each baby delivery, and cared for us during those early newborn weeks. They have always included me in their celebrations and lives. They have helped me move, watched my children when I was called to work or out of town. They even cleaned up my vomit when I was sick in the ER while on call—again getting me and the patients through safely. They shared funny stories, pictures, hugs and prayers when I was struggling with balancing the needs of three young children and full-time academic surgery. I cannot say enough about their selfless love, encouragement, and care—not to mention their superb clinical insight. When certain nurses call, I know it's serious and I run. I have seen them touch countless patients' lives with their loving nursing care.

I have been blessed with several mentors, but have never deliberately sought them out. My parents were both fiercely independent and instilled that in me. They were the smartest people I know. My father was a gifted student, expected to get top academic honors in a small town Alabama high school, when his father took his hard-earned book money that he had saved for his senior year (to buy alcohol, I'm told). My father was so devastated that he ran off and joined the Navy at the age of seventeen. He completed his education, graduated from school through the Navy, and never looked back. He never spoke of his childhood, and I found out about this incident much later from my mother. His hardships turned him into a dedicated family man who devoted himself to my mother and us children. He was an air traffic controller who turned down leadership promotions so that we would not have to move. He believed in the importance of his work in air safety, and refused to strike when his colleagues walked out. He lost some friendships but he always followed his principles. I feel the same way about surgery. You can never walk out on those in need. Do your best and fight the system to make changes, but never make a stand at the expense of patients.

My mother grew up in San Francisco, graduated from nursing school at UC Berkeley, and was living on her own, aged twenty-three when she met my father, serving in the Navy, who was three years younger. She played piano at a soup kitchen and also played violin in a symphony. My mother was the ultimate phone-a-friend lifeline. She could answer any question about history, literature, even pop culture. My parents fell in love and were married three months after meeting. They remained married for thirty-nine years, with utmost devotion until my father's death. My mother never remarried. My parents never went with the pack, and deliberately sought out the narrow path. Thus, I was encouraged to make my own way.

Deciding that the brain was the last frontier in research, I looked for research opportunities in this field. Early in my studies at the University of California, Irvine, I embarked on research projects at the Center for Neurobiology and memory, for Dr. Norman Weinberger. For two years I worked with students, faculty and postdocs, perfusing, extracting and analyzing rat brains after a conditioned behavior. I learned a tremendous amount—about brain cell types, neurochemistry, and also, how to critically analyze research papers. But our work was not published during those years, and I felt deficient when applying to medical school. Dr. Weinberger was a wonderful mentor, who encouraged analytical thought and research development. Years later, I understand his parting encouragement not to let medical school be a "waste" of my intellect. During my career, I came across many types who seek mentorship only to get ahead and publish. I gave no thought to publication at the time, and joined in research because of the subject. He cared about my intellectual development, which is a far greater gift than a publication.

I knew I wanted to be a doctor early on, but did not know what kind. In my third year of medical school, I began my clinical rotations with Surgery, because everyone said it was hard and it was best to get it over with. I loved it! I had no prior surgical experience and I was awed when, at the end of my rotation, I was handed the scalpel to perform an appendectomy, from skin to skin. The attendings were rewarding my hard work and interest. They complimented my technique! I don't think my feet touched the ground for days. Although I loved every clinical rotation, I realized that nothing was as exciting as surgery. I had no real mentors during my rotation, so I asked to meet with Dr. Philip Donahue, then Chairman of the Surgery Department at Cook County Hospital. He was kind and offered to write me a letter of recommendation. Thus, I experienced another great mentor moment. Sometimes, mentorship comes with brief encounters!

Another brief encounter changed my perspective. As a brand new intern, I sat in Vascular Conference with Dr. Julie Freichlag and my Surgery Department Chair from Harbor UCLA. My Chair could not remember me from interviews and orientation and thought I was on Dr. Freischlag's service. But Dr. Freischlag remembered me as a medical student interviewing for residency over a year earlier. I was stunned. She actually remembered enough details about me so that it was clear that this was genuine. I was forever impressed that an important surgeon could remember a lowly student and express caring. Mentorship is about caring, not just advice.

My husband and I have never vacationed away from our children. We've never had the desire, so have never felt that we missed anything. We appreciate the occasional date night, and have found that day dates are easier to schedule weekly. Our hospitals are not too far from each other, so whenever we have a free moment, we meet for coffee or lunch. I am blessed with a husband who loves to spend time with me and the kids. We both believe family time is so precious that we don't want to waste a moment away from them. Perhaps having children later in life adds to the charm. I've taken the whole family to medical meetings, when our schedules allow, so we can have family adventures even when I have to work. Many of my medical colleagues do this, and I think it's a wonderful way to stay connected.

After a General Surgery residency and a Surgical Oncology clinical fellowship, I moved to Reno to join the VA under the leadership of Dr. Ralph DePalma. I had found home. I loved the beautiful outdoor lifestyle of Reno and was honored to work at the VA. I am passionate about caring for veterans and believe they deserve our very best. Dr. DePalma supported my academic development and has continued to encourage me in scholarly activities. He walked me down the aisle to give me away when I married Jeff, after the death of my father.

A year after Dr. DePalma left Reno to become the National Director of Surgery for the VA, many faculty members retired. They were upset by the loss of surgery residents from the University of Nevada Las Vegas. Everyone was leaving because the residents were being taken away, and I was left in charge. After calling several department chairs, I was fortunate to connect with Dr. Claude Organ, at UCSF-East Bay. I showed him what the Reno VA had to offer educationally, and we started the UCSF-East Bay Surgery program in Reno within a year. I began with one resident (hand-picked by Dr. Organ), Dr. Linda Barry, who embraced the challenge! She was the perfect pioneer resident, who rolled with the changes and provided great feedback and leadership to subsequent residents. Over the next few years, we gradually built the program to four Surgical residents and one resident in Family Practice. I feel fortunate to have known Dr. Organ. When he and Dr. Gerald Peskin first came to visit Reno, I was nearly nine months pregnant. They still believed in my ability to lead the program, and never once questioned my intentions or commitment during or after maternity leave. After Dr. Organ retired, Dr. Alden Harkin became Chair of UCSF-East Bay Surgery Department. I have truly been blessed by his mentorship.

I have loved working with the residents over the years, and my children have great memories of residents at every holiday gathering. Residents have played long games with my kids, listened patiently to their stories, watched impromptu plays and puppet shows, and been serenaded by piano concertos, waltzes and lullabies. My kids have heard about other countries and traditions, and now have adventurous palates and an appetite for travel.

After completing my residency, I learned important things about myself and others during a month of volunteer surgery in Cameroon, Africa. Surgery is not just about procedures and skills, it's about caring enough to pray for patients and make a connection to their circumstances. I believe surgery is a calling. So much of what we do on a daily basis is above and beyond what's required that we must keep our purpose in mind when the hours get long and hard. I feel so blessed to give my best to my patients that I sometimes forget how hard it can be on my family. I know that my children do not have as much mommy time as they could, and thus they sacrifice as well. I hope that the lesson they learn is that life is about service. Parenthood and surgery are both about using your skills and abilities to their full potential and knowing when to lead and when to listen. I credit God with transforming my life and guiding me to a life with purpose, and I pray that my children will not be limited by my shortcomings.

I'm just starting my next chapter in Surgery at "Kaiser Permanente." I am invigorated by this challenge and growing in new ways! As only my husband truly understands, "More later!"

Inspiring Quote:
"Happiness is not a goal . . . it's a by-product of a life well lived."
— Eleanor Roosevelt

Heather Lillemoe, MD
General Surgery Resident

M.D. Means "My Daddy"

It may come as a surprise to learn that growing up with an academic surgeon for a father wasn't particularly unusual. In the Lillemoe household, as in many others, dinner conversations revolved around sports. Generally, my father focused on how his beloved Yankees were doing, but he would always ask about our games and practices. I have three older siblings and all of us participated in sports. We didn't sit around and discuss the hepatobiliary system or hear details about the eight-hour procedure my dad had performed that day. In fact, as it is with many fathers, we were lucky to pull him away from SportsCenter once he made it home for the evening. Honestly, it wasn't until I was a bit older that I realized what it meant when I told people my father was a surgeon. Now, as a medical student about to embark on a career in surgery, I realize the meaning of the word better than ever before.

As a child, I can remember a poem we had framed in our front hall that was entitled "M.D. means My Daddy." The poem perfectly described my feelings toward my father's profession. I knew he was a doctor and I liked to tell people that. He wore cool-blue scrubs like the doctors on TV and looked at fascinating pictures of things like the pancreas, which I would show to my friends to gross them out. He could even save the day at our sporting events by running out onto the field and offering his expertise (which was not in orthopedics, might I add). When I was five, I decided I would become a doctor so that I could save the day, too. And although I wavered back and forth about the idea for the next twelve years or so, here I am in medical school finishing up my clinical rotations.

Throughout my time in medical school, I slowly discovered that general surgery is where I belong. There was no single moment that led me to this realization, but I think it is a perfect fit. My experiences up until medical school were biased. I only had exposure to surgeons. In fact, I went into medical school with a goal of *not* pursuing a career in surgery. I wanted to do something different. However, as I experienced all of the other specialties, none could compare to surgery. I loved the fact that I could interact with patients, collaborate with a team, and perform procedures all in one day's work. Working with my hands and dealing with the anatomy I loved so much during my anatomy course was an additional bonus.

To be honest, the fact that I am a woman has not affected my choices thus far. As I first explored my interest in the field of medicine, my father made sure that I met many female physicians. In fact, I met so many women in the field of surgery growing up that I never even thought about the male surgeon stereotype. I know that many women in the field of medicine have remarkable stories about the adversity they have faced. Female surgeons, especially, have had to deal with the challenges of surviving in a male-dominated field. After hearing these stories and meeting many outstanding female surgeons, I have learned that being a woman should not hold me back from anything. Even after exploring my interest in orthopedic surgery, where I met very few female physicians, I felt comfortable and confident even when I was the only woman in the room.

My mother constantly tells me that I am just like my father (this is her explanation for why we butt heads so often). We both deny it, but I presume it is true. And it wasn't until these past few years that I realized she was giving me *quite* the compliment. I remember the first time my father took me into the hospital with him. He had this confidence around him like nothing I have ever seen. It truly amazed me. When we finally entered the OR, his eyes lit up like it was Christmas morning and I finally understood there was a whole other part of him that I had never known. This man was not the goofball of a father I knew; he was a brilliant surgeon. As his youngest child and the only one embarking on a medical career, I felt honored. I realized from that point on, that I had the opportunity to share something with him that no one else did.

I have tried to keep that feeling with me now that I am in medical school applying for a residency in general surgery, especially when I feel pressured to become the person my father wants me to be. I remind myself at the end of the day that he just wants me to find the happiness that he found in what he does. He has always said, "I've never worked a day in my life," and that is something I hope I can say for myself one day. While I do not feel like I have an advantage over any other student in terms of knowledge or skill because my father is who he is (unless having skills in fantasy football will score me points in the OR), I know that the fire that has driven him is inside me as well.

I don't know for sure what the next phase of life holds for me, but I do know that I have a lot to live up to . . . and potentially some pretty big clogs to fill.

Inspiring Quote:
"Believe me, the reward is not so great without the struggle."
— Wilma Rudolph

Editor's note: This essay was written when Heather was in medical school.

Madison Griffin, MD
General Surgery Resident

What It Takes to Be a Surgeon

As a third-year medical student, my perspective on women in surgery is even more limited than my experience with surgery itself. Only one week into my cardiovascular surgery rotation, I can now boast about scrubbing in on four surgeries: two CABGs (coronary artery bypass grafts), an AVF (arterio-venous fistula) and a neonatal arterial switch. All four were very interesting, and all four were performed by men. The most interaction I have had with women in surgery has been through a newly formed lecture series I was fortunate to have founded called "Women in Surgery."

The lecture series was to serve a similar role as this book—to highlight women in surgery and to explore the pathways, roadblocks and lifestyles of different women involved in surgery. My task was to find our speakers. Seemingly a simple task, I began by searching all the women surgeons associated with the University of Texas at Houston. There were less than ten. I needed a few more speakers, so I expanded first to Baylor College of Medicine, then to the Texas Medical Center, and eventually to Houston, in general. It was through this process that I realized how few women surgeons exist. It was through their speaking that I realized not only how special a woman must be to be a surgeon, but also how special a surgeon must be to be a woman.

These surgeons, all of whom are highly sought after and extremely respected in their individual specialties, told story after story about their life as a student or resident, favorite case, children, vacation, favorite hobby, and more. From an ironman triathlon to a long-distance relationship to a child's championship tournament to saving a life, these women's stories and lives have inspired me to work past my school requirements, past my exhaustion, and past my self-imposed limits.

I don't know much about the struggles these women went through to get where they are now. I know it took hard work and tons of time. I know it took priorities and sacrifice. But I also know that they did it and did it really well!

At the beginning of the lecture series, I was disillusioned. I thought that surgeons, male and female, were the medical field's version of "the best at everything." I have learned, though, that while surgeons are all very good at whatever they do, that is not because they are superhuman. They cannot do everything, and they especially cannot do everything well—they have to choose and sacrifice. A great surgeon can also be a great mom, but a great surgeon cannot necessarily be a great mom and great marathon runner and a best friend to all. A great surgeon, male or female, must know him- or herself, his or her limits, his or her priorities, and act on these things.

Society in the past has told us that a female should be a wife and mom and therefore complete all items on a wife and mom's traditional to-do list. Though these social rules are changing, albeit slowly, when I started the "Women-in-Surgery" series, I thought there were so few because of this discrimination. After this WIS lecture series and my work with some incredibly talented male surgeons, I have since decided it may instead be due to the special personality traits required for anyone to make it, male or female.

Surgery is a unique field. It requires intelligence, fine motor skills, strength, creativity, confidence, dedication, hard work, time-management, self-awareness and very understanding family and friends. Male or female, a surgeon must be willing to sacrifice part of his or her personal life for the wellbeing of the patient. He or she must be willing to be a perfectionist for others' benefit, not for his or her own glory.

Who cares that every time I walk into the operating room I only see male surgeons? The most likely explanation might be that the female surgeons have already finished. Just kidding, but I do know that somewhere there exist women who have set many examples of success and life balance.

I would like to end, therefore, by saying thank you to certain individuals: Dr. Ahmed, Dr. Alexander, Dr. Alford, Dr. Austin, Dr. Hayes-Jordan, Dr. Kao, Dr. Kozar, Dr. Letsou, Dr. Love, Dr. Moore, Dr. Moore-Olufemi, Dr. Souchon, Dr. Weltge and Dr. Wiatrek. I will take the life lessons you have taught me, and because of them I will be a better doctor, wife, mother, daughter and friend.

Inspiring Quote:

"The secret to getting ahead is getting started." — Sally Berger

Editor's note: This essay was written when Madison was in medical school.

SECTION 4—WOMANHOOD AND SURGERY

Claire Cronin, MD, FACS, MBA
General Surgeon

"What's It Like Being a Woman Surgeon?"

I am frequently asked by medical students and patients, "What's it like being a woman surgeon?" They ask it in a tone that makes me believe they wish to hear a tale of triumph over the odds of making it into a male-dominated field. They are hoping for a GI Jane-type story, where Demi Moore not only completes Navy SEAL training but gains the respect of her fellow men in the process. There are many similarities between the military and the field of surgery: the hours and food are awful, there is a hierarchy that you must abide by, you are pushed to your limits, and some people go AWOL. Unlike the SEALs, however, women are allowed to become surgeons and, therefore, have the opportunity to achieve equal amounts of success as men do.

I can only speak for myself, but my thirteen years of experience as a surgeon carries very little of the anticipated drama expected by the person asking the question. At least not enough to get a movie made about me. This doesn't mean, however, that men and women are treated equally in surgery. They aren't. It's just that the differences run both ways as far as fairness goes. The real answer to the question is more complex than the typical girl versus boy conflict. Biases are more subtle, often not intentional, and take on different characteristics at different stages in a woman's career.

I was the only medical student in my third year core surgical rotation who expressed an interest in surgery as a career. My desire to become a surgeon, along with some technical abilities learned during my research years, afforded me special treatment. The residents would assign me to first assist one attending in particular, who allowed me to do most of the operation. Unlike the other interns who were doing one hour cases, this very nice attending would allow me to scrub into his four-to-five-hour cases. I was delighted to be treated like an intern instead of a medical student, and was convinced that gender discrimination was a thing of the past. It was only later in the rotation that I learned that inguinal hernias were not supposed to last half the day, and that I was being used to free the house staff from having to scrub with this surgeon, who was later diagnosed with an extremely underactive thyroid that contributed to his slowness in the OR. This experience has nothing to do with any female prejudice in surgery but, rather, the usual flow of sewage down the hierarchy, which in a way is the point I am trying to make about my third-year experience.

When I was an intern, one of the senior residents started her graduation speech with her answer to the same question as at the start of this essay. She recited a very funny yarn about how, as a new surgical intern, she had to accompany an intubated ICU patient for an MRI of the brain and stand by the ventilator, while the patient was having the study. She imitated the tedious task of removing all the metal objects from her person before entering the MRI suite. This was particularly amusing because she wore more jewelry than your average rapper. She described the glares coming from the team of nurses and technicians, who were impatiently waiting for her to help move the patient into the scanner, as she slowly pried the rings from her fingers and unclasped each chain from her neck. Finally, when she was all set, she was locked in the room with the patient and the study began. Suddenly, she felt this intense gravitational pull arising from her chest and her breasts began to vibrate. Unaccustomed to female surgery residents, the MRI technicians had not thought to warn her about the underwire in her bra!

I doubt that this was the only obstacle she had to overcome in her five years of training, but for her surgical residency it was not a big deal. I tend to agree with her from a training standpoint. Our chief of surgery hired more women into our program than was statistically necessary. He truly believed that women made great surgeons and was proud of his stable. Many of my former co-residents have successful careers at major medical institutions across the country. Unfortunately, his charity towards women did not extend outside of the hospital environment. He would often say that women belonged in the operating room but not on the golf course. My ability to play golf never resulted in an invitation to his country club along with the guys, but I did get into a good training program without a handicap.

As far as the surgical attendings go, we had the usual roster of char- acters. There was the cowboy, the old guard, the legend, the insecure who never left after residency—because the thought of making an independent decision was overwhelming—and the ones who should have gone into something that didn't require the use of their hands. Most of them accepted the female residents without complaint and enjoyed teaching us. The women interns tended to be better organized on the floors and were less arrogant than the men. The older surgeons who were reputed to be brutal in the operating room were often downright sweet to us girls. I can't decide if this difference in behavior was due to chivalry from a bygone era or if they were just afraid that we would cry. Either way, we often got a buy.

Some attendings found all residents an annoying necessity, and we learned not to draw too much attention to ourselves in their presence. After my transplant rotation, one of these misanthropic types stopped me in the hall and told me that I did a great job. He had never voluntarily spoken to me throughout the month except to tell me that I was doing *it* wrong. The best part about his compliment was that it didn't come with "for a girl," because he disliked everyone equally.

Very few of the surgeons disliked women on principle. We did have one misogynistic chief of surgery who came after I had left residency. When I was introduced to him at a surgical meeting, he looked at my outstretched hand as if it was unsterile, before walking away. He is currently being sued by some other hand that he didn't shake, which makes me a believer in karma.

I never had a male surgeon come on to me either. Of course there were the "dears" and "honeys" from the older guys, but that was kind of endearing. I was therefore surprised when I overheard my no-nonsense attending engage in a racy banter with a fellow resident in the operating room. The possibilities were there but I never went down that path, and I believe that my message of "not interested" was received.

There were only a few female attendings during my training. None were in real positions of authority and few did large surgeries. As we all know, bigger cases equals more respect. Most were excited to mentor another woman but some were competitive. It's since been explained to me that some women have worked their whole life to fight for airtime with men, and they find the idea of competing with another woman intolerable. If you ever hear a female in a position of authority tell you she is a great mentor to women residents, stay away. Real mentors don't need to say it.

Although my breasts never did vibrate in an MRI machine, I think residency was a fairly neutral experience. This sentiment also applies to my surgical colleagues, now that I am out in the working world. Most surgeons are hard-working and, despite some competition for patients, they're just happy to have another set of hands to help. I think of us as a group that is standing shoulder-to-shoulder digging ditches. There is so much emergency work that they are just happy to have another body digging next to them, no matter what the gender. If one of us falls, it means more work for the others, and thus there is a mutual respect . . . mostly.

The one caveat applies to the perception of breast surgeons. Just like in high school, the surgical world has cliques and stereotypes, and breast surgeons are close to the bottom of the ladder. A lot of women enter this field intentionally for a number of reasons, which include research, interest and lifestyle. Others are brought in by default, because they own a pair and therefore must be good at it. Most full-time breast surgeons no longer take emergency room call and limit their practice to what is considered minor surgery, which is the source of disrespect from colleagues. These same women have changed breast surgery, so that it is a fast-growing field. I am still trying to figure out what it is about staying up all night and removing foreign bodies from patients' rectums that make one a real surgeon, but I still do it out of peer pressure.

As surgical residents, we had no need to cultivate relationships with the internal medicine residents, and we did all we could to avoid their annoying consults. Private practice requires an adjustment in attitude in order to generate referrals, which then lead to operations and ultimately a paycheck. The superiority we felt as surgical residents over the "fleas" (a term used to describe internal medicine residents), because we worked the longest hours with the fewest people, is quickly replaced by deference and availability to the internists.

Referral patterns from the primary care physicians (PCP) have a curious pattern of gender prejudice. Who knew, but there are "boy-surgeries" and "girl-surgeries." Internists have a tendency to refer breast surgery to girls and male hernias and colectomies to boys. When I first started practice, I could not understand why I was getting all the breast referrals and none of the colon patients, when I was one of the few doctors who could do laparoscopic colectomies. There is a subconscious urge on the part of the referring doctors to send women problems to women and men problems to men. This theory may not hold in academic centers where sub-specialty training by women overcomes this bias, but it does in the community hospitals where everyone is a generalist.

I get sent a lot of patients that resemble me demographically. My most common non-breast patients are young women with children who need cholecystectomies and herniorrhaphies. This is a wonderful population of patients to have, because they are healthy and have very treatable problems. These women come in saying that they heard from their PCPs that I have just had a baby as well. In reality my baby is twelve years old, but when I started practice and met the internists in the hospital, I was visibly pregnant. The internists no longer come to the hospital, but their impression of me pregnant remains in their mind forever, and influences who they send to me. I am convinced that patients will be asking about my baby when I am in my sixties, with looks of confusion.

The most impartial stakeholders are the patients. The sicker the patient the more gender-blind they are. They're just happy there is someone available to take care of them. Occasionally I'll have a patient ask me, at two a.m., if I've ever done an appendectomy before (as if they really have any chance of finding a second opinion at that time), but I attribute that to age mostly. My answer is usually, "No, but I have the book in the room." To show how sick they are, I usually get an "Oh, all right then," for a response.

The geriatric patients are great. Some, like my father-in-law, can hardly wait to tell their friends that they have a woman doctor, in the same tone they would use to brag about mastering the Internet. They feel modern. Others can't quite grasp the concept. On more than a few occasions, after explaining how I perform a hernia repair and getting a signed consent, they will ask me, "So who's going to do the operation?" The first few times, I was insulted with the implication that a wise, grey-haired man would be do- ing the surgery, and that I was some sort of assistant. Now I laugh and say, "That would be me." When they show up for a post-op visit, these same enlightened souls undoubtedly ask me, "Do you know what *they* found at the surgery?" and I have to answer, "*They* is still *me*—and *I* found . . ."

The only other patient interaction that I believe there is a big difference in has to do with time spent during a consultation. Patients ex- pect to sit down with women physicians and have a good, long chat during every visit. It's not the same with the men. One of my male partners can meet a new breast-cancer patient and book a mastectomy in twenty minutes. I can barely do it in an hour. I am torn between rationalizing this from the patient's perspective—as a male surgeon's time is more valuable than a woman's time versus women are more approachable. I am less productive because of it but, then again, I would want someone to spend an hour with me before removing my breast.

Despite women representing close to 50 percent of all medical school admissions, we represent only 30 percent of surgeons, and even less as hospital and departmental leaders.[1] As a former trustee of our hospital and associate chair of surgery, I realize that this form of discrimination permeates all academic and hospital administration positions. This is the true glass ceiling that still remains. Part of it is the time commitment it takes to be a chair and run a practice. This requires the ability to negotiate a salary that allows you to be away from your practice. Many female chairs I know are not paid at the same rate as men are, and find it difficult to ask for more money when they have just been flattered with the offer of the position.

To answer my original question, as to what it's like to be a woman in surgery—it's great. It's definitely not worse than being a man but it's different. Some things are easier and some are harder. I have opportunities open to me that men don't have and vice versa. For example, the next time a patient that I just operated on asks on rounds, "Do you know what *they* found during surgery?" and I am in a rush, I can always answer, "I'll ask."

[1] www.acshpri.org/.../ACSHPRI_Surgical_Workforce_in_USapr2010.pdf; http://www.facs.org and www.womensurgeons.org

Inspiring Quote:
"Everything is copy." — Phoebe Ephron to her daughter Nora

Helen Cappuccino, MD, FACS
Surgical Oncologist

Girl Surgeon

As a woman with a surgical career, I have taken a meandering path. Being a woman, a wife and a mother has prompted me to change my job positions, and my gender and appearance have also given me some unique challenges.

My grandmother is ninety-five years old this summer, and she has almost no wrinkles. Her husband, my wonderful ninety-seven-year-old Grandpa Jack, calls me the "little girl surgeon." Even now as I knock on the door of fifty, I have always looked young for my age. This has been a mixed blessing for me as a female surgeon. For the rare patient who has not stayed with me after a consultation and who has gone on to have surgery elsewhere, I genuinely don't think it had anything to do with my gender or appearance. For the most part, I think these characteristics actually set people at ease. Once I get talking, and people understand that I have the requisite surgical knowledge, they are happy to sit back, have a conversation and ask questions, because they aren't intimidated. I like that patients feel comfortable with me and find me easy to approach.

Fresh out of residency, I returned to my childhood hometown and started a solo private practice. It was very scary and lonely, but I longed for the old-fashioned, small-town feel of practicing medicine in a community that truly needed doctors and respected the treasured few they had. I especially liked this type of surgical practice because we had almost no surgical specialists; and we general surgeons performed a wide variety of cases, which I felt well-trained for. The other wonderful thing is that we had patients across the near-full spectrum of life. I cherished getting to know not just individuals but families. Within the same family, I might retrieve a hot-dog from the esophagus of the three-year-old who had chewed poorly; suture the canthus or chin of the boisterous eight-year-old; do an appendectomy on a teenager; a cholecystectomy on the young mother; a thyroidectomy on her a few years later; the colon resection on her husband; a carotid endarterectomy on her father; and then a gastrostomy tube on her grandfather. For more than a decade in this small town, I grew close to many families and patients, as I treated them across the span of their lives. I really valued the relationships I built. I liked seeing them in the grocery store, chatting with them, catching up on how each was doing. They also seemed happy for this familiarity, and more often than not it made our professional relationship better too.

The only negative was the occasional patient who simply stopped by our house on a Sunday afternoon, in an attempt to avoid a busy emergency department for a quick surgical problem. Happily, it didn't happen too often. It was a small enough town that I would still occasionally visit patients in their homes as needed. I loved seeing patients in the context of their fuller lives. I never regretted making this special effort. The patients and their families were always so appreciative.

As our family grew and our surgical careers went into high gear over the next twelve years, it was increasingly difficult to juggle my very busy practice with my growing family. I couldn't recruit good enough help with the practice. I was at a terrible juncture and ultimately made the decision to close my practice and take a position at our cancer hospital, Roswell Park Cancer Institute (the oldest cancer hospital in the US).

It all started when I sought additional training in sentinel lymph node biopsies there. As a female surgeon, I seemed to see a disproportionate number of women who had breast cancer. I wanted to deliver them the very best care, even though I was in a "small-town" hospital. While getting trained in the cancer hospital in this technique, I was asked to stay on and help. I did so, on a very limited part time basis for two years, and then eventually closed my practice and worked more at the hospital, but still on a part time basis. Being a specialist in breast cancer surgical care at an academic institute ironically provided me with some of the same professional joys that small-town surgery did.

I have come to love the protracted relationships I have with patients as I follow them from their diagnosis, perform their surgery, and then do their long-term follow up care. I am sad that surgeons may not do as much of this in the future, as more and more follow-up is designated to physician extenders, such as nurse practitioners and physicians' assistants. I am not sure my proclivity to real friendliness with patients, or appreciation of the long-term aspect of the relationships, is unique to female surgeons, but it seems common enough among my female colleagues that perhaps it may be related to gender. I know many surgeons prefer the "quick hit" problem-focused nature of surgery, more than the relationships built across a patient's or even a family's life.

I talk with many of my female medical colleagues who grapple with the crossed interests of patients and their practices. Patients have an innate expectation that women will be more communicative, and that we will spend more time with patients, which directly conflicts with the current push to productivity and volume by medical centers. I am grateful that so far I have never had external pressure from my wonderful hospital to speed up my patient interactions. I cherish the connection that patient interaction can bring. While I don't ever initiate it, I am often tempted to give patients a hug. Happily, because they don't feel threatened or intimidated, they often reach out and hug me instead. It makes me feel great, and I think it makes them happy to have that connection too. In this increasingly "politically correct" and "watch who and how you touch world," real human connection is wonderfully affirming. It seems especially comforting to the breast cancer patients I treat. That level of comfort seems to give them peace, as they struggle emotionally and physically through their cancer journey with me at their side.

I think being female really helps to open up the lines of communication. Two-way communication is vital to every patient partaking in their understanding of the disease process, the proposed surgical intervention and what their post-operative course will be. Anything that makes it easier for them is a great thing in my opinion. Being easy to approach, easy to talk to, listening carefully and actively, and spending the requisite time for a relaxed dialogue is vital. Things that are now stressed in medical school such as open-ended questions, taking time, making eye contact and being non-judgmental somehow seem (to me) more intuitive and natural to women historically. I am thrilled that these approaches are now actually part of what is stressed in the classroom.

All patients need to feel comfortable communicating with their physicians—not just women. Male patients also seem at ease when they can be open with me. They ask a lot of questions and don't seem intimidated.

I remember early on in my practice, as a solo general surgeon in a small town with no specialists, I did a very wide variety of surgery. I once cared for a kind but frustrated man who was an oxygen-dependent pulmonary cripple. He was physiologically older than his tender age of mid-sixties. He had a lot of hard living and smoking on his frame. His FEV1 (forced expiratory volume in 1 second) was less than 30 percent, and much of both his thoracic cavities were consumed by massive pulmonary blebs, especially on one side. He refused a referral to a tertiary care center, even though he was confronting choices about a permanent ventilator versus death. He clearly wasn't willing to endure a lifetime chained to a ventilator. We discussed a thoracoscopic blebectomy (at that time a much newer procedure in which I had gratefully been well-trained), and I quoted him a 60 percent mortality rate. He immediately agreed to the surgery, but I made him mull it over for a couple weeks. He came back, expressed his comfort and faith in me, and presented me with a teacup as a gift and a card, which stated that he'd rather die in the care and hands of a beautiful surgeon trying to save him than live his life "crippled" by his poorly functioning lungs. Happily, his surgery went beautifully and he enjoyed a new lease on a much better life.

Not all outcomes are as heart-warming and happy. Like any surgeon who operates frequently, I have had rare fatal outcomes. These are so difficult to live with. Like any surgeon, I grapple with every single detail of the case, trying to understand what I could have done to change the outcome, and usually not finding an answer. But I do believe that after a negative outcome women surgeons are more inclined to communicate feelings such as sorrow, regret, sympathy and our own fallibility to the family. On these rare occasions, it was my habit to attend the patients' funerals and/or memorial services. I always expressed my sorrow, often in a card too. Sure, the lawyers would advise against it, but I need to live with myself, I have to be able to sleep at night, and I trust my instincts. I think, in general, women—and many women surgeons—are willing to "put themselves out there" when things aren't as perfect as we'd like, or when our outcomes are not what we worked so hard for. I strongly believe it's important for patients to understand our fallibility and our humanity.

Medicine will always have new frontiers to explore, and an interesting one is communication. I just accepted a "friend request" from a patient on Facebook. I feel it is a new boundary that must be explored and defined. It's a new way to know our patients and have them know us if used judiciously. Since the old, pre-digital days, I have maintained a file of cards and letters from patients. On days when things aren't perfect—a bad schedule, a difficult surgery, a challenging patient or family—I derive such peace and pleasure reading through notes that now span nearly thirty years. They are a reminder of why it is a true joy and privilege to practice surgery. In the new era of electronic medical records, excessive documentation and litigation, it is a beautiful thing to see a hand-written note from a grateful patient. In the end, we as healers and our patients are first human, and it is good to start understanding each other in every way we can.

Inspiring Quote:
"The good, the bad, the hardship, the joy, the tragedy, love and happiness are all interwoven into one single indescribable whole that is called life. You cannot separate the good from the bad. And, perhaps, there is no need to do so either." — Jackie Kennedy Onassis

Kerry Bennett, MD, MPH, FACS, CPCC
Breast and General Surgeon

A Celebration of Women In Surgery!

I want to celebrate women surgeons. I used to think that being a woman surgeon was no different than being a male surgeon. I was wrong. When I hear the phrase "Women in Surgery" it reminds me of a few stories from residency. I shall title these "I Will Change You," The "WIS or Wus Service" and "Life Lessons." The first two stories are brief but "Life Lessons," from having children, is a bit longer and continues each day of my life.

"I Will Change You"

When I was a third-year resident, I was called into the residency program director's office to discuss my high enthusiasm and energy levels. As with all stories, I can only speak of my perspective. What I heard from him was that my enthusiasm and kindness were "not surgical enough." I remember him telling me, "We are going to beat it out of you," and that to succeed I would need to become more somber and controlled. Well, nothing could have made me more focused on retaining my enthusiasm and kindness. On the other hand, I did temper it and try to fit in better. It was with great pride that I shook his hand, as a fourth-year resident, to win the prize for "most competent surgical resident," which included being kind, good with patients and staff, technically proficient and reliable. At the time he told me to change I was so angry. Years later, I see that his talk with me strengthened my desire to be a wholly competent surgeon: one who cared, listened, was easy to work with and was technically meticulous. I swore they wouldn't beat my difference out of me, and I retained my essence but tempered it to fit in better.

The Women in Surgery: "WIS" or "Wus" Service?

This service has no such change in interpretation. I can still feel the fire of anger begin to burn as I remember being in that hallway of Four North in the new building at Tufts-New England Medical Center. I was on a service with two other women: a resident completing her residency and another fourth-year resident. The Chief Resident and Residency Program Director/acting Chief of Surgery (both men) passed the three of us in the hallway. As they passed, the Chief Resident said, "Oh, it's the wus service." One of the other women said, "What?!" The Chief Resident repeated, "The wus service . . . the Women in Surgery Service." The fire sparked in me and began to rage. I said, "The wus service, huh? Women in Surgery is W-I-S, which is much closer to *wise*." Good for me. I was able to retort back quickly. It may have been the only time in my life!

Life Lessons

Being a woman in surgery with children is different than for men in the same situation. I see it in my residents as they grapple with the decisions of whether to marry or have children. There is no right answer. There is only a personal choice.

I did have children and it changed my life completely. When I was a resident, I believed there was no difference between male and female surgeons. For me, I first realized that perhaps there was a difference when I got hypoglycemic and felt dizzy during an open cholecystectomy, while in my first trimester as a Chief Resident. There wasn't much support for my bodily weakness from others or myself. In June of my chief year, I was called into my Program Director's office. He reamed me. It seems that my obstetrician informed him (can you say HIPPA violation?!) that I had been put on bed rest. I was 4 cm dilated with an "incompetent cervix" (Hrrumph! I was a Chief Surgical Resident and wanted nothing to do with anything incompetent!). I had neglected to inform him about the bed-rest order and had continued to work. He spoke emphatically of how the last few weeks of residency were not worth the risk to my unborn child. I heard blah, blah, blah (think Charlie Brown). My ears were full of whooshing and my body shook in rage. How could I dump the last two weeks of call on my colleagues?! How could my body, not to mention my obstetrician, betray me like this?!

The program director called my colorectal fellowship program at Cleveland Clinic, Florida, and told them that I needed to put my fellowship on hold, that I had been advised to remain on bed rest and was not due until September.

Wonderfully, I received many job offers in the next few days from hospitals locally, where I had worked as a resident. When the next year rolled around, I didn't want to leave New England. I had the support of family and friends. So I stayed until the second child came—eleven days before September 11, 2001. As I held my eleven-day-old child, and as my twenty-three-month-old son played on the floor, I watched events unfold on television. I wasn't sure if I should go to New York or what to do. I felt guilty for bringing children into the world. I felt angry, vulnerable and confused.

Over the next few months of maternity leave, I decided to move even closer to family and leave academic surgery. I tried community practice for a bit but missed academics, so I drove into Boston (a forty-five-mile ride that takes a minimum of ninety minutes each way) for many years.

"Life lessons" here were that family is more important than work, yet work was vitally important too. The balance is difficult to strike and constantly moving, like a dance. Constant movement and adjusting are needed. Support from others such as nannies, babysitters, carpools, spouses, friends and family must be relied upon to balance motherhood and surgery. We each find our own way and, hopefully, can learn from one another while accepting each other's choices without judgment.

In 2008, my son became critically ill. He had a learning difference that led to many somatic symptoms. I chose to quit my academic job and focus on creating stability for him and our whole family. I lost my identity as a surgeon. Best thing that ever happened to me. I learned that the "work" in life is to be happy, healthy and whole, no matter what roles we take on. It's learning that wholeness is more important than perfection. This is why surgeons often quote Voltaire: "Better is the enemy of good." We are each vital and important no matter what we do.

I am back practicing in an academic setting and truly love my work. I am immensely grateful to practice and learn in all of my roles. As a "woman in surgery," each experience from work, home and life makes me (and each of us) wiser, kinder and more competent. That is reason to celebrate!

Inspiring Quote:
"Trust your body. It does not lie." — Kerry Bennett

Anjali S. Kumar, MD, MPH, FACS
Colon and Rectal Surgeon

In the Hands of a Woman

Women are often discouraged in pursuing surgery as a career because men are supposedly much better suited for such militaristic careers. We hear that men possess the crucial skills of strength and tenacity. But in my experience as a female surgeon, this story ignores the many ways in which a woman is the superior practitioner.

Take the simple example of a woman's hands. They are usually smaller than a man's. As more patients demand minimally invasive surgery, the dainty size of our hands confers an advantage during surgery. It is a pleasure to tell a patient that if I need to convert from laparoscopic-assisted to hand-assisted laparoscopic colectomy, my incisions will be up to 3 centimeters smaller because my hands are a size 6, compared to a fellow surgeon's whose hands may be size 8 or 9.

Then there is the matter of what women do with those hands. Since time immemorial, women have been engaged in activities that demand fine motor skills, such as knitting or quilting. Many of the practitioners of these crafts I know are ultra-perfectionists. They develop exceptional deftness in the hands and fingers, not to mention a microscopic attention to detail and an unwillingness to accept errors. If a woman at her knitting needles discovers that she pearled something wrong two lines ago, she will most likely undo several lines of work to fix it. As a seamstress myself, I find that this obsessive attention to detail is of immediate benefit to my patients, in the quality of my work and the tying of my knots—the mechanical parts of the job in this most hands-on of medical professions.

I learned of another advantage women surgeons possess over their male colleagues, from a female pediatric surgeon who trained me. When she was done sewing, she was not content to leave a 4 x 4 bandage and occlusive dressing that might contain oozed blood and remind a child of his distress. Instead she went to pains to disguise it with a false bandage that also had a sparkly sticker that he could show off to his parents. At the time, I remember wondering, having completed the child's operation flawlessly, what then compelled her go to this extra effort? Was it her unique ability to empathize with the child's plight? Or was she influenced by her own role as a mother? A woman's sense of empathy goes a long way in patient care.

Finally, women are capable of being excellent surgical leaders. We have the ability to think really big. Many women are excellent event planners, which not only gives us great joy of pulling off a successful event, but also brings joy to those who participate. In more serious situations, we often look to find ways to change the entire paradigm.

My role model in this respect is one of my mentors, Dr. Laura Esserman, a breast surgeon at the University of California, San Francisco. She walks into a situation and, if she feels something could be done better, she does a root-cause analysis and improves it, regardless of the extra work.

Once she took on something so pervasive it almost seemed impossible to correct: the obsessively sterile hospital environment. Like many people, Laura saw that its Spartan character and lack of warmth were almost hostile to patients and families suffering and trying to heal. Laura was not someone to walk by the halls and tolerate it. She worked through piles of red tape at the university to find a way to transform an area within the hospital into a courtyard for healing, reflection and serenity. The centerpiece was an interior hall of ceramic tiles created by medicinal botanists, poets, artists and cancer survivors—intended to link emotions of cancer with images of medicinal herbs. Those tiles now decorate the halls, and their inauguration was a giant event, which still receives inordinate positive press and patient gratitude.

These are the kinds of things of which women physicians are capable. I don't intend to be derogatory to men, but I observe that men compartmentalize their work life from their home life. They see their workplace as just that—an office. Women, on the other hand, regard their work environment as a home away from home, so they often have no problem putting in just as much work to make their workplace homey.

So when you hear someone say how men make superior surgeons, know there is a counterargument that has the weight, force and alacrity of experience—the experience of a growing number of female surgeons whose temperament, training and outlook make them every bit as good, if not better!

Inspiring Quote:
"Be faithful in small things because it is in them that your strength lies."
— Mother Teresa

Sheri Slezak, MD, FACS
Plastic and Reconstructive Surgeon

Woman Surgeon—From Boston to Baltimore

I first fell in love with anatomy when we dissected a mink in seventh-grade science. Most kids liked the fur. I liked the heart and the intestines. The next thing I know, I was in Harvard Medical School.

At Harvard, 30 percent of the class was female—a great feat in 1980. I did surgery as my first clinical rotation to get it out of the way, because I definitely didn't want to be a surgeon! But who knew that it would be so much fun to do a physical exam on someone, then cut them open to see if you were right. Anatomy really is beautiful. The only "role models" in surgery were a woman cardiac surgery resident who packed a gun in a shoulder holster, and a pediatric surgery resident who consistently managed to alienate people every time she uttered a sentence. Considering this, it was pretty worrisome to want to go into surgery. A rotation in plastic surgery with Joseph Murray taught me that you can be humble and kind and still be a surgeon.

I did general surgery residency training at Columbia Presbyterian. I was the only female in my intern group of twelve, but there were four other women residents in general surgery and orthopedics. We had informal "girls surgical service" dinners and supported each other. I was the fifth woman to finish general surgery. Columbia is a great teaching institution.

I interviewed for plastic surgery residency at Johns Hopkins Hospital. Here, they told me about previous women who had left, told me that I could never have babies in their program, and that they had never had a good woman resident. During the interview session, I was sent to lunch with the chair's secretary. One of the general surgeons there was often heard to proclaim that "Women do not belong in surgery." It was like going back in time fifty years—or maybe a hundred. Nevertheless, I needed to be in Baltimore, so I signed on. You can learn anywhere, I told myself.

I had my first child in my research year. I told my Chair about a cute thing that my child did, and he looked at me and said, "I hate babies." So he missed out on all the stories about my brilliant infant. That will teach him a lesson!

91

After nine years of training, I took a job as attending plastic surgeon at the University of Maryland, and have been here twenty-five years. I had my second child at the age of forty. I asked the Maryland chair of surgery about the maternity policy and he said he would have to get back to me. He called in a week and asked what I wanted it to be. I was surprised that they did not have to close the hospital while I was away for six weeks of maternity leave; but everything seemed to run well without me—a good lesson for me!

My third child was born when I was forty-two years old. It was always a dilemma how to position myself in relation to the OR table: Did I place my ever-expanding belly below it or above, so I could rest the baby on it? I learned that sitting down occasionally during surgery helped my legs a great deal during pregnancy. Dr. Ralph Millard always said, "Why stand when you can sit while operating?"

I eventually became a full professor and Chair of plastic surgery. Now that I am Chair, I can tell you that men ask for a higher salary and a promotion every other month.

We recently had a picture taken of twenty-three women surgeons at University of Maryland, and many have had children. I am enthusiastic when my faculty members are pregnant. It all works out.

I am proud to be a surgeon. I learn every day from my patients, but my proudest moments are still as a mother of three.

Inspiring Anecdote:
I went to a lecture by Margaret Mead in 1977. The question and answer period turned to domestic and work balance. One woman asked her, "Can you really come here and give a talk knowing that there are dust bunnies under your bed?" Margaret Mead replied, "Damn right I can!"

SECTION 5—SURGERY, PREGNANCY AND MOTHERHOOD

Amy L. Friedman, MD, FACS
Transplant Surgeon

The Elephant In This Room Is Fertile

Years after graduating, my five minutes as a returning Ivy League alumni panelist were spent imploring the eager pre-medical students packed into the auditorium to honestly engage their intrinsic biologic drives to procreate, instead of necessarily suppressing them to attain career goals. I was honest, witty (at least I hoped so) and received more questions than my co-speakers.

Thus, I was stunned when the pre-medical advisor virtually accosted me afterwards. Her fury was so intense that I was convinced steam hissed out of her ears. Her gripe? Since she had personally been successful in bearing children at the age of thirty-five, surely all women could similarly do so. Thus, my topic had been inappropriate fodder at this pivotal moment in these young peoples' lives. Wow! I could not have differed with her position more strongly then, and still do now. And as a mature (yes, older!) woman who emerged from training, in general, and transplant surgery with an intact marriage and three children, it seems so apparent that for women interested in surgical fields, the stakes are higher than in virtually any other career imaginable.

The elephant in this room is fertile—or, at least, one hopes so. Actually, the fact that one out of six couples experiences infertility troubles[1] is highly germane. At least for me (and my husband) it was, between the first two babies. Today, it may seem evident that surgeons should become parents, if and when they so choose, and are fortunate enough to be capable of doing so. This figurative pachyderm is the reality that such an assumption is much more complex for women than for men surgeons because of biologic limitations. By the time a typical trainee begins residency at the age of twenty-six or twenty-seven, peak female fertility has already passed. By definition, then, the woman surgeon in training is faced with a choice of overlapping the rigors of residency with one or more pregnancies, or further delaying procreation and thus accepting the associated risks of steadily declining fertility. Either strategy involves stress about the unknown elements of family planning, stress about the response of other trainees whose own schedules will be impacted by any pregnancy, and anxiety about the response of academic supervisors (Chair and/or Residency Director). Finally, of course, are the considerations for any woman who works in a physically demanding job while carrying a pregnancy, particularly when fatigue and sleep deprivation are added into the mix. Tough enough to imagine for a medically uneventful pregnancy— right? And what if it isn't?

In reality, can it all possibly work out successfully? The answer is often resoundingly *yes*. But, it isn't easy. The key ingredients for me were biologic good fortune, an incredible partner, a very strong support network, resilience and a sense of humor. Finally, was the crucial revelation that— while unfair that we women must bear the greater share of family building—men did not intentionally design such a system. In other words, although it would be easy to blame men for assigning women the physically demanding portion of family planning, it isn't their fault. Besides, I actually regret what any individual misses who will never know the wonder of giving birth to new life. No matter what one says about the awesome, frightening, unpredictable birth process, it is truly remarkable to be the giver of life. I have personally never been prouder of my own body than on each of the three days it gave me (and my husband) healthy babies. This miracle forever changes the woman who has the experience—even when she is a surgeon. I would not have traded my own three births for anything in the world!

Since my training was in the olden days, when 120-hour work weeks were routine, few women surgeons were mothers. So, as I pondered family issues in the middle of residency, I had few mentors or role models to turn to. I was extremely fearful of having a baby under such circumstances— honestly doubtful that my child would recognize me as his/her mother, because of the minimal amount of physical time we would spend together. And that would have been devastating. As I equivocated about becoming pregnant, the wise words of the only woman surgeon/mother I knew were incredibly helpful. Gentle Dr. Francisca Velcek did speak the words I will never forget: "Amy, twenty years from now, which would you regret more, not having a family—or not having a career?" She so clearly put the decision in the proper perspective! And that was that—my equivocation was over!

Once pregnant, life for me and my growing belly was not straight-forward—challenged by even the simplest personal thing like keeping

Ob/Gyn appointments. Perhaps the funniest was the Lamaze class I was forced to skip, but that my husband did attend with my sister as the stand-in pregnant mom! I will never forget those reports. Apparently, my husband was considered quite the lothario. I also learned to laugh at my own adjustment issues. Fortunately, in my sixth month, I hadn't instantly complained to the anesthesiologist about inadequately medicating my patient while we were still operating. I finally recognized that the movement I felt was not the patient's arm moving against the outside of my abdomen, but my baby on the inside. My masked grin was undoubtedly more sheepish than Madonna-like at that moment.

In those days, pregnancy and surgical residency were simply not expected to coincide. The responses I encountered from those whose lives my choice (choosing to be pregnant during surgical residency) impacted ranged from incredible insensitivity to extraordinary kindness. I have long ago moved beyond the hurt induced by my co-resident's anger, when he found me briefly elevating my edematous legs in the on-call room. But, I will not ever cease to be astonished by the silent generosity shown to me by Dr. Peter Kottmeier, the grandfather, patient advocate and mentor. Somehow, within twelve hours of my request for his help in repairing the call room's non-functional air conditioner, a brand new unit suddenly materialized, transforming the few moments of rest available to my swollen body into relative heaven. There was no need to ask how—hospital bureaucracies don't function that effectively!

Holding my husband's hand and listening to the inner voice that often sent me in tough directions has ultimately granted the satisfaction of being both the mother of three independent and interesting adults and an academic surgeon. Many mistakes were made along the way, but none intentionally so. In choosing to openly share this perspective with you, I may once again induce wrath in pure academics and/or feminists who might have preferred my contemplations on the issues they consider to be at a higher level. In contrast, my core strength has always stemmed from a foundation of love and family at home. The need to justify a legitimate desire for that footing, even at some cost to those around us, is not generally shared by men. It should not arise for women either. Yet, the effort and planning ultimately required to create such an infrastructure in my own life were so substantial as to now merit your honest and direct consideration. I fear that failure to similarly do so may predispose others to subsequent regret. Wouldn't it be a bit wiser to admit she is there even now, while she is in her prime?

Any accomplishment I have achieved is shared fully with my husband/partner of thirty years, Simon, without whom I could never have created a family of two marvelous adult sons, Ben and Jeremy, and one terrific daughter, Sharon— each of whom is forging a path in which I take pride. Though I still thrill at the moment of restoring blood flow to a dormant transplant organ, I am finally learning to take the time to care for myself too. Through the camera lens, I try to see and capture the beauty around me. I have also come to recognize that my years and experiences authorize a modicum of expertise to my perspectives. Hence, I am emboldened to document my observations in texts as well as photographs. Above all, I believe in following my heart, for if it is unhappy, the rest won't matter. And I celebrate change while striving to respect tradition. There will always be a way if you try hard enough.

Reference:
1. www.americanpregnancy.org

Inspiring Quote:
"You are what you are when nobody is looking." — Abigail Van Buren, advice columnist

Christine Rohde, MD, MPH, FACS
Plastic Surgeon

"Surgimom"

I hold the bead bracelet in my hand, rubbing the pink and purple sparkly globes and the M-O-M blocks, like a sacred rosary. I am about to head into another twelve-hour operation and yet another day without seeing my kids. My daughter proudly gave me her bead creation and I proudly wear it at work, tucking it into my coat pocket when I head to the OR. All thoughts of the challenges and rewards of my chosen profession are tucked away at that instant as well. My patient and a successful outcome to her cancer reconstruction surgery are my only priority for today. And that is how it should be, for everyone going "under the knife" should be assured of the commitment of the person to whom he or she trusts to cut, to sew, to repair, to heal. And to know that that commitment exists whether it is day or night, weekend or holiday.

Women in surgery have unique gifts to offer but unique sacrifices to make as well. As I go through my career, every year moving faster than the last, I realize that, although I knew how hard it might be, I never knew how fulfilling it could be. I thought I would be a surgeon even when I had no idea what that meant. My mom saved my elementary-school writing— oversized letters on thin paper with wide lines—"I want to be a doctor someday, maybe a brain surgeon." I still don't know where I got that idea. No one in my family is a doctor, let alone a surgeon. Maybe it was just because it seemed like the hardest thing to do. Except for a brief time auditioning for music schools for voice, I barely wavered in my path to medical school. Once there, I realized that nothing appealed to me like surgery. I usually advise students that, if there is anything they would like to do in medicine besides surgery, they should probably do that. But for me, there was nothing else.

So I went on to general surgery residency, which, come to think of it, is a lot like delivering a baby: 120-hour-work-weeks and sixty-hour power-weekends, pre-rounding at three a.m., passing by people just coming home from a night out. If I try hard, I can remember some of these tough times, but mostly I remember being part of a team, wanting to be nowhere else, learning to be at my best at all times of day or night, no matter how little sleep I had had, and the overall sense of accomplishment. So, like childbirth, I don't remember the pain of it; I only appreciate the good that came out of it.

I never really thought about having a family, other than my family of surgical residents. I was swallowed up whole. But I did manage to sing in one opera during residency, playing Zerlina in Mozart's "Don Giovanni." Several of my surgical mentors came to the performance, and it was wonderful to see them in another context.

I got married during residency, but waited until after finishing plastic surgery residency to have children. There is, of course, no right time for a female surgeon to have kids. I remember hearing the regret of some surgeons who said they waited too long and were never able to have children. I also remember how hard it was for already overstretched residents to cover for fellow residents if the need ever arose.

Now, many years later, I realize that balance is not possible. It is possible to be a great mom and a great surgeon, a great wife and a great researcher. But balance is not possible. One day, the scale will be tipped more on one side; the next day it will tip the other way. And so you can end up feeling off balance and torn.

I am only able to do what I do because of a supportive spouse and family. My husband works as hard as I do, both at work and at home. My mother, who helps with my children, thinks of it as her contribution to my patients, to enable me to work early and stay late. In this regard, we are the same as our male colleagues with families. It is only with the support of others that we can do what we do. (However, I doubt that most of my male colleagues worry about packing school lunches or cleaning toilets when they get home.)

So what are the challenges? Being torn between work life and home life. Feeling like I could always do more in one place or the other. The drive to work harder than everyone else, so that no one can ever complain about "female surgeons."

And the rewards? The hugs I get from patients. The tears of gratitude. The knowledge that at the end of the day (even if that is in the middle of the night) someone has been impacted positively by my hard work. I don't have to wait for a medicine to kick in or a laboratory test to come back—I see it at the end of an operation done well.

And what's more, I get to go home to the rewards of kids running around yelling "Mommy's home," or a sleepy, soft post-bedtime kiss.

Mommy' home. And I get to do it again tomorrow.

Inspiring Quote:
"Life is not measured by the number of breaths we take, but by the moments that take our breath away." — Maya Angelou

Elizabeth Warner, MD
General Surgeon

Plans, Priorities, and Other Moving Targets

On the last day of my maternity leave, I took pictures of my son, Jack, and loaded them onto my Palm Pilot so that I could see his face when I was back at work. He was three months old, that magical age when babies seem to suddenly shed their wizened, squinty-eyed look and take on definitive features. Jack has almond-shaped, blue eyes with long, feminine lashes, and they can look mischievous or far away and pensive. Looking down into his crib, I locked eyes with him and he held my gaze while playing with a fabric giraffe called Alice. Click. I reached down to stroke his fuzzy head, trying to feel and smell as deeply as I could. I was a fourth-year surgical resident, in Washington, DC, and my first day back would be a call night; I would leave for work that morning and return sometime the following afternoon. I rolled Jack onto his belly and watched as he pushed himself up on his pudgy forearms, his stern little brow furrowed with the effort. His head wobbled. Click.

Jack had come as a surprise. My fiancé, Graham, was also a surgical resident, a year ahead of me at another hospital in Washington, and we were in the midst of planning a wedding when we found out that we were expecting. I had just arrived home from purchasing my wedding gown, when it occurred to me that I hadn't had a period in almost two months. To put my mind at ease I took a pregnancy test. The line turned blue and I clapped my hand over my mouth. Parenthood had seemed like an abstract, no doubt special thing that happened to other people; now it was barreling down on me. After taking a confirmation test at Planned Parenthood, I walked the thirteen blocks to Graham's work. By the time I got there I had shared the news with three friends, a kindly Planned Parenthood employee, and the man who owned our wedding reception facility. When I met Graham, I said, "I have something to tell you." He looked into my face and said, "Oh, no." I was seven weeks pregnant.

Three weeks later, Graham and I were crying in the emergency room of our hospital. At work that day, I had started cramping and bleeding. We had taken to calling the tiny embryo inside me "Fennel"—like the seed—

and we gripped hands in the dark as we watched a radiologist peer at an ultrasound monitor. The heart was beating. The obstetrician on call prescribed a week of bed rest for my threatened abortion (that is the clinical term) and advised me to share our news with my chairman. Graham and I rode the elevator up to the fourth floor of my hospital and sat down with Dr. Evans, a general surgeon who had also trained as an obstetrician and gynecologist. He congratulated us, smiled with genuine warmth, and said, "Lizzie, let me tell you what *bed rest* means."

Certainly there are surgical residency programs where a pregnant resident would be regarded as a liability—not because surgeons hate women or babies, but because these programs function most smoothly with a full complement of trainees. Surgical residents are divided into "teams" led by a senior resident or a chief and staffed by both mid-level residents, who typically spend their days operating, and junior residents (or interns), who take care of patients' needs—ordering medications, requesting consultations, following up on test results. A few years ago, a national regulation limited residents to eighty hours on the floor each week, and, now more than ever, the loss of one team member means more work for the others.

My own program's solution to the issue of my bed rest was to wish me well and leave me alone, then to ignore the two interns under my wing, who were now without leadership. Thankfully, another third-year resident saw what was happening and absorbed my old team into hers. When I returned to work the following week we sorted out our teams and went back to work. I felt fantastic, relieved to still be pregnant, and also relieved to have escaped the exhaustion and nausea of the first trimester. My co-residents seemed excited for me, and if there was resentment or complaining, I never heard it.

The last rotation I did while pregnant was in the surgical ICU, tending to sick pre- and post-liver transplant recipients, general surgery patients with sepsis from various intra-abdominal catastrophes, and the occasional thoracic or vascular surgery train wreck. As my third trimester dragged on, I developed elephantine swelling in my legs and feet, and my junior residents and I howled with laughter (and a bit of disgust) at my ankles, which made me look like a freakish lower-body transplant recipient. I woke up in the morning and squeezed my feet between both hands to milk the edema up my legs so that my clogs would go on, and, when compression socks failed,

I took to making rounds riding on a swiveling chair. Fennel kicked and shoved, causing my scrub tops to shift and stretch.

One morning during week thirty-eight, I couldn't get my clogs on, even after wringing out my feet. That day I had chest pain at work and a headache that wouldn't go away. At Labor and Delivery, the nurses took my blood pressure—190/110—and then repeated the reading to be sure the machine wasn't in error. The attending obstetrician told me that I had severe preeclampsia. "Call your husband," she said. "You are going to be induced and have the baby today." My labor lasted fifteen hours, most of which I remember only hazily. The doctors gave me high doses of magnesium to prevent seizures, which can accompany severe preeclampsia, and by the time Jack was born, at five a.m., I had double vision and was barely able to move my limbs. I held Jack for a moment, and then a nurse took him from me and placed him under a warming lamp. When we went home, two days later, climbing the stairs left me winded and my heart pounding.

Graham had only a week off for paternity leave before he went back to work, and then I was alone with Jack. The weeks were harder than I had expected. We settled into a routine of sorts—naps, daily baths, diapers and frequent pumping in between sessions of nursing, in an effort to store up milk for my return to work. I knew that our time at home together was limited. Each day was a race to build a bond with him before I essentially relinquished my daily mothering duties for my resident duties. But being at home with a newborn baby, who was fussy and not easily comforted, left me feeling helpless. Wasn't I supposed to feel blinded by love, engulfed by a halo of peace and light? Jack didn't want my efforts at snuggling and comfort, and nothing I did seemed to bring us closer. One particularly desperate night, when Jack had been crying for an hour, despite swaddling, nursing, taking off his clothes and bundling him back up, I finally called Graham's operating room. The circulating nurse told me that he was unavailable, scrubbed into a case, but something in my voice (maybe murderous hysteria) told her that she had better interrupt him. When he came to the phone, I unraveled, sobbing and yelling at the same time, "I can't get Jack to stop crying! I can't do this anymore! You need to come home, now!"

Graham came home to find both of us crying, castaways who didn't particularly get along but struggling to make do with each other. I probably should have put Jack in his crib, closed the door, and poured myself a pint glass full of wine, but the thought never occurred to me. Maybe those are more advanced mothering skills that I've only now honed.

From the early days of my pregnancy I knew that eventually I would have to find a nanny. We had no family nearby, and my hospital's daycare opened at seven a.m., long after our workday began. Because finding a nanny made final, in my mind, the fact that I would need to return to work, I put it off for as long as possible. In the end, the process was quick, because so few applicants were interested. We lived in a small house and could not accommodate live-in help, nor could we offer health care benefits, a car, a private phone line, exotic vacations—all the perks a good nanny could get from one of the more affluent families in Bethesda or Great Falls. What we could offer was cash, under the table (in fact more than I took home) bolstered by the proceeds of selling our old apartment in a nicer neighborhood. I made a dozen calls and two women agreed to be interviewed. One sat politely at the table and asked detailed questions about salary, while nodding blandly at Jack. The other, Rabia, immediately took him from my arms and began clucking and cooing. She was Bangladeshi and had a grown son back at home and a grandson she had never met. She spent a few trial days with us learning routines, and we agreed to work together.

On my first day back to work, Graham left at five-thirty a.m. As chief resident on the transplant service, I would be spending the night at the hospital, on call. The plan was that I would pump breast milk for Jack every three hours at work and continue to nurse him when I was home. A lactation consultant at the hospital had showed me the nursing lounge (basically a modified bathroom) and told me that if anyone interfered with my ability to pump, I should let her know immediately. God bless her, she was serious. That morning I carried Jack around the house, nervously assembling my white coat, my ID badge, my backpack with socks and underwear and toothbrush. Rabia arrived and took Jack from my arms, crooning and smiling. We reviewed once more, mostly for my benefit, the procedure for warming the pumped breast milk in the freezer. I rushed out the door feeling nauseated, knowing that I would not see Jack again until the following day. Driving down the Rock Creek Parkway to the hospital, I did my best to ignore my constant thoughts of "*turn around*," and resisted the urge to drive into a concrete bridge support.

In the grubby resident work room on the transplant unit, I gathered my team, ran the list, and went to the OR to scrub on a distal pancreatectomy with Dr. Johnson, the chief of our hospital's transplant division. On the way I ran into two other attendings. "Brought your digital camera, I see!" one of them said, pointing at the black case slung over my shoulder. "No," I said, "That's my breast pump." I scrubbed my hands and arms in preparation. A distal pancreatectomy is the sort of case I looked forward to; the foregut is masterfully designed, a circuit of interlocked blood vessels and just-so relationships between organs. The pancreas lies with its head in the curve of the duodenum, its body snugly behind the stomach. My anatomy professor had always said, adding with a lecherous snicker, that it "gives a little tail" to the spleen.

Working with Dr. Johnson was always a lesson in economy of technique: Not a single move was wasted. Errors were noted and corrected with a cool, clipped rebuke. Still, I knew that he liked me, and so I let my thoughts return to Jack. A resident the year ahead of me had had a baby during her chief year, and had advised me about breastfeeding. Just scrub out when you need to pump, she'd told me; the attendings will understand, and if they don't, fuck 'em. So after we mobilized the greater curve of the stomach, dividing its vascular attachments to access the body of the soft pancreas, I told Dr. Johnson that I had to go pump, and that I would arrange for another resident to step in for me briefly. His eyebrows rose, barely. All right, he said. I found an empty call room, looked at those pictures of my son, and willed my milk to let down quickly. When I returned to the OR, I was too late. The pancreas was out; the crucial part of the operation was over, and I had missed it.

* * * * *

I always planned to be a doctor. As a kid, I had friends who wanted to be garbage men because it was cool to ride around on the outside of a truck; I wanted to be an MD. I was one of those little nerds who wear the plastic pince-nez from the Fisher-Price medical kit and a pair of argyle pants and are always trying to look into relatives' ears at parties. Growing up in a single-parent household where money was tight made the prospect of a respectable, secure career even more attractive.

I didn't decide to enter surgery until my fourth year of medical school, after I had already started interviewing for a spot in internal medicine. While tour guides led groups of us around the hallways of hospitals, droning on about Diabetes Clinic or electives in Rheumatology, I would gaze longingly at surgeons striding by in their scrubs, white coats buttoned and stethoscopes pocketed. The surgeons I had worked with as a student seemed fearless in the face of chaos, decisive and determined and inexhaustible. The best of them were also capable of great tenderness with their patients, and, to me, that was the Holy Grail: to comfort and to cure. I wanted to be one of them.

I was twenty-five when I made the choice to match in surgery, and hadn't given much thought to how this role might play out if I had a husband or children. Like the national-debt-size loans I took out to pay for medical school, I assumed that things would somehow work themselves out. In my naiveté, I never gave serious consideration to the logistics of being a practicing surgeon and a mother simultaneously. Certainly role models were few, but even that fact eluded me. One grows up—perhaps even enters parenthood—with untested ideas of what constitutes a "good mother." At the core of being a good parent, I thought, was unconditional love, along with the duty of ensuring your child's safety and providing for his basic needs. There were the higher tasks of conveying truths about the world. There was nurturing and tenderness and, I hoped, a deep supply of patience with the growing child. If I was going to provide these things, it seemed necessary to be available, both emotionally and physically.

After I went back to work, all of Jack's daily needs would be met by Rabia, a virtual stranger. Friends assured me that I could breastfeed Jack when I was at home, to keep our bond alive. But I was away from home every third night, and it didn't take long for Jack to realize that milk from a bottle took much less work than nursing. Within a few weeks, he refused to nurse at all; he would struggle and cry if I offered him my breast. One call night not long after that, I sat in front of Dr. Matsumoto, one of my attendings, as he told me that my team was out of control, and that I needed to do a better job as their leader. We had just spent two hours rounding, much it of punctuated by his berating residents for not having information he wanted. I agreed. I was not leading my team effectively. I would do better I promised. At the same time, I knew that I was unable to fulfill either of my roles in life effectively. I told one of my attendings that as soon as I could find another way to pay off my medical school loans, I planned to quit.

The next day Dr. Johnson summoned me to his office. "Liz," he asked me, "what is this I hear about your wanting to quit?" I avoided his eyes. On his desk were pictures of his family on a beach, dressed in identical khakis and white shirts. Trying not to cry, I told him that I was a failure as a resident and a mother and a wife. He reminded me that he was married to an obstetrician, that they had four children, that indeed it was not easy, but that it could be done. He invited my family to his house for dinner. Graham and I went and had dinner at their well-appointed home in Virginia, while they told us about how they managed their lives. We left Jack with the nanny, which now strikes me as a little ridiculous.

Dr. (Mrs.) Johnson worked part time. They had a live-in nanny, who drove a van that they had bought her to shuttle the children to various events and practices. The love and closeness among them was clear. To leave training now, he told me, would be a mistake and a loss for you and for us. Please reconsider. It was a tiny seed of reassurance in a year of painful failures, but it gave me hope.

What got me through was redefining my own beliefs about motherhood. If being a good mother meant nursing until the baby turned two, knitting booties from hemp, hosting art-centered play dates, and preparing organic locavore baby food, then I was failing utterly. So I decided that, for me, being a good mother would have to mesh with working in a grueling job. If I failed to finish my training, I would be a tremendous financial burden to my family, with limited prospects for employment; and I never wanted to put us in financial jeopardy.

The rotations got harder. I spent six months at a sister institution, a sprawling inner-city center where residents were routinely told to under-report their work hours. A co-resident and friend of mine stuck her finger with a needle during surgery, and her attending mocked her for rinsing the cut with Betadine before continuing to operate. I got by with telling myself that there was no way I would let these bastards get between me and what was best for my family. And, in that way, I finished my fourth year of residency.

Conversely, I also had some serious work to do on my beliefs about what it meant to be a good doctor. In my first few years as a surgeon, I tried to put to use all of the skills I learned in training. I fixed hernias, removed cancerous colons and took out innumerable gallbladders. I enjoyed the variety and got a little rush seeing a new consultation come across my desk. But I found it very difficult to wear two hats at the same time—my mommy hat and my doctor hat.

Trying to bundle *two* toddlers and all their gear into car seats so that I could respond to a call from the ER—ruptured spleen!—was a special challenge. (I had my second child, Chloe, during residency training.) When a patient really needed me at work, my kids' needs had to wait. I have left home on a Christmas morning to go to the operating room. I was able to accept that because sometimes a patient's life truly depends on your presence. That's the basic responsibility of any physician with emergency call. But even at home, I obsessed about the sick patients on my service.

After a few years, Jack started to ask me why his friends' mommies didn't have to go to work or take call. Chloe, my daughter, would tell people that when she grew up, she planned to stay home with her kids. Oof. And balancing my call schedule and Graham's, plus my responsibilities as a mother, was getting harder. I started exploring the idea of working part time, in a breast-only practice. It seemed like a failure to walk away from such a large part of my training; I worried that my partners would resent me and that my non-surgical colleagues would lose respect for me. But when I started taking anti-anxiety medication in order to tolerate being at work, something had to give.

I'm now in my sixth year of practice, working part time as a breast surgeon in a small community hospital. It's enormously satisfying work. The help one can offer as a physician ranges broadly. It often means offer-ing the cure to a disease, of course, but it can also mean acting as a reliable source of expertise in an information-saturated world. It can mean providing comfort by easing physical pain or by offering an empathetic ear to patients who feel out of control of their own bodies. (Almost every day in my office a patient cries and then apologizes for crying.) What I enjoy most is the emotional connection with patients, which can be a more powerful tool than any surgical instrument. Of course, I also find it deeply satisfying to remove an offending process from a patient's body. In my practice, that is usually breast cancer, but to cure a person using your hands and familiar tools is thrilling, even when what's troubling him is as unglamorous as a hemorrhoid or a hernia.

My baby boy is almost seven years old, and Chloe is five, sweet and goofy and a little crazy. The work-life balance is a moving target, and it may shift again for me. I feel extraordinarily fortunate, and I'm glad almost every day that I made the choices I did—until I get the annual prospectus from my old training program, full of articles about my co-residents who are now heading their own transplant and thoracic divisions. Then I feel that tiny stab of self-doubt, of not quite measuring up. Students from a nearby college occasionally shadow me to get an idea of what it's like to be a surgeon. The young women, in particular, tell me how inspired they are to see that it's possible to "have it all." I laugh and tell them that "having it all" is a myth.

Inspiring Quote:
"Whatever you choose, however many roads you travel, I hope that you choose not to be a lady. I hope you will find some way to break the rules and make a little trouble out there. And I also hope that you will choose to make some of that trouble on behalf of women." — Nora Ephron

SURGERY, PREGNANCY AND MOTHERHOOD

Nicole Fox, MD, MPH
Trauma/Critical Care Surgeon

The Day She Was Born

She sighed deeply when I touched her for the first time. My single hand spanned her entire torso. Limited by the small opening in the isolette, I could only rest my hand there gently, feeling her inhale and exhale. My head bowed, humbled and defeated as tears fell onto the polished wood floor. Two thoughts surfaced immediately: "I failed her" and "how will I ever go back to work?" The first thought will resonate with any mother. The second may seem inappropriate considering the circumstances, but a surgeon will understand.

36 Hours Prior . . .

The temperature in OR 6 was perfect and the room was spacious and bright. I handed my favorite Castro to the scrub tech so he could flash it before the case. In my fourth year, residency was more tolerable; I was able to run the service and staff cases that interested me. The water from the scrub sink was warm, and in my thirty-third week of pregnancy I had to stand back slightly from the sink. The ritual of scrubbing, dressing and preparing to start an elective case was soothing and familiar. As the vascular attending dissected out the femoral vessels, I settled onto a stool at eye level with the popliteal fossa. This was a milestone in my training, becoming a participant rather than an assistant—performing the dissection, asking for instruments, sewing the anastomosis. Through my loupes I watched the prolene suture carefully as it passed through the popliteal artery, then the vein graft, merging the two. I ignored a vague discomfort in my upper abdomen and tried to relieve it by changing position as hours passed. After the final dressings were in place I rose from the stool.

Pain, unexpected and intense, took my breath away and almost brought me to my knees. No one noticed as I exited the OR and leaned heavily against the wall. In the call room, I collected my keys and jacket and turned towards the parking lot exit. But somewhere within me I knew. The adrenaline that carried me through the case was gone, and in its place was terrible pain. And fear. Slowly, reluctantly, in scrubs stained with my patient's blood, I shuffled down three floors to Labor and Delivery/triage. They were so accustomed to seeing me arrive for consults, they barely looked up. "Who are you here to see?" they asked. "Me. I'm here for me."

She moved gracefully on the ultrasound, tiny legs thrown in the air over her head like a diver in pike position. Her appearance was reassuring, but my blood work was not. With elevated liver enzymes, decreased platelets and epigastric pain I was a textbook presentation of "HELLP syndrome" (a life-threatening obstetric complication characterized by hemolytic anemia, elevated liver enzymes and low platelets).

Hours after leaving one OR as a surgeon, I found myself lying on my back in another OR as a patient. I felt the same, cold prep on my abdomen that I had painted on my patient that afternoon. I stared up at the CRNA I worked with almost every day, his face solemn as he brought the mask to my face. The anesthesiologist rubbed my arm gently while she injected midazolam. Before my eyes closed, I saw the obstetrician turn and silently hold out her hand, as I had done so many times in the last three years, waiting for the scalpel.

The transition from surgeon to patient was abrupt and unwelcome. This hospital was home to me. Countless hours were spent working, sleeping and eating here. Yet there were places I had never been and never knew existed, like the high-risk maternity ward and the Neonatal Intensive Care Unit (NICU). There were people I had never met who became part of my daily routine—the neonatologist, pediatric residents and neonatal nurses. Details from those days are difficult to access now, but the feelings are not. Residency had changed me. The hours, the patients, the relentless death and illness had taken their toll. At some level my faith in the medical profession and my original optimism had faded. I was exhausted, frustrated and lost. My role as a patient, therefore, was well timed. There were many lessons I needed to learn, some of which were new and others that were long forgotten.

There were two lives at stake that day, and the degree of skill and experience necessary to manage the birth of a premature infant and a life-threatening maternal complication is tremendous. On a normal day, I would be a member of a similar team. Once we were finished, I would move on to the next patient, the next crisis, with very little thought or reflection.

In this role, however, I was merely an observer. I had the privilege of witnessing a group of professionals deliver exceptional care. I was humbled, as the same nurses who frustrated me with what seemed like endless pages and requests changed my sheets, administered pain medication and coordinated visits to the NICU. The neonatologists, sensing our fear and uncertainty, included us in bedside rounds, explained our daughter's progress in detail and consulted us on decisions about her care. My colleagues graciously filled the void I left in the schedule, took turns spending time with me and stopped by the NICU to check on her. When the day finally came for us to take her home, it was bittersweet. Somewhere along the way I had lost faith in a system that I was deeply invested in. It was only as a patient that I was able to see and experience what I could not as a physician: the impact our care has on the patients we treat. Those two weeks restored my faith and changed me forever, as a physician and a human being.

Three Years Later . . .

"Tell me the story!"

"What story?" I ask innocently, but I know what she wants.

"The story of the day I was born."

After a twelve-hour day in the hospital on the trauma service, I stretch out on her pillow as my husband starts. "It was a warm August day . . ." He takes her through the narrative and she giggles when he tells her, "They rolled you past me and you cried 'Wah!Wah!'" She laughs when he imitates the shocked look on his face when the obstetrician told him, "You're going to be a daddy tonight." He recounts the hours I was unaware of, when he went down to the NICU and saw her by himself for the first time because I was too sick to go. "I held you first," he likes to tell her. And with all of the wisdom of her three years, she corrects him. "No, *she* did," she says, pointing to my abdomen, "in there."

Inspiring Quote:

"You gain strength, courage and confidence by every experience in which you really stop to look fear in the face. You are able to say to yourself, 'I have lived through this horror. I can take the next thing that comes along.' You must do the thing you think you cannot do." — Eleanor Roosevelt

Adriana Laser, MD, MPH
Vascular Surgery Fellow

Becoming "She"

I was lucky. I was able to time my first pregnancy and new-mom experience during the required research years of my general surgery residency. At the time of the second baby, I was in a clinical year. I was trained in an overall sensitive residency program that had attending surgeons who were understanding about my pregnancy. I had accommodating and supportive co-residents. I was lucky.

The American Board of Surgery's (ABS) leave policy includes the statement: "For documented maternity leave, the ABS will accept 46 weeks of surgical training in one of the first three years of residency and 46 weeks of training in one of the last two years." Despite the program following this officially, and my close colleagues' attitudes, I had many interesting encounters on a daily basis as a resident who was pregnant. I tried to attribute most of it up to the usual stares pregnant women get anywhere (on a bus, in a store, or at a restaurant). However, on many occasions I felt as if I was the first pregnant colleague, or the first pregnant doctor people had ever seen in the hospital! I had multiple strangers in elevators comment on my size, proclaim they knew what gender my unborn child was, or even practice their "date wheel" and predict when I was due.

Most comments I received in the hospital I knew were well intentioned. There were wishes from older patients who were reminded of years ago when they had young families. Many of my attending surgeons shared memories. I was inundated with stories of when their children were born, including several near-elevator babies! "There are now five people at the operating room table," one of my attendings proudly stated at the start of a case one night. As we all looked around at the three of us present, we turned back to her, puzzled. She smiled. She was announcing her pregnancy and acknowledging mine.

At other times the comments I received were concerning. "You don't want this chair, do you?" "Are you coming back after you have the baby?" "You don't have to do this case because it will probably be too long." "I can refer you to the bariatric service for a consult." And "You might want to get that ascites addressed." And on occasion it was just plain weird: "Let's walk to see that consult patient on the 13th floor" (mind you, we were on the fourth floor, and I was eight months pregnant.) Hmm? My response was to push the "up" button for the elevator.

I was fortunate enough as a junior to have witnessed two of our previous female residents have their first children during chief years, and I came to realize I was "*She*" for some of the junior residents. Once I announced my pregnancy, several of the females came up with a million questions. How did the program receive my news? Well . . . considering. What was I doing for child care? A live-in nanny, to help in a household with two residents who had two children and unforgiving work hours. And how on earth did I manage to breastfeed for over six months? Well, you "pee when you can, sleep when you can, eat when you can, pump when you can!"

So, despite some strange experiences and challenges, I was lucky. I hope any surgical resident who chooses to start (or continue) their family during residency is as lucky. There is no perfect time, but it is so worthwhile whenever it is.

Inspiring Quote:
"Only she who attempts the absurd can achieve the impossible."
— Robin Morgan

Amanda V. Hayman, MD, MPH
Colon and Rectal Surgeon

The Balancing Act

My friends not in the medical world frequently ask me, "Why do you have to work such crazy hours?" I explain to these law-firm partners and stock-market traders that, unlike the New York Stock Exchange or the circuit courts, hospitals never close. Patients get sick twenty-four hours a day, and don't really care if you have an anniversary dinner planned or haven't eaten lunch yet. Further, surgeons are not interchangeable, which is why surgery does not translate well into shift work. With some caveats, anesthesiologists and emergency room physicians can perform acceptable patient handoffs, even in the middle of a procedure or critical illness. We, as surgeons, do not scrub out of a case and tell our colleague, "I just finished the bile duct anastomosis, so take it from here." Despite the eighty-hour work week, surgery still demands more time and offers less flexibility than most other medical fields, and, despite making many strides, is still far from "family friendly." Whether it is possible to make it so without sacrificing the trust and responsibility inherent in the intimate relationship between patient and surgeon remains to be seen.

I knew that being a surgeon would require incredible responsibility and sacrifice. When I was in medical school, one of my chief residents said to me, "Before I went into surgery, if you would have asked me what one word identified me, I would have said 'man' or maybe 'American'. Now I would say 'surgeon'." The practice of surgery becomes all consuming; it becomes your identity. At the beginning of residency, "surgeon" was my primary identity, too. At the end of the day I lingered in the hospital, checking out other cases, thrilled with my burgeoning responsibilities. Surgery was my job, my passion, and my sole focus. However, at the end of intern year I added "wife" and, three years later, "mother" to my list of identities, and everything got a lot more complicated. Being an academic surgeon is difficult. Being a working mother is difficult. Choosing to be a surgeon and a mother presents unique challenges and is frequently a lonely place to be.

Even today, surgeon-mother role models for young female residents are scarce. Although half of the students entering medical school are female, only one third of general surgery residents are women, and even fewer go on to become academic surgeons or have children. These numbers are even more appalling in the most highly compensated surgical sub-specialties, such as orthopedic surgery (4.4 percent women residents) and neurosurgery (6.5 percent women residents)[1]. At the time of writing, nearly half of the current categorical general surgical residents in my program were female, but were three times less likely to be married than the men.[2] Further, only two of us had children during residency, as compared to five of the men, and both occurred during our research sabbaticals.

One reason for this is the current American Board of Surgery rules. All residents are required to complete forty-eight clinical weeks each year, with an exception of forty-six weeks for illness or maternity leave, up to twice during residency. However, if you have a child during your final clinical year and are also interviewing for fellowship, presenting at conferences, and take a week or two of vacation, you are left only a few weeks for maternity leave. Many women are neither emotionally nor physically ready to return to work two or three weeks postpartum, especially to a grueling eighty-hour work week. Further, as most fellowships start the same weekend that residencies end, usually July first, there is no easy option to extend a week or two of residency and still start fellowship on time. This is a major issue that, although politically difficult, is imminently fixable (for example, the orthopedic surgery fellowships start a much more humane one month later). Until this is addressed, childbearing options for female surgery residents remain limited.

More troublesome is the fact that women are woefully represented in the highest echelons of the surgical world. Although the increase in numbers of women surgeons should be applauded, a very small proportion succeed in obtaining academic or leadership positions, perpetuating the gender disparity in surgery. 2011 marked the year in which the ACS had only the second female president, after the elected president had to step down. He had made comments that were interpreted by many as being sexist, and it had become a well-publicized controversy.

As of January 2012, out of 245 academic surgical departments, there were only five (2 percent) full Department Chairs who are female.[3] Out of the twenty-two members of the American College of Surgeons (ACS) Board of Regents, only three (14 percent) are female. The first woman surgeon to chair the Board of Regents was elected in October 2012, and there has never been a female Executive Director of ACS.[4]

If we expect fundamental cultural change regarding the roles of women in surgery, we must increase our representation in our leadership organizations. We would do well to heed President Obama's advice: "Change will not come if we wait for some other person or some other time. We are the ones we've been waiting for. We are the change that we seek."

It is also discouraging to note that many female surgeons do not remain in the full-time surgical work force. A significant proportion of women surgeons switch to more "family-friendly" fields, such as anesthesia, or work part-time once they have children. Some quit altogether to become stay-at-home moms. Many people judge the women for this decision, although I would argue that, for many, this decision was a result of a lack of support at work and/or home for their career.

The father of one of my old boyfriends was a cardiothoracic surgeon. After I told him I was applying to medical school, he responded that the "problem with women doctors" was that they take up a spot a man could have had and, in the end, drop out to have children. Instead, I find it unfortunate that these women feel that they *have* to choose between a family and a career. His son later remarked that my "career was going to make it hard for us to have children." However, I concede that my career *did* make it difficult for me to have children, and that it would be naïve to think otherwise, but it wasn't impossible. Apparently he wasn't up for the challenge.

Although I had endured all-day OR cases late in my pregnancy, recovery after my protracted labor and delivery was even more difficult than being seven months pregnant during a ten-hour neck dissection. I soon learned that the beauty of being post-call is that you get to go to sleep when you are done with your shift, but that you are never off duty with a newborn. I returned to work the day before Christmas Eve, when my daughter was five weeks old. Wistful, I handed her over to the nanny and left the cozy living room to drive through the snow to the VA call room. Ironically, the nurses woke me up fewer times than my daughter usually did. I slept better than I had in weeks, minus the occasions for when I had to set my

SURGERY, PREGNANCY AND MOTHERHOOD

alarm to pump every four hours. One of nature's cruel post-partum jokes is that, just when you are suffering from extreme sleep deprivation, you can't sleep more than three hours without waking up in pain from breast engorgement. Once I was pumping around two a.m. when the intercom went off. "Code blue, room 5246." This was the surgical floor. Normally, I'd throw my white coat on and run out of the call room. But that day with a moderate amount of guilt, I spent about thirty seconds removing the pump, sealing the bottles and putting them in my fridge pack, before rushing down the stairs so that the milk would not spoil. In this first of many instances, being a good mom was in direct contradiction to being a good physician.

These days, being a working mother in America seems to require being on a merry-go-round of guilt, resentment and judgment. Last year we attended a birthday party in the neighborhood. The girl's mother had handmade the invitations, baked and frosted the cake and carefully planned creative activities to fit the party's theme. My inner surgeon self was simultaneously dismissive ("must be nice to have so much time on your hands") and scornful ("how incredibly indulgent"), whereas my inner mother self was simultaneously guilty ("I didn't go to half this length for my daughter's birthday"), remorseful ("I'll never be able to do this for her"), resentful ("Why can't I just have a normal nine-to-five job?") and panicky ("Does this mean she'll resent and hate me?"). I've since grown used to these conflicting feelings and accept them as the price of having so many choices at my disposal. When my daughter recently said her first sentence— "Mama, bye bye," a.k.a "My mother is leaving me (again)"—I reminded myself that if I want to raise an independent-minded daughter who could grow up to be anything she wanted, that she would see me as a strong role model, a mother with her own interests and career, and, if not thank me, at least respect me for it. And hopefully I'll be able to make her a few birthday cakes along the way.

I am acutely aware that the dilemmas I struggle with are privileges. These choices were non-existent for most female physicians a couple of decades ago, especially surgeons. There were no part-time academic surgical positions, protected maternity leave, "pump rooms" in hospitals and, of course, no eighty-hour work week. The days of the tongue-in-cheek words of a chief of surgery, who, when his fellow told him that his wife was pregnant, said, "Then we're not working you hard enough," are mostly over.

However, the most important development that has facilitated work-home balance for female physicians is the relatively new invention of the supportive husband. I was lucky enough to marry a man who sees himself as my equal partner in both life and parenting. Between conferences and overnight call, my husband often performs the bedtime and morning routines alone, and gets our daughter to the day care center with both shoes on (usually). My mother certainly didn't have this luxury, nor did most of the female physicians who trained before me. These women felt forced to either not have children or to curtail their professional responsibilities and, thus, their potential accomplishments.

I recently attended the American Society of Colorectal Surgeons where a women's luncheon was held, with over fifty women attending. I got advice on nannies and breastfeeding, as well as contract negotiation, from a range of female colorectal surgeons, from new fellows to those already well-established in their careers. This community is essential to all women surgeons who want families, as well as professional accomplishment and fulfillment. We need to know that it will be lonely and hard, but that we are not alone. Only decades earlier, this meeting could have fit in a phone booth.

Perhaps one of the reasons fewer women than men pursue surgical training is that we surgeons are inadvertently discouraging them. Although we all need to prepare students to realistically understand the rigors of surgery, we also need to express to them that surgery can be incredibly rewarding and intellectually fulfilling. As a medical student, I was told dozens of times that "If you can see yourself being happy doing anything else other than surgery, then do it. If you truly can't, only *then* consider being a surgeon." One female attending often added, "And then *still* do something else." One bleary weekend on my surgical sub-internship, a junior female attending and I were scrubbed into surgery for thirty out of thirty-six hours. At the end, ripping off our bloody gowns, she looked at me intently and said, "Do *anything* other than general surgery. It's an awful life." A friend who gave birth to twins during medical school was told by an attending that she was "crazy" for considering going into surgery, with two children.

So what convinces female medical students to pursue surgery? Is it performing well on the shelf exam? Or realizing they are technically adept? Not really. The strongest factor found to be associated with choosing surgery as a career is a strong mentor. I was lucky enough to have an outstanding mentor in Karen Deveney. She was one of the first female surgical residents at UCSF (University of California, San Francisco, School of Medicine) and my first attending during my university surgical rotation. I was fascinated by the complex colorectal procedures she performed. When she asked me anatomy questions during an ileoanal pouch or ileocecectomy, I surprised myself by usually knowing the answers. It just made *sense*.

During one case she asked me what I was going into. I replied, "Infectious Diseases." I had spent a good amount of time working on communicable diseases in the developing world, and, given my joint Masters in Public Health degree I was pursuing, it seemed the right choice. She replied, "No, you aren't. You're going into Surgery." I was taken aback and, although I disregarded the comment, she was obviously right. She took the time to foster my growing interest in surgery both in and out of the operating room. To my surprise, on the last day of my rotation, she let me sew in the mesh during an inguinal hernia repair, knowing full well it would get me "hooked"—which it did. To honor Dr. Deveney and the many surgical residents who gave me advice and encouragement, I always try to engage my medical students in the operating room and let them close incisions whenever possible, despite the occasional grumblings from anesthesia and surgical attendings. I try to make the students a valuable part of the team and give them frequent feedback. I also make sure I tell interested students that it *is* possible to have a life, one that includes children, and be a surgeon. I try to get them "hooked." If they thank me, I just tell them, "Someone did it for me."

References:

1. www.acshpri.org/.../ACSHPRI_Surgical_Workforce_in_USapr2010.pdf
2. Personal data, unpublished
3. Distribution of U.S. Medical School Faculty by Sex, Rank, and Department. https://www.aamc.org/download/169810/data/10table13.pdf.
4. http://www.facs.org and www.womensurgeons.org

Inspiring Quote:
"If you want to change the culture, you will have to start by changing the organization." — Mary Douglas

SECTION 6—MEMORIES, MINDFULNESS, MAGICAL MOMENTS

Carol Sawmiller, MD, FACS
General Surgeon

The Inconvenience of Compassion

"Sawmiller, you're getting good enough that sometimes I forget you're a girl. All right, I'll be out in a minute," Dr. Nayhan said, disappearing into the men's locker room.

Was that a compliment? I wasn't quite sure whether to feel pleased that my abilities as a general surgery intern had been acknowledged favorably, or to be offended on behalf of my gender. I don't think he even realized that his comment might be construed as being very politically incorrect, if not completely chauvinistic. But he was my attending, and I was the intern on his surgical service, so my lecture on equality and the value that women brought to medicine would have to wait.

After we had finished surgery, Dr. Nayhan wanted to go over the things that he needed done for his patients in the hospital. This meant he was going to give me a list of things to do. He was in a hurry as we headed down the hall towards the locker room, already running late for his office hours. "Let Smith eat; he can have a full liquid diet. Get that epidural out of McKane so we can get her out of here, and make sure Minah gets her CT scan today," he continued as he opened the door to go into the men's locker room. He held the door open as if he expected me to follow him in, and he kept right on talking.

"Dr. Nayhan, I can't go in there," I said. So I stood outside the locker room door, waiting for Nayhan to change out of his scrubs and return. "You sure spend a lot of time hanging around the door to the men's locker room, Dr. Sawmiller," remarked Edith, the PACU nurse, as she passed by.

Dr. Nayhan came out and we finished talking about the patients. He had a woman patient to be admitted for surgery. Mrs. Gates was a rather large lady, and finding her veins and maintaining an IV had been a problem on her previous admissions. I was supposed to put in a central line to alleviate this problem and get her ready to go for the OR tomorrow.

A central line is a large caliber intravenous catheter that goes into one of the big veins of the neck or shoulder. The technique of placing this line involves simply relying on knowledge of anatomy to find the vein with a needle, then sliding the catheter in over a guidewire. It takes doing a few to get the feel of when you are in exactly the right place, the correct angle to guide the needle, and how deep in you can safely push the needle.

I had done enough lines that they would send me out on my own to do them, but most had been on reasonably thin people with good anatomic landmarks, easy shots. I had to call the senior resident on the last three lines I had tried because I couldn't find the vein. All those patients had been either obese or old and twisted up from severe degenerative neck and back arthritis. I was beginning to lose my confidence, and I was sure the senior resident was beginning to get annoyed at my constant need for help.

I gave Mrs. Gates my little talk on central lines, the risks and benefits, and had her sign the consent form. She was a little on the large side, but I had to get this line in. I could not fail again and have to call the senior to bail me out. I laid her down flat and prepared all my supplies. I prepped her skin, then dipped the head of her bed at a steep angle. This maneuver causes the veins up near the head to become engorged with blood, giving you a much bigger target in terms of veins. However, this also allows any extra weight the person is carrying to mound up and obscure all the carefully sought landmarks that help guide where you will place the needle. I injected some local anesthetic and inserted my long needle, probing for the vein, waiting to see a flash of that nice dark, red venous blood. I passed the needle in and out, varying my angle slightly with every pass to sweep the area. No blood. I couldn't find the vein.

"Are you doing okay, Mrs. Gates?" I asked.

"Yes, are you almost done?" she inquired from under the sterile drape.

"Well, I'm just trying to get into the vein now."

I passed the needle deeper, and felt it stop against the hard bone of the clavicle. She winced with pain. I angled the needle a little and tried to slide it under the clavicle, as this is where the subclavian vein would be. Again, the needle tip hit against hard bone. "Let me give you a little more numbing medicine. This may sting and burn a little," I said as I injected additional anesthetic.

She was starting to move a little. I was starting to get irritated that I couldn't find the vein, again.

"Can you please hold still, Mrs. Gates?" I said.

"Are you about finished?" she replied.

I did not answer her. I decided to try a new site, lateral to the first try. I injected more anesthetic and poked the needle through the skin. She shifted position as I tried to find the vein.

"Hold still," I instructed.

"That hurts. That's a sharp pain. Is it almost in?" she asked.

"Not yet," I said, thinking that maybe it would be in already if she was seventy-five pounds lighter and I could tell where her clavicle and sternal notch were, instead of having to guess and blindly stick this needle in and out a thousand times. I glanced at the clock. I had been working on this for half an hour. The procedure should normally take ten minutes. I grabbed the local anesthetic and injected more. I tilted her head down a little more to see if that would help, and went back to the needle. I tried several new angles with no luck. I was determined not to call for help. I was becoming increasingly irritated that this was so difficult. I was angry at the patient for being so heavy that I couldn't clearly identify any anatomic landmarks and for having such a thick clavicle that I couldn't get the needle into her vein. I took down the sterile drape and told her I would have to put it on the other side. Sometimes one side was hard for some unknown reason, but you could get the other side easily. I was hoping this would be the case. I got a new set up and started on the other side. I flipped the drape up over her face and instructed her to hold still. I injected some local anesthetic and passed the needle through her skin, slowly advancing it and hoping to see some blood flash into the syringe. She flinched, causing the drape to drop down so I could see her face.

"I'll give you some more numbing medicine; you shouldn't be feeling any sharp pain. I need you to hold still. Are you feeling pain, or just the pressure?" I asked impatiently.

"That was sharp pain," she replied quietly.

I injected more anesthetic and glanced at the clock. I was going on fifty minutes now to get this ten-minute job done. I cannot fail. I cannot call for help again. The vein has to be there, I thought. I was getting more and more annoyed that this wasn't going well. Then I finally got the flash of dark blood. The syringe started to fill, and I was so relieved I almost forgot what to do next. My hand was shaky from fatigue, but I managed to get the guidewire through the needle and it slid in easily. I felt like jumping up and down for joy. I got the catheter sutured in place. I happily put on the dressing and assured the patient we were done. I felt like I had passed a test, like I had achieved a milestone. I could do a difficult line. If I could get this in, I should be able to get a line in anybody. It couldn't get much worse than this. I cleaned up the mess of supplies and explained to the patient we would get an x-ray to check catheter position and to make sure there was no lung collapse. She just nodded her head, not saying anything. I left the room feeling pretty good, proud of myself that I had persevered and was triumphant. I got the line, with no help from anyone. I could walk back over to the surgery office, and when Marcos asked, "Did you get the line in?" I could say, "Yes, it was a little hard, but I got it in." It was a small victory in my long, miserable day.

About a year later I ran into that patient again. She had gone through her surgery and recovered fine, with no problems. She was back for a repair of a small hernia, and I was in pre-op clinic to do the History and Physical. I went into the exam room and introduced myself.

"I remember you," she said, not sounding very pleased. At first I didn't recognize her or recall what we had done on her.

"Oh, you've been in before, right?" I casually responded.

"Yes, last year. I had surgery, and you were on Dr. Nayhan's team; you were the one who took care of me before surgery," she replied, giving me a seriously dissatisfied look. Then I did vaguely remember her. She had done very well with surgery. Most patients I ran into after being involved in their care expressed thanks, or said they appreciated the nice job we did taking care of them. She was obviously not impressed with me.

"You put a central line in the day before my surgery," she went on.

"Yes," I replied, "Now I remember."

Then this nice, sweet, grandmotherly lady looked me right in the eye and said, very solemnly, "If I would've had a gun while you were doing that, I think I would have shot you dead."

"Oh," I stuttered, completely taken aback by this unexpected statement. "I'm sorry. What made you feel that way?"

"After you had been working for a while, when that drape fell and I looked at your face, you had a look in your eyes that you were going to keep poking and sticking that needle in until you got it in, even if it killed me. I don't think you cared at all, not one bit, if you were hurting me. And I don't understand that, because after the surgery you seemed nice, everyone did.

But I will never forget that look in your eyes. It was like I wasn't even a person, not even a human being," she said. She spoke in a very matter of fact tone, not emotional or angry. Her words hit me like a huge tidal wave of bitter cold, stinging salt water, rolling me over and pushing me under so I couldn't catch my breath. I had trouble speaking for a moment, but finally choked up some words of response. "I'm sorry. I certainly didn't mean for you to feel that way," I stammered. "Some lines are difficult to get in, just because anatomy varies between people. I usually give plenty of anesthetic so it's not painful. I try to keep people as comfortable as I can."

"Listen, my comfort was the last thing you were worried about that day. I don't know what else you had going on that day, you may have had fifty other things to do and maybe you were up all night. I don't know. I just remember that look in your eyes," she said quietly.

And she was absolutely right. Somewhere during that long struggle to get that central line in, she had ceased to be a person, and had become a project I had to complete. She had become a means to prove to myself and my seniors that I could accomplish a task. She had given me confidence and had restored my faith in my ability to get this procedure done. What had I given her? A sense of worthlessness. I had blamed her for being difficult, even became annoyed at her for having the bone structure she had, for moving, for complaining. The safe, responsible thing to do would have been to let someone else try the line, instead of continuing to torture this poor lady. But I had been at a point where I needed to be able to do this independently, to build my confidence. I had no perception of how aware the patient was of all this. I had left her room with a great sense of accomplishment, feeling like I had overcome a great obstacle, whereas she was left feeling like something less than a person.

I didn't know how to reply. I was a little embarrassed and ashamed. I thought I was a sincere, empathetic person, but I hadn't been. I just simply said, "I'm sorry." I didn't try to explain it away, because she so clearly understood what had gone on, what I had been thinking about while putting in that line. "Would you prefer someone else do your physical?" I asked, half expecting to be kicked out of the room.

"No, you can do my physical. There's no sense in holding a grudge. You're a young doctor, and there are some things you need to learn that aren't in any book. I always just wondered if you had any idea how hard that was on me, or if you even cared at that moment. I thought you should know."

I listened to her heart and lungs and examined her abdomen in sort of an awkward silence. I got the sense she had forgiven me long ago, that she just chalked it up to me being an inexperienced doctor. I occasionally think of her now, years later, when I am beginning to get annoyed or frustrated because something isn't going as smoothly or quickly as I think it should. I begin to focus on the fact that some thirty-minute case is taking an hour-and-a-half to finish, and I'm going to run late, and I'm going to miss a soccer game or dinner with my family, again. It's amazing how easy it is to lose sight of the fact that you are working on a human being with needs and feelings. Your patient is someone's mother, or grandfather, or spouse. Someone is waiting, counting on you to safely care for their loved one. A patient's need for comfort or reassurance can seem like just another barrier to getting the job done, so you can move on to the next things you have on your list of things to get done. However, as Mrs. Gates taught me, everything we do or neglect to do does have a lasting impact on our patients, even if it makes no impression on us at all. The key is to remember that respect and compassion are always necessary, even when it's inconvenient.

Maria Basile, MD
Colon and Rectal Surgeon

How I Chose a Date for My Surgery

Since the year 2000, the first week of May has always been a rough one for my family. That was the year my mother passed away.

This past Sunday we all had dinner together. I could feel each person—my dad, my brothers, my sister, even my husband, going through his own personal history of Mom's last days with us. The phone-calls, the drive for us from Erie, the different hospitals that week. In one of those hospitals in Brooklyn, New York, my dad had practiced as a general surgeon his entire career. After my residency, I even worked there, first-assisting on bigger cases, fulfilling a dream my mom always had for me—that I would operate with my father. It was the last place my children, then just two and three years old, would see my mother alive. The hospital where she was transferred next was a big heart hospital on the North Shore of Long Island. Here they were equipped to do everything, which is of course what we wanted them to do, since none of us was ready to say goodbye. My dad and I, having experienced through our years of training that certain procedures can save lives, let them cath her, crack her chest, and try for hours to patch the shredded fibers of her heart. Then she died. Nothing will ever be as painful.

Even six years later, the first week of May is still rough. My youngest brother, thirty-six, recently had a pacemaker placed. The cardiologist came out of the procedure and told him in a heavy Indian accent, "Both your nodes are dead! Boat of dem!" I think my brother knew this. He has had vague complaints since our mother passed: trouble sleeping, chronic fatigue, pains in his shoulder, palpitations. In September 2001, he was visiting my mother at the cemetery and took a day off from work to rest, still tired all the time. The next morning, running late for work, his subway stopped working a station away from his office in Manhattan. When he got to the surface, he was carried by a wave of people coursing north. He turned to see his office building crumble to the ground.

May fifth is the day my mother died. I remember explaining her death to my children. I told them that her heart broke a little each time her

131

children moved away. And that she died so she could be with all of us at once, no matter where we were.

As I stated before, nothing will ever be as painful. I am thinking of all this as my surgeon helps me select a date for my own upcoming surgery.

Post-op Day Five

Post-operative day five is always the one that surgeons fear. And when the surgeon is the patient, that fear is doubled. After the assault of any major surgery, the body undergoes endocrine, immune-mediated (inflammatory), cell-mediated, metabolic, and nutritional responses to injury that culminate on or around day three, and reach homeostatic balance by day five. Day five is the day that many surgery-related complications will present. Wound infections, fascial dehiscence, eviscerations, small bowel obstructions, anastomotic leaks, stump blowouts . . . the first hints of these conditions often manifest on post-op day five.

Probably why I feel so horrible today. Every time I laugh, cough, urinate—especially urinate—I feel like they are doing the operation again, with me wide awake. Like my pretty, healing, bikini-line Pfannensteil incision is being torn open again, and some ungodly retractor like a Balfour is being used to hold the edges wide open and apart. Ouch. And we won't even discuss the gas pains, in shockwaves. It hurts from my pelvis to my eyes. No relief. Am I doing too much or not enough? What should I eat? High fiber, to make the bowel movements softer, or low fiber so as not to produce so much gas? Take more pain medicine and walk around more or stop taking pain medicine because of its constipating effects? Dunno.

Maybe I should just be happy. Cancer is out; and you can't die from gas pains. It's post-op day 5 and I don't have any of the major complications listed above. The Yankees have another chance to beat the Red Sox tonight. My vote for Taylor (on "American Idol") went through. I watched "Love Actually" last night and remembered how cute Hugh Grant and Liam Neeson are. Yeah, I should just be happy.

Inspiring Quote:

"I postpone death by living, by suffering, by error, by risking, by giving, by loving." — Anais Nin

Preeti R. John, MBBS, MPH, FACS
Critical Care Surgeon

Up at Dawn

Fluorescent white lights flickered on as we walked into the patient's room. As a resident training to be a surgeon, I was up at dawn each day to begin "rounds" with a team of medical students and interns, donned in scrubs and white coats. Starting at five a.m. we examined patients who had been operated upon, to check on their progress after surgery.

Most patients had to be woken up from deep slumber as we greeted them, and some remained disoriented while we asked them questions, poked and prodded their abdomens and inspected their surgical wounds.

"Do you know where you are, Mrs. Jackson?" I asked the first patient, standing at her bedside in the surgical oncology ward.

"Jom-Opkins!" she replied, her words refracted through her toothless mouth. She clutched at her bed sheets, squinting at the lights and frowning, as she asserted her independence and dignity over and above her "Patient Exhibit Number One" status.

Part of her colon had been surgically removed a couple of days ago, for a mass that was probably cancerous.

"Yes, that's right!" I replied. "You've had surgery, and we've stopped by to make sure you're doing alright. Can I have a look at your belly?"

She reluctantly let go of her bed sheets as I peeled them off her frail body. Her abdomen was covered with a dressing and seemed distended. I placed my stethoscope on it after rubbing the diaphragm against my thigh to warm the instrument, but she still let out a faint gasp as the metal rim touched her skin.

I listened intently for bowel sounds and heard occasional gurgling—a reassuring sign that the intestines were gradually beginning to function again. She looked at me expectantly, her frown slowly easing.

"Well? Can I eat today?" she queried.

"Let's start with clear liquids to make sure your body can handle it," I suggested.

"Watermelon," she stated, blinking hopefully. "I want watermelon."

133

This was an easy negotiation. I nodded my consent. It was an unobjectionable choice, and if it made her look forward to relishing something, all the better.

Clearly pleased at the prospect, she flashed me a toothless smile as I left her room. I marveled at the clarity of her thought and simplicity of her request. She focused on something satisfying that would get her through the day. The remarkable adaptation of the human spirit coping in a bleak situation.

I moved on to the neighboring room to examine the next patient, medical students in tow . . .

Inspiring Quote:
"Some of the most important contributions to our world are made by caring for one person at a time. We each have to chart our own unique course and define which goals fit our lives, values and dreams."
— Sheryl Sandberg

Fatima Khambaty, MD
General Surgeon

Exam Room 29: Notes from the District

I manage to return to the United States from Eritrea, the Horn of Africa, where I was living and working for a small mom-and-pop nonprofit medical organization for two years, after finishing medical training. Leaving the dysfunction and glory of the Emergency Department and eight-year-old victims of grenade blasts behind, I exchange this for a fellowship in small-incision surgery, strangely, for not-so-small-people in the District of Columbia.

I hobble across the fellowship finish line and eagerly start my new job at Kaiser Permanente, where the prospect of having a life outside the hospital, owning a set of un-chipped dinner plates, paying a mortgage, and getting the occasional dental cleaning for myself loom large.

So, I have been seeing tits and asses (professionally) all day. Breast lumps and butt abscesses abound, and at 8:30 in the morning, no less. Although I think caffeine is essential, it just doesn't do what the scent of viscous pus does at that time of the morning to turn your headlights on. But why digress? I am greeted by a forty-something-old-man in the standard San Francisco position, who stutters something about a throbbing ache in a slightly sheepish tone. Not to worry, I reassure him, I get paid to boldly go where no man has gone before, adjusting the light, now illuminating the area where the "sun don't shine." I knowingly use all the bad clichés I can possibly muster up, hoping to make him a bit more at ease. I inject some numbing medication into his anus, and ask him to "just let that simmer for a while."

"So you cook?" he says, picking up on the use of that verb "to simmer."

"Yes," I reply.

"What do you make?" he says, making small talk I assume, to ease the uncut tension.

"Shrimp," I counter, and then proceed to slice into an abscess in his anus.

"Oh. What does your husband think of your cooking?"

He is smart, or at least diplomatic; and the numbing medication worked well, I think to myself.

"I'm not married," I add, as I squeeze out thick, yellow pus. I then insert some gauze into his anus.

"Yeah? Maybe you could cook for me some time?" he mumbles.

"Sure," I say, thinking to myself, *I'll cook for you when Mumia Abu-Jamal walks free, or when the after-effects of Chernobyl wear off.* I finish with the procedure on his anus, and give him a prescription for antibiotics. He looks at me, quizzically.

"Is that all?" he says.

"Yes," I answer.

"Are you sure?" he asks.

At this point, I am confused. What more could he want than me cleaning, draining and packing his anus?

"Your number?" he asks.

I gather myself into a five-foot-two-inch spit wad of fire, take a deep breath and set aside the fact that I have spent the past twenty minutes having a conversation with this man's buttocks. I remind myself how much I loved the book *Guns, Germs and Steel* and that men have two testicles. Not one, but *two*, that churn out the very stuff of life itself, constantly. "Umm, no," I counter, with the best of a DC head wiggle.

He leaves the office, prescription in hand, and walks out to where his wife patiently waits for him, clearly unaware of the nature of her husband's booty call.

Inspiring Quote:
"The truth will set you free. But first, it will piss you off." — Gloria Steinem

Sarah Blair MD, FACS
Surgical Oncologist

"Criers" versus "Yellers"

The two most common categories of women I encountered during residency were the "criers" and the "yellers." These were the coping mechanisms I saw my fellow residents use to get through the stress of surgical residency. I couldn't commit to either extreme and ended up just falling back on sarcasm to release stress.

I started my residency in 1992 at a New England Medical Center. Only 5 percent of surgical residents were female at that time, but certain programs attracted a higher number of women. In my program, there were three women out of the eight categorical interns. Given the enormous demands of residency, only five out of eight would actually finish. The faculty factored in that several were going to quit because of the torture of training. We worked 100 hours per week, including 36 straight hours every third day. We were routinely shouted at and publicly humiliated when we made a mistake. Thus it was crying versus screaming to cope with the physical and mental anguish.

I was the only woman in my class to finish the five years of training. One older woman quit after the first year—or they asked her to leave. I think it was a mutual decision. Medicine was her second career; she had already worked as an architect. Her kids were grown up and she wanted to do something new. She was definitely a crier but, in her case, it was a disadvantage. She cried to everyone including the nurses. When something went wrong with the patients at night, the nurses never called her, because they just could not deal with her crying. Invariably, she was reprimanded the following day for not taking care of the patients, which meant a lot of yelling from senior residents and more crying on her part. It was a vicious circle. Lesson number one: don't cry to the nurses. The other female resident left under mysterious circumstances when I was away on a research fellowship. I never heard from her again.

One of my first chief residents was a yeller and a "dragon lady;" her name was Cynthia. She yelled at everyone and was very controlling. She had quirks in managing patients that she insisted we observe, even though they did not always make sense. These quirks were more "voodoo" than real medicine, but she insisted they be followed in great detail. Most people think medicine is a science, and for the most part it is, but surgeons are a superstitious lot. When we have one patient who has a bad outcome after an operation, we blame it on weird things—like the patient had carbonated soda or scrambled eggs too soon after surgery. We would much rather blame the diet than our surgical skills. Cynthia was one of those surgeons who believed that if we followed her superstitions, her patients would always do well.

Cynthia had perfectly coiffed hair that appeared to require daily early morning blow-drying. This was quite an accomplishment since we all started patient rounds at five in the morning before going to surgery at seven a.m. Getting up even an extra fifteen minutes early around four a.m. to blow-dry your hair was a commitment I was not willing to make.

Cynthia also had this annoying habit of playing with her necklace during rounds. She would slide the charm along the chain back and forth during the "sign out" process, when discussing what happened the night before and the plan for the day. What follows is an example of such an exchange.

Susie: Mr. Jones had a fever last night. We checked a chest x-ray, urine culture and a blood count.

Suddenly Cynthia would stop moving the charm—and here it came:

Cynthia: Susie, what is the most common cause of fever in the first twenty-four hours after an operation?

Susie: Atelectasis?

Cynthia: What did your chest x-ray show?

Susie: Atelectasis

Cynthia: What is the treatment for atelectasis?

Susie: Incentive spirometry.

Cynthia: How come I did not see an incentive spirometer at Mr. Jones' bedside? Did you go to the bedside and make sure he knew how to use the spirometer?

Susie: No.

Cynthia: No. Instead, you ordered a bunch of useless tests and rolled over in bed.

OK, so now would be the time that the crying or yelling would begin. A crier would start bawling and say, "I couldn't go see Mr. Jones because I had to draw blood work on Mr. Springer, who is on a heparin drip for a deep vein thrombosis, but is 300 pounds and I could not find a vein. Alternatively, a yeller would get indignant and say, "I spoke to the nurse but she was too busy, so I took it up with the nurse manager between drawing Mr. Springer's labs. Of course the crying worked better on male residents, who still felt the need to help a damsel in distress.

I myself would have resorted to sarcasm. "I ordered respiratory to do supervised spirometry and get a spirometer from the store-room; but it was during their mid-shift second coffee break so it would have to wait for changeover at eight a.m. to turf it to the next team."

I always assumed that the criers and yellers would never get along—that they would resent each other's tactics. The criers would feel the yellers were too bitchy and mean and the yellers would feel the criers were taking advantage of their femininity and not acting like equals to their male counterparts.

I was once on a team with both a yeller and a crier. Cynthia, chief resident, and May, who was a third year resident. May was pretty. She had a heart-shaped face with big brown eyes, a strong nose, thin lips and a pretty smile. She was tall and thin. She had a boyfriend Jim who was also a surgical resident. They were an attractive couple and very popular with the other residents. May was a superstar crier.

The fourth-year resident on the team was Charlie. Now Charlie looked like the iconic surgical resident. He was tall and handsome with a strong chin. He looked like Clark Kent. He even had tortoiseshell glasses like Clark Kent. You felt like he could always save you from any surgical emergency when you worked with him. He never got flustered during a code. He always gave the right advice, including which nurse to talk to and how to stay on each attending's good side. Following his advice you could avoid getting yelled at in the operating room for asking for the wrong suture or putting on the wrong dressing. Of course Charlie was the kind of guy who would try to help all the criers.

I was the intern on the service. I was a short, attractive woman with light-brown hair and green eyes. I was thin in those days, since there wasn't much time for eating or sleeping. I typically was quiet. When I got yelled at

I just sucked it up. Of course that made me lash out at the nurses or respiratory therapists with sarcasm. They in turn got back at me by sabotaging me in small ways. It was a vicious circle.

May would burst into tears with the slightest bad news. She would literally have tears roll down her face in front of the whole team. I just could not put myself out there like that. Cynthia as the Chief resident would make the call schedule. We were each on call every third night; and every month you were supposed to have one day off. When you were on call on Friday, you could go home on Saturday around midday and then you got Sunday off. That month May did not get a day off; and she started crying in the middle of rounds when she found out. She would not get time to spend with Jim. Charlie could not stand the crying.

Charlie: May, don't cry I'll switch with you. You can have Friday and I'll take Saturday.

Cynthia: Charlie, that's not fair. May had two days off last month because she had her sister's wedding in Springfield.

Charlie: I don't mind. I don't get much sleep at home these days because of the baby. He only sleeps a couple of hours at a time. I get more sleep on call than at home.

Cynthia: Suit yourself. Let the operator know about the change. Can we get back to sign-out now? Sarah, give me the ins and outs for each patient today.

Sarah (me): Mr. Jones had two liters in and three liters out. He is starting to mobilize fluid so we turned down the IV fluid rate. No fevers, out of bed twice, no flatus.

Cynthia: Did you start him on non-carbonated clears less than 300 ml every eight hours and crackers?

Sarah: Yes.

(I knew that starting on a precise amount of non-carbonated clears was voodoo medicine).

May: I saw his nurse in the hall and he wanted a coke. I told her it was okay. (May tried to avoid the nonsense since she was a more senior resident.)

Cynthia: May, do you know what non-carbonated clears means? It means no carbonation. If he has an intestinal leak it will be your fault for letting him have carbonation and distending his anastomosis. OK, let's continue—but I would like to speak with you after rounds.

May looked appropriately scared. Cynthia could publicly yell at rounds but in private she could get really scary. May left after rounds and followed Cynthia into the call room to get her "beating." Charlie and I hung around to cheer up May afterwards. We made phone calls and updated the list of patients. Charlie was never anxious to go home early because of the baby. His wife moved to New England to be with him but had not found a job, so she decided to become a stay-at-home mom. That's what you did when you married a surgeon. I hung around because I was on call and this was the most interesting thing going on. Better than the crappy cafeteria food waiting for me. Besides, it was always safer to be around Charlie in case some patient disaster happened. I could always get Charlie's input. May came out of the call room looking shocked.

Charlie: May, what happened? You look shell-shocked. Did she yell? Did she threaten to fire you?

May: No.

Charlie: Then what happened? I have never seen you at a loss for words.

May: Cynthia got engaged. I didn't even know that she had a boyfriend. Who would put up with her? The pressure would be too high. Can you imagine if he does not follow her instructions at home? What if he does not bring home the right kind of non-carbonated clear liquids from the grocery store?

Charlie: Does she want to go on a double date with you and Jim? What did she talk to you about?

May: She wants me to go look at wedding dresses with her. She considers me her best friend. Or maybe she just does not have anyone else to go with. *She is going to give me time off to go shopping with her!*

Sarah: Well that's a surprise. She can go from yelling at you to asking for help in two minutes flat. Do you think she realizes how loud she gets on rounds? (I didn't want to bring up the public crying a few minutes prior.)

May: I don't think she realizes that she is yelling; or she is really good at compartmentalizing. I told her I would go. What woman does not like looking at wedding dresses—*and* I get next Saturday off. It's a win/win situation.

Charlie: Fair enough. I didn't see that one coming.

Of course these kinds of things happened twenty years ago and surgical residency has changed. It is no longer a grueling "survival of the fittest" physically or mentally. We are all a kinder and gentler society, and I have not seen any teary eyes in quite some time; but I'm pretty sure that the dragon ladies are still around!

Inspiring Quote:

"A woman is like a tea bag—you can't tell how strong she is until you put her in hot water." — Eleanor Roosevelt

SECTION 7—TRAILBLAZERS TELL THEIR TALES

Carol Sawmiller, MD, FACS
General Surgeon

Ship's Surgeon

In the entire history of the United States military, there have only been a handful of women who have served as the Ship's Surgeon onboard an aircraft carrier. I am one of those women. The military has allowed women onboard combatant ships since 1993, and the carriers are the only ships that have a surgeon attached as part of the crew. The Navy currently has twelve active aircraft carriers, so there aren't that many ship's surgeon billets to fill. This assignment was the last thing I had in mind when I signed my Oath of Office, swearing to support and defend the Constitution of the United States against all enemies, foreign and domestic. It sounds rather naïve now, but I was totally shocked and completely unprepared for any possibility that I would be going to sea.

When I signed my oath early in my residency, I had romantic visions of being an officer in the department of surgery at a nice shore facility in Italy or Spain. I would practice general surgery all day. I would go home to my family every night or at least nearly every night. No general surgeon I knew got to go home every night. I planned to spend my free weekends traveling Europe with my family. The recruiting team assured me this was usually how the assignments worked out. A good portion of the very generous debt I accumulated for medical school would be paid back and the extra money would allow my husband to pursue his education and go back to school and finish his PhD. After we finished college, he went to work to support us through my medical school years, so I felt like it was his turn now to be able to follow his dreams. My life was perfectly planned. But I had joined the Navy, for God's sake. The Navy, whose official mission is to maintain, train and equip combat-ready naval forces capable of winning wars, deterring aggression and maintaining freedom of the seas.

Four years later, it was payback time. When I got my orders to the USS Carl Vinson, I was completely devastated. My decision to join the military had not accomplished a single goal that I had set. As it turned out, my husband had no interest in returning to school. I had been accepted for a Vascular Surgery Fellowship at the Ohio State University, but the military would not allow me a year of deferral. I had to start my active duty obligation immediately following residency, giving up my fellowship position. I would not be assigned to a shore hospital, but would spend the year living onboard an Aircraft Carrier. This was particularly distressing to me since I had a three-month-old son at home. I was utterly despondent about having to leave my infant son, my home and my husband, and live on a ship for a year. The military was separating me from my family, taking away my career choice and sticking me on a ship where I wouldn't even be doing much surgery. I had a passionate bitterness towards the Navy before I ever even put on a uniform. The idea of being the Vinson's Ship's Surgeon brought nothing but disappointment and frustration. But I had signed on the dotted line, and the military owned me, at least for a few years. I had one-year orders as the ship's surgeon onboard the USS Carl Vinson.

The ship was in its work-up phase, leading up to a six-month deployment to the Persian Gulf. We would go out to sea for six or eight weeks while different departments, like the flight deck, trained and got certified or qualified. We would be back in port for four to six weeks for maintenance and updates, then back out to sea. Every time we left for a training mission, every time I had to say goodbye to my husband and son, it felt like someone ripping a hole right through my soul. It's hard to adequately describe the intense loneliness that engulfs you in the last few minutes, when you hand your child over to your spouse and walk away. You touch his skin, stroke his hair, breathe in that fresh baby smell, cling to every little sound he utters, because you know this has to last for weeks or months. It feels like an eternity will pass before you get to be his mother again. Some people thrive on deployments, but I am not one of those people.

So here I was, the exact polar opposite of where I thought I would be at this point in my life. I was a Lieutenant Commander in the United States Navy, stuck in the medical department down in the depths of a massive ship, a thousand miles away from home, feeling useless. This was our fourth underway, and we were somewhere in the Pacific Ocean, continuing carrier qualifications and participating in a COMPTUEX (Composite Training Unit Exercise). I rarely did any surgery—the main reason a surgeon is onboard the carrier is to take care of potential trauma. The flight deck of a carrier is an incredibly dangerous place, staffed by inexperienced nineteen- and twenty-year-olds. Any little mistake could result in life-threatening injuries to crew or pilots that would need immediate care. Luckily, this almost never happened. But it left me with very little to do. A year ago, I had been the chief resident running a busy surgical service, supervising the junior residents in the SICU (Surgical Intensive Care Unit), managing car accidents and gunshot wounds in the ED (Emergency Department) every day, and doing big cases almost daily. I was used to constant action, always being needed, and no spare time. On the ship, I had almost nothing to do. The crew was young and healthy, and didn't have the problems that typically lead one to end up on an OR table. The GMO (General Medical Officer) and the hospital corpsmen took care of all the primary care type stuff for the crew. A GMO is a doctor who has completed medical school and one year of intern training. They are sent out for one to three years on a general medical tour, where they provide primary care for their unit. The corpsmen are enlisted personnel with specialized training in medical care. They were usually pretty busy with sick-call duties. I had done only two or three appendectomies, an incarcerated hernia and a handful of minor procedures in the last few months. I was miserable, always feeling like my years of training—all my skills—were just being wasted out here. I spent my days seeing an occasional patient, doing administrative tasks and going to the gym. I did some lectures for the corpsmen. We had a fantastic group of hospital corpsmen, eager to learn and very competent in what they did. HM2 Bradley was my surgical tech. Everyone in the Navy is identified by initials that signify their specialty and rank. HM signifies a hospital corpsman, and "2" refers to the rank as a second class. He would eventually progress to a first class, then a chief. During my first week on the ship we organized the OR and took inventory of everything we had.

"Okay, we'll go over all this and get a list together of anything we might need, and see what we can get from the hospital," I instructed.

"Yes, Sir," he responded, then quickly corrected himself. "I meant M'am, yes, M'am." He was slightly embarrassed, and explained that it wasn't very common to have a female surgeon on the ship. Poor HM2 Bradley continued to address me as "Sir" frequently, quickly apologizing and following with "M'am." Over several months it became an almost automatic "Yes, Sir, I mean M'am," then progressed to a more consistent "Yes SirM'am," just combining the two into one. I didn't mind; it seemed odd to be called "M'am" anyway. He was a good tech. He had experience in the OR and he had that natural surgical intuition, just sort of knowing what was needed for the next step in whatever we were doing. He did a great job as the surgical assistant in the few cases we did, and was always on top of things and well prepared. If calling me "Sir" was his biggest flaw, I could certainly live with that.

As the weeks at sea passed, I helped organize protocols for mass casualty drills and a trauma response team. I read books. I studied for my general surgery oral board exams. I did a lot of things that didn't involve me being in an operating room. It was a slow form of torture, and left me feeling like this whole idea to join the Navy was an exercise in futility. Had I been busy on the ship, I might have felt some justification for my being dragged away from my family on a regular basis. I was determined to be professional and do a good job with whatever I was tasked to do, but it was hard not to let this resentment overwhelm me.

One of the ways I spent my vast amounts of free time was running on the various treadmills in the ship's gyms. If my talents weren't needed, at least I could do something for myself. I was hoping to get a few miles in before dinner, but the Medical Alert sounded just as my foot hit the belt. If anyone on the ship had what they thought was a medical emergency, they could initiate the Medical Alert System. Three loud bongs sounded over the ship's intercom system, followed by an announcement of the location of the emergency. A team from the medical department, usually the PA (physician assistant) or GMO, and two corpsmen would respond, running to the site with the bag of emergency medical supplies. The Medical Alerts usually turned out to be something completely lame—like someone vomited or someone had a fever.

"Medical Alert . . . Medical Department Treatment Room. Medical Department, Treatment Room."

This caught my attention. If the alert was in the Medical Department, then one of our own corpsmen or the PA or nurse called it. Maybe this was more than a sore throat. Almost immediately my phone went off.

"Sawmiller," I snapped as I answered.

"Oh, thank goodness. Sir, can you come down here, like yesterday. We've got a real problem, a guy who can't breathe, he isn't looking good." It was HM2 Bradley. I was already down the ladder well and halfway across the hangar bay, ignoring the "Sir;" nothing like a compromised airway to get you moving.

"I'm getting a tracheostomy set ready, and a chest tube set and we are calling anesthesia. I don't know what's going on with him, but we'll be ready for anything," he continued, as I slid down two more ladders and sprinted to the treatment room.

The kid was sitting upright on the treatment table, leaning forward, diaphoretic and breathing fast. I had seen him down in the Dental Department. He was one of the enlisted DNs. (DN refers to a "dentalman, nonrated," representing an enlisted sailor very early in training towards becoming a dental technician.) He had been at work all day, just fine, then suddenly developed terrible pain in his right chest and started gasping for breath. His buddies grabbed him and literally carried him up the ladder to our department, convinced he was having a major heart attack. The corpsman had a pulse oximeter on him, which was showing an oxygen saturation of 70 percent. GMO was getting his blood pressure and directing someone to get oxygen on him. "Has this ever happened to you before?" I asked, as I grabbed a stethoscope.

The only word he could get out was "die," and it seemed to be a question he was asking me. He had no breath sounds audible in his right chest. "His pressure is 60," GMO informed me, getting worried. My eyes found HM2. "Get me a long needle, like a spinal needle, right now." "Tension pneumo, I got it. Get his shirt off and get him down, get some Betadine," he instructed HN Shafer as he disappeared into the OR. "Oh, man, were gonna needle-decompress this thing right here, aren't we? You think this is a tension pneumo?" GMO chimed in, excited. He always liked to be involved in a procedure.

A tension pneumothorax occurs when air leaks from inside the lung into the space surrounding the lung. This can occur from an injury, or sometimes from underlying lung disease. As air leaks through torn lung tissue, the lung collapses. If there is continued leakage of air, the space fills enough that it starts to shift the heart and major blood vessels towards the other side of the chest. With every breath in, the situation worsens. With enough shift, the blood can no longer fill the heart. The blood pressure drops, and soon cardiac arrest will follow. The air has to be vented out to relieve the tension pneumothorax.

For the first time in a long time I felt like I was exactly where I should be. All the months of wearing a uniform, returning salutes, going to sea on the carrier, all this felt awkward, like I had been thrust into someone else's life. I had spent these months not knowing exactly what to do with myself. But now I had a young kid dying in front of me, likely going into shock from decreased cardiac output due to a tension pneumothorax. If I didn't act quickly, with the correct intervention, he would not survive. And I felt a wave of relief sweep over me. I hadn't felt better in ages. I relaxed, relieved to finally be right back in my comfort zone, right where I belonged. This was a situation where I knew exactly what I should be doing.

I pulled on some gloves as HN quickly swabbed Betadine over the upper right chest. I briefly told the patient I was going to need to put a needle into his chest so he could breathe. He was more diaphoretic and on the verge of going unconscious. At that moment he would have let me do absolutely anything I wanted, if it meant he could take in a breath of air. HM2 handed me the needle and I plunged it into the chest wall, midline, second intercostal space below the clavicle. I sank it about six centimeters, and got that very satisfying hiss of air as the pleural space vented. He drew in a deep breath and looked at me with sincere astonishment in his eyes. His pressure jumped back up to 100 mmHg, and his oxygen saturation rose to 98 percent. The dramatic and immediate resolution of the life-threatening symptoms of a tension pneumothorax with a simple needle decompression is hard to beat. The patient goes from being on the brink of death to feeling pretty good, in seconds.

"Can breathe," he said gratefully, grinning at us. "Good, but if you want to stay that way I need to put a tube in there that will keep your lung up, okay?" I informed him. He readily agreed. HM2, being his usual one step ahead, was setting up the chest tube tray and had several sizes for me to choose from. The needle bought us some time, but he needed a bigger tube placed to reestablish the negative pressure in the chest cavity and maintain lung expansion. We got an intravenous line going and gave him some midazolam (a sedative) and a dose of morphine. This would make the chest tube placement a little more tolerable. As we set up, I explained to the corpsmen the mechanics of tension pneumothorax. I prepped the right lateral chest wall with my sterile solution, and carefully injected a generous amount of local anesthetic. I made an incision and dissected down through the tissue to the muscle, and guided my Kelly clamp through the muscle between the ribs. With a vigorous push, I popped into the pleural space, releasing another puff of air. DN winced a bit, but the drugs were doing a good job for him. I slid the tube into the pleural space, hooked it up to the Pleurovac suction device, and sutured it into place. HM2 placed a dressing, teaching HN just the right way to do it. X-ray rolled in to get our film. Everything looked good on his chest x-ray. His lung was nicely expanded, and the tube was in good position.

"If you hadn't gotten down here and put that needle in, how long would it have been before he died?" HN asked me.

"Six or eight minutes, maybe ten, in someone as young and healthy as him," I replied.

"You totally saved that guy! That was awesome. That guy would have died without you on this ship. This is what medicine is all about. This is why we are here. Awesome!" GMO raved.

He congratulated the corpsmen on their good work, and we updated SMO (Senior Medical Officer) and XO (Executive Officer). The higher-ups always needed to know what was going on, as they were ultimately responsible for everything that happened on the ship. XO usually showed up for all the Medical Alerts. "Good work, Doc. The crew counts on you being here for them," XO said as he left, satisfied that things were under control.

I wrote some orders for his care and got him tucked in on the inpatient ward. Sometimes people have a lung condition where they form thin-walled bubbles on their lungs, called blebs. These can rupture, causing the lung to collapse. It is more common in tall, thin people. Our DN was thin but not very tall. Sometimes these areas heal and the tube can be removed and the lung stays expanded. I tried three or four times over the next week, but every time I took the tube off suction his lung collapsed. We finally got close enough to San Diego to fly him off the ship to the Navy Hospital. He ended up having thoracoscopic lung surgery, where the ruptured bleb was stapled closed. He did fine and was back on the ship for our next underway.

"The crew counts on you being here for them." That's the thing that had been missing. That was the thing I never really understood until DN came in with his collapsed lung. For months I was resentful and angry, crushed by this sense that my time was completely wasted out here because I wasn't operating every day. I thought I could have been so much more useful somewhere else, anywhere else. But the crew of the Vinson needed me. They needed my years of training and my experience. All other jobs on the ship could be done by someone else if the primary person was not available. If the CO (Commanding Officer) was incapacitated or unavailable, the XO was fully capable of taking over. All the other department heads had a second in command, all the maintenance and safety and nuclear jobs had multiple individuals capable of functioning in the same position. But there was only one person on the ship qualified to do surgery, with no back-up available. If there was a life-threatening injury or emergent surgical problem, there would be no one else capable of handling it. They needed me because I was the only person on this ship capable of saving someone's life, if it came down to getting an airway or stopping a traumatic hemorrhage or getting a chest tube in when needed. I finally appreciated the importance of this position. Even if I never actually did a single procedure or operation to save someone's life, the crew needed to know that someone could do that for them if needed.

The next time we left for a ten-week mission it was hard, but at least I knew I had a reason to be going. My load felt a little lighter, not having to pack up all that bitterness and carry it with me. I had been looking at this assignment as the Ship's Surgeon and only seeing how much I was limited in what I wanted to be doing. Now I was able to look at it from the perspective of what the crew needed. There was one kid now who still had his whole life ahead of him, because I gave one year to this ship. There was a whole crew depending on me to be ready for them.

We had about 5,000 people on board when we loaded on the air wing. Many of the jobs on the carrier involved heavy machinery and fairly dangerous work sites. There is a safety net that extends about ten feet out surrounding the perimeter of the flight deck. If someone happened to misstep and fall, the net was there. Everyone up there knew the net was there, so they were able to do their work without worry. The idea of being the Vinson's Ship's Surgeon now brought satisfaction and pride. I didn't realize it earlier, but this position came with all the responsibility that I craved, all the merit and value that I thought was missing. My time was not being squandered at all. I was the safety net for the crew. Even though they may never need me, they all knew they had a Ship's Surgeon on board, ready and waiting.

Inspiring Quote:
"No one can make you feel inferior without your consent."
— Eleanor Roosevelt, later repeated by Rosa Parks

Kathryn D. Anderson, MD, FACS, FRCS (Hon) Eng; Irc; Edin.
Pediatric Surgeon (Retired)

Musings of an Accidental Pioneer

I think that I began my road to being a surgeon at the age of six, right after World War II, when my aunt took me and my sister to the newly re-opened Manchester Art Gallery. I gazed at a pencil drawing of "Theatre" by Barbara Hepworth, who is better known as a brilliant sculptor. It depicts an operating room with the table surrounded by mostly men and one woman, undoubtedly a nurse. Nothing changed my mind, although being a woman surgical resident in the 1960s almost destroyed my resolve. No one in Boston would give me a surgical internship, so I became a pediatric intern at the Children's Hospital and entered surgery at the residency level at Georgetown. There, getting through the next rotation occupied all my time and energy. Children remained my first love, and I became a pediatric surgeon, one of the first to take the new pediatric surgery board certification exam. "Firsts" followed thereafter and I eventually became, among other honors, the first female Surgeon in Chief of a Children's Hospital (Los Angeles), first Chair of the Surgery Section of the American Academy of Pediatrics, first President of the American Pediatric Surgery Association and, my ultimate honor, the first woman President of the American College of Surgeons.

My life did not begin in the United States, as perhaps the reader has realized. I began my medical training at the University of Cambridge in England and met my American husband there. I had not wanted to go to Cambridge, as Oxford and Cambridge added a year to the training. Most English Universities train physicians in five years, right after high school, with no degree until the medical one. Cambridge gave a Bachelor degree half way through medical school, hence the extra year (there were three pre-clinical and three clinical years). However, Fate intervened; and the night before my final exams in high school (the infamous "A" levels without which I could not get into any University nor receive a much needed scholarship), I came down with appendicitis. I missed the exams and had to stay an extra year in high school as the exams were only given once a year. So I took the Cambridge entrance exams for something to do!

Although there was no formal arrangement between the universities of Cambridge and Harvard, they were "kindred souls," believing that each was the best university in the world. It was difficult to get into Cambridge, particularly from a state high school rather than a private school, but I passed the entrance exam and they must have liked me. I was only the second in my high school to be admitted there. My husband was already scheduled to enter Harvard Medical School at the second-year level after his two years in Cambridge, so it was relatively easy to follow him a year later. I finished the last three years at Harvard.

Life in the United States versus England was as different as the languages are similar. First of all, crossing the road was a hazard (hint: the English drive on the left), and there was a local traffic cop who yelled at me every day because I always looked the wrong way. Medical school exams were not essay type, and my abject failure at the first "hour exam" at Harvard sent me to Professor Bernie Davis, who kindly taught me how to take a multiple-choice exam. Once I finished the second year, a non-clinical year, and started to learn clinical medicine, I did not look back.

However, I did run into overt sexism when I told the Dean of Students that I wanted to do a surgical internship and residency. I was told that women could not be surgeons, and if I even applied the Dean would make sure I did not get *any* internship in Boston or elsewhere. So I did a year in Pediatrics at the Boston Children's Hospital, a year I very much enjoyed and have never regretted, in spite of the reason I had to make a fallback choice at the time. Said Dean obviously forgot his remarks and could never understand why I would never speak to him again.

Residency: Oh dear! In the 1960s it was very much okay to make sexist remarks and be overtly averse to training a woman ("You'll only get pregnant and quit, wasting a place which could be better occupied by a man.") Some of the situations I endured I still cannot talk about. There was no point in complaining in those days. There were a few notable exceptions of surgeons, mostly in the community hospitals I rotated to, rather than the University, who were willing to train me. Once I reached a senior level (third year of residency) I was good enough that the surgeons fought to get me to assist them, and I did more than 600 cases in that one year, having previously done a total of six cases the prior two years. This included resection of an abdominal aortic aneurysm! I mention this because this surgeon's son eventually became Chief of Surgery at Howard University, sadly not while his father was alive.

Mostly my fellow residents, who were of course men, were supportive. A minority who resented it when I was given cases they wanted to do undermined me at every opportunity. I was only the third woman to go through the Georgetown residency. By the time I finished as Chief Resident, a total of five, including myself, were in the program. There were no support systems, only the sporadic support of individual surgeons, and, for me, a constant—my husband, who was an unending source of comfort and encouragement.

Nurses were marvelous. I made a point in each rotation to meet with the Head Nurse and find out her routines. This worked wonders and many of the nurses became friends. There was *never* a problem with patients; they were only too happy to have attention paid to them and I was a fairly good listener. At first they were only interested in my English accent, but that was fleeting—I guess as my accent faded somewhat. I have always had the policy of treating the whole family, whether in my pediatric practice or when I was training in adult surgery, and this worked well for me as well as for the patients.

I would like to say that things have much improved, and it is now common for women surgeons to combine a successful career with bringing up children. We chose not to have children for a number of reasons, and although I have no personal regrets, I applaud those women who are able to manage career and family with all the difficult choices inherent in "having it all." This is not to say that the playing field is completely level as yet, and there is still some way to go. But the time for stridency (metaphorically chaining oneself to an iron railing) is gone. It is entirely possible that integration will occur to such an extent that there will be no need to be distinctive as a "woman surgeon"—just a surgeon.

Grateful patients always claim their doctor "saved their life." In fact it is quite rare to really cheat death on someone else's behalf. But when it happens it is the most moving experience. For me one of those rare privileges was when my grandnephew was born with a heart murmur. The neonatologist assured my nephew that the baby could go home, as the defect would close by itself. In the dim recesses of my brain I remembered that a VSD (Ventricular Septal Defect) most often did not present with a murmur at birth. On my advice my nephew insisted that the baby have an echocardiogram; he had critical aortic stenosis, which most certainly would have resulted in early death if he had been forced to go home. My grandnephew is now a lusty lad, who has no idea of the role I have played in his life, nor that he was the inspiration for me to finally write a book that had been in my head for decades. "Who will hold *my* hand?" is for parents whose children need surgery, and it is published by the American College of Surgeons.

How have I managed my complicated life? I pass my philosophy on to the readers of this book: You walk one step at a time, and so you must achieve milestones one at a time, whatever your role in life turns out to be.

Inspiring Quote:
"I've always tried to go a step past wherever people have expected me to end up." — Beverly Sills

Patricia J. Numann, MD, FACS, FRCPSG (Hon), FRCSEd (Hon)
General Surgeon (Retired)

What a Great Life!

I cannot imagine a career that could have brought more pleasure, excitement or fulfillment to my life than being a surgeon has brought. I will admit there have sometimes been challenges, but even then there has always been the enjoyment and sense of accomplishment to balance the challenges. Sserving as President of the American College of Surgeons has been incredible. I wish each woman surgeon could have the experience! At least in the future I am sure more will. Not only have I been able to bring forth the mission of the American College of Surgeons [ACS] to "Inspire Quality," but I have also been able to advance my own agenda regarding surgical education and women's inclusion in surgical leadership.

I believe strongly that every surgeon should belong to the ACS. For me joining and getting involved in the College shortly after finishing my training shaped my career in ways I could not have anticipated. I learned the value of having colleagues throughout the country and world. I was able to influence thought on surgical education and to advocate for women. I continue to see surgeons develop amazing programs through their affiliation with the College. Actually, I believe involvement is essential, particularly by women. The collective intelligence of a group far outweighs that of an individual. Decisions made by diverse groups are always well reasoned.

I feel fortunate to have grown up in rural New York. Living in Denver, NY, population eight-two, taught me to be self-sufficient and self-motivated. My best friend as a child was my great aunt, "Auntie" (my parents worked and my sister, brother and neighborhood children were older, and not particularly interested in a child). She taught me to read, spell, sew, can jam, pick berries and to amuse myself. She created a curiosity in many things, which led to a life-long diversity of interests. I was also always allowed to make decisions and choices. My school, Roxbury Central School, with a graduating class of sixteen, being small, allowed great flexibility. The teachers knew me personally. We were all encouraged to participate in every activity. When I wanted a course that no one else did, a teacher agreed to teach me.

The most useful thing I did in retrospect was participate in public speaking competitions. Everyone should have that experience. It is never too late. Being articulate and comfortable in front of a crowd can be learned and is invaluable for a professional person. I graduated with confidence, accomplishment and empowerment. My full-tuition scholarship and NY State scholarship certainly helped. So although perhaps poor as judged by my parents' meager income, I was rich in the opportunities I had received and the security and confidence I had in my own ability.

Becoming a doctor had always been my goal. Fortunately my family and special teachers throughout high school and college always supported me, and gave me the encouragement to pursue this dream, even though the naysayers outweighed them. I have never understood why when someone has a dream you discourage them. Certainly it is reasonable to tell them what it will take to get there, but not to tell them they cannot do it. This is particularly for women—to be told they cannot do it because they are women. Fortunately, as my father would always tell me, you will do it your way. The women in my family were always strong, which I am sure also shaped my determination. Education and excellence were always expected and rewarded in my family. I realized as I aged that many of these experiences in childhood allowed me to be who I became and weather the challenges presented to me.

I wasn't enthralled with college or the first two years of medical school, but I survived. Third year was exactly what I had been waiting for. Unfortunately during the fall of my third year my mother was diagnosed with metastatic pancreatic cancer. She had been ill for a while. It was the surgeon who made the diagnosis. I admired his knowledge and his compassionate care of my mother and our family. I was doing a rotation in the Department of Surgery when my mother was dying. She wanted to remain at home to die. I was the most logical person to go home to help. Dr. Barber Mueller, the Chair of Surgery (and my mother's surgeon) allowed me to leave. He would call regularly and check on her progress. Long after she died, I asked why he had made me tell him her problems. He told me that if I could be objective about my mother, I would always be able to be objective with patients. He was correct. He never required me to make up that time, but did allow me to take Surgery during the summer. I worked with great residents—the best doctors I had known. My fate was sealed. I knew I had to be a surgeon.

A training position in a surgery residency program was difficult to obtain. I ultimately made a deal with the chair to take a mixed medicine surgery internship. If at the end I still wanted to be a surgeon and had performed well enough, he would give me a residency spot. Being the first and only woman had its advantages and disadvantages. Some surgeons were really paternal and nice while others felt I did not belong and tried to prove it. I just worked hard and tried to always do my job. Those were the days of the pyramidal programs, so you never knew if you were going to make it until you did. I decided, during those days, that I had to endure whatever came my way, as the decision as to who stayed and who went was pretty arbitrary. Some of it was not pretty. I find no point in dwelling on the negatives of sexual harassment and abuse, call room difficulties, nurse and patient rejection, etc.

There are still a number of issues that need resolution; however, I find it more useful to assess the current issues and continue to improve them. I also decided that when I was in a position to change things I would. I think some people try too hard to change things when they are in the midst of them, and do not have the power to do so. If they would seek help from those who are in a better position to change things or until they themselves were, they might be more effective. I deplore the "I did it, so can you" attitude. I found the open bias was much easier to deal with than the unconscious bias that one deals with today. I try and politely point out unconscious bias or create a process that does not allow it. One advantage of being unique was that you were very visible. You got noticed and had many opportunities as the token woman. In many ways that led to a career guided by serendipity.

When I finished my residency I had no job. The private group that told me for years they would give me one just had someone else to whom they had made the same commitment, come back from the military. I was given a part time job at the VA Medical Center by Dr. Lloyd Rogers, Chief of Surgery, who had also been acting Chair during my residency. As I started my career in academic surgery, I realized I needed to do research, which I had not done. I loved endocrine surgery—a realization that related to the excitement of diagnosing a pheochromocytoma as a third-year student, then watching its removal. I recall thinking that the next one I found I would take out myself. So I decided on endocrine research. Two medical endocrinologists, Drs. Arnold Moses and Myron Miller, who had good research labs at the VA, allowed me to work with them. They helped me understand how to do research and write abstracts, papers and grants. Ultimately, I got peer-reviewed funding and a laboratory. I was a terrible scientist and didn't really enjoy the work. I also became seriously allergic to rats. I decided after nine years to close my lab and give the remaining money back to concentrate on surgical education. I was told I had just ended my academic career. By then I had become very involved in surgical education, administration and endocrine and breast surgery, which I did like. Thus, quite serendipitously, this became my career path.

My interest in surgical education began with my love of teaching the residents and students during my residency. Shortly after joining the VA staff, I was offered a position in the Department of Surgery by the new Chair, Dr. Watts Webb. The next year the student program coordinator left and I was assigned that job, not based on any experience or desire, I might say. I did see it as an opportunity to fix many things that I had not liked about the program. I got really interested in fair testing and evaluation. At that time "surgical education groups" were just forming, and I started being involved with those groups.

A few years later the Dean, Dr. George Reed, asked me to be Associate Dean. Not a job I had ever thought about. I liked him. He was a strong leader and allowed me pretty free range as far as developing pro-grams went. He taught me a lot. Outwardly, he was "gender insensitive" at best, always making sexist comments, etc. You would think him not overly supportive of women, but he treated women very fairly, supporting and promoting their best interests.

He funded my participation in the first Women's Academic Leadership meeting in Tucson Arizona, which was a life-altering experience for me. I learned that the obstacles I was experiencing were not just because I was a surgeon but more because I was a woman. *All* women in academia were treated unfairly. At that meeting we committed to do something locally and nationally to benefit women. Since I knew no women surgeons, I decided to put up a notice inviting women to join me for breakfast at the American College of Surgeons in 1982.

During my time in the Dean's office, I also learned to figure ways around obstacles. When the Dean would not increase the pay for my women pelvic teaching models, I held a bake sale outside the Dean's office to raise the money to pay them more. I never had a problem getting their pay in the future. I have held a few other "bake sales" to support projects. The Comprehensive Breast Care Center was initially funded by an art benefit held by the Hospital Auxiliary, at that time essentially all women. There is always a way to accomplish what you want—you just need to figure out *how!*

Dr. Webb pushed us to be involved in national organizations, present papers and become involved in committee work. The department always funded those meeting expenses. Although I have great concerns about the changes in funding of young surgeons' activities, seeing the enormous participation in the Academic Surgical Week encourages me. Luckily as a child I had gotten over stage fright, so I could present. My involvement in national work has been incredibly fun and meaningful as well as a saving grace on more than one occasion. I got to know people all over. They brought new ideas to my teaching and practice. This was particularly useful as I was the only academic endocrine/breast surgeon in Syracuse—which meant I was the mainstay of the student teaching program.

When a new Chair arrived who fired me regularly and tried to discredit me nationally, I had numerous job offers and strong support nationally, so I survived. I found, as I looked at other jobs, that there are problems and benefits *everywhere.* I decided to stay, as I knew the problem where I was, and had sufficient support to continue to accomplish the things I wanted to accomplish.

Through the International Society of Surgery, I now have a group of people throughout the world with whom I communicate regularly. I love that group. Dr. Hilary Sanfey has been so very valuable putting programs together and arranging events for us at those biennial meetings. I hope our women's group there grows as well as the Association of Women Surgeons has. We learn so much from each other. Even though now you may have to pick and choose what you participate in more than I did, I would encourage you to be sure to get involved.

Becoming medical director of our university hospital was also serendipitous. I didn't look for the job but rather was recruited, perhaps because I was always there to be counted. I always came to meetings and did my committee work. I believe it was because I was rather matter of fact, learned to listen to both sides, could keep things to myself and didn't worry about everyone liking me. Each is a valuable characteristic in a leader. I learned to deal with difficult people and believe I had a role in slowly changing the culture.

Perhaps I have been able to do many of the things I have because I am single and childless. I am not sure. I see many women accomplish a great deal while having families. I am often asked if I regret not having children or a spouse. I don't have regrets. I have had a few wonderful men in my life. I am sure I have saved each and myself an unpleasant divorce. They remain good friends. I basically like living alone and making decisions by myself and for myself. I also think I have been gifted with many very close friends, including their children. Having both my parents die by my first year of surgical residency changed the way I lived my life. No one was asking when I would get married and give them a grandchild. That was the order in those days. My brother and sister were older. They had young children and busy careers, while I was very busy finishing my surgical residency; so I relied on close friends for support and companionship. I am not sure it is easy for people to understand that just because your life is different than theirs you can love it just as much.

I had planned to retire when I was sixty-five years old for many reasons. I have many other interests. I was getting physically more tired working long days. I had done it all so to speak. I didn't want to get to the point that people would wonder when I would retire and say, "Thank God she's gone," rather than "Isn't it a shame she retired."

It takes planning to retire. I recruited a woman from our residency, Dr. Kara Kort, who was a bright, nice, technically excellent, good doctor to join me. I did so early enough so that my colleagues and patients could know and trust her. She has been a perfect replacement for me as far as I am concerned.

I have had time to pursue other things. I had a retirement project planned, which was to develop the ACS Fundamentals of Surgery Curriculum. There were many organizations I wanted to work with more closely. I love to travel and wanted to be able to go for as long as I wanted when I wanted. I technically retired when I was in Bamako, Mali. The opportunity to spend more time with my family, friends and hobbies was appealing. My sister died in 2000. One of my real regrets is that I didn't spend more time with her when she was well. I wasn't going to have that happen again. You can never get some things back. I think everyone should have a strategy for the next phase of life. I am working on one for when I have more limitations, and working to have that happen as late as possible. It is hard to recoup what you have lost, so my advice is to take good care of yourself along the way.

In retrospect, looking at the things that shaped my life, I would have to say that I can attribute much of it to my childhood. The incredible freedom to choose and make decisions as a child stood me in good stead forever. The emphasis on education, encouragement of broad interests, and being involved has always been helpful to me. The encouragement by those who really counted, my family, teachers and friends, helped me deal effectively with those who tried to thwart my ambition.

As much of a feminist as I am, most of the great opportunities were given to me by men. I learned early that hard work, honesty and involvement can really open enormous opportunities. Being a utility player, seeing what needed to be done and doing it without needing to have it spelled out or asked is always desirable. Not bemoaning the past but looking forward to the future should be one's attitude.

All in all, it has been a great life!

Inspiring Quote:
"It is not fair to ask of others what you are unwilling to do yourself."
— Eleanor Roosevelt.

Barbara Lee Bass, MD, FACS
General Surgeon

The Day I Almost Quit

Beautiful Grace. She snuggled calm and close in my arms, a brand new little one. This time, not one of my own, but rather the new daughter of one of my surgical faculty members, who two days earlier had performed her "last" surgery before delivering this little bundle a few hours ago–at the age of forty-two! "Grandmotherly awe" is the only accurate description of my affection for that child at that moment—the newest member of our "family"—a dear, dear treasure.

Pausing, I had the unusual sense that this moment of awe was somehow different. It took me a few minutes to orient myself before realizing why this baby was so uniquely special to me, for I have held with happiness many new babies over the years. This time, however, evoked an array of confluent unexpected memories and events.

First, of course, I had watched my very special faculty member—a fearless, indefatigable happy surgeon and courageous keeper of home, grow that long-awaited precious baby girl, day by day, until she was ready to pop. Thankfully, she had a wondrous pregnancy: happy and perfect. I worried every day for her, so was relieved the morning I held the baby. Watching the mother reminded me of so many other women surgeons I have known, who have run the gauntlet of pregnancy through training and practice with success. I felt proud and happy.

But the moment was poignant for another unexpected memory flash. Holding Grace returned me to that very same day in January, a generation earlier. For on precisely that morning, at just about that hour, twenty-nine years earlier, I had delivered an equally long-awaited son. Weeks past due and after a long night of labor, he had finally come to me—wide-eyed, silent, beautiful—and he, too, had nuzzled close and quiet. Until this moment with Grace, I had not recalled the moment so clearly in decades.

As I sat and held Grace, a rapid series of moments in my son's life (now a magnificent grown man) that had changed mine came back to me. Ten days after his birth, my "infrastructure," my mother and father, escorted the two of us to Chicago, so I could present my first paper at the

165

plenary session of the Society of University Surgeons. I remembered how my research mentor and now good friend, John Harmon, had been visibly anxious that he, himself, was going to have to present that paper—fearful I would be "unable" to travel. (Never doubt the resourcefulness of supportive grandparents and ambitious children!)

Then I remembered a phone-call from my mentor, who was also the first woman surgeon I had ever met, Dr. Kathryn Anderson. She inquired as to why I had not yet initiated my application for pediatric surgery training. Although I had resisted a change in direction, I had within a few months of my son's birth recognized that my goal to be a pediatric surgeon had unraveled, in the flood of fierce affection I had for him. I could no longer objectify the fearful eyes of sick children in a way that would allow me to participate in their care as a surgeon. I had lost my pediatric "edge."

I then recalled the great six months of springtime and freedom with my perfect little boy during those last months of research fellowship. We were a family at last—my husband, son and I—before I had to return to my fourth year of residency training.

This morning in January, with Grace in my arms, I remembered again—for this is one memory that has come back to me many times over the years—the day I almost quit. That day was the same day in January, twenty-eight years ago, on my son's first birthday. I was on call and had, of course, left home long before he woke up for the day. I had seen him briefly before bed the previous night, just a touch. But that day, twenty-eight years ago, I could only remember the year before when he had arrived, and now I realized that I was not going to see him awaken on his birthday.

As the hours rolled by on that day, I became immersed in sadness, anger, conflict. What was this outrageous choice I had made to give up so much of my life to becoming— and then being—a surgeon? What was driving me, why was this so important? Was this more important than seeing my beautiful son awake, to touch him, kiss him, feed him, on the day he had been born only 365 days before? I decided I had made many bad choices in my life, but this one to pursue surgery was one that would cost me too much. I decided to give it up—to quit. And I meant it—as much as I had meant anything in my life.

Now here is the happy part and, perhaps, the most important message. We surgeons have the capacity to understand each other—our ridiculous ambitions and commitments, our drive and passion—more readily than others possibly can. We can help each other and we need to. For throughout our careers, and particularly as residents, we spend many hours together in our hospital homes. As a cohort of surgeons in training, we grow up together; and if we are lucky, we really do behave as a good family.

Well, I was lucky. I had a fellow resident who I am proud to say I helped raise from "puppyhood." He joined our program as an intern when I was a third-year resident. He was a silly puppy—good-natured, tireless, kind, loyal—and, incidentally, a superb doctor and resident. He was my dear friend in residency, and we spent many, many hours taking care of patients together; he as my loyal junior resident, me as the doting senior basking in his growth. He saw me that evening and knew something was very wrong. This may seem like a little thing—what came next—but for me it was the act that saved my career in surgery.

He sent me home. He said he would take care of everything. "Stay home as long as you want—go see him." So, I went. I woke my little one up; he was cheery, even if a bit confused, and we sat and snuggled. I'm quite certain we ate something or other—sharing food is essential. Life was good. He happily went back to bed and I went back to the hospital, calm and grateful.

My fellow resident, Steven Teich, is now an accomplished pediatric surgeon, who started his own family many years later. I don't think he knew at the time how his intuition and friendship had saved my ambition to continue—but *I* did.

It has turned out to be a good choice, one that has come with many missed dear moments, but many others filled with joy, from one January to the next, and one generation to the other.

Inspiring Quote:
"As for accomplishments, I just did what I had to do as things came along."
— Eleanor Roosevelt

Julie Ann Freischlag, MD, FACS
Vascular Surgeon

Women Surgeons—Still In a Male-Dominated World[1]

"There are two ways to live your life. One is as though nothing is a miracle. The other is as though everything is a miracle," said Albert Einstein.

My approach, as I reflect on the thirty-two years since I first began medical school at Rush, in Chicago, has been according to the second part of Einstein's quotation. It has always seemed a bit of a miracle to see my patients survive incredible ordeals, to have my family and friends continue to support me and my occupational choices, and to have my career take a frequently serendipitous path.

I went to college with the goal of becoming a high school biology teacher, but the education program had closed because of a glut of students who wanted to be teachers. So my love of science led me to the pre-medical program. In medical school, my ambition was to become a pediatrician. However, I did my surgery clerkship first, just to get it out of the way because I was convinced I wouldn't like it. That clerkship changed everything. I went to UCLA to train to be the best academic vascular surgeon.

My career path led me to taking on leadership roles as Chief of Vascular Surgery at the West Los Angeles VA, Chief of Surgery at Zablocki VA Medical Center in Milwaukee, Chief of Vascular Surgery at UCLA, and currently Chair of Surgery at Johns Hopkins, Baltimore. Initially in one's career, one wants to do it all, accomplish much in a short time, and for women in surgery I think we can blaze ahead and just do it. It is like most surgical emergencies: Get the data, make the diagnosis, and go for it. It is our nature.

Monica McGrath describes this as the first phase of women's careers, not only in medicine or surgery.

In the middle portion of our careers, we develop a symbiosis with work and life accomplishments. Perhaps it is because we then have families and need space and time to be many places, seemingly at once. Life can get complicated with divorce, health issues, child issues, and parent issues, yet most women find this to be a part of what we need (must? want?) to do. McGrath describes a third phase, sort of where I am now, that asks, "Now what?" Inner meaning is essential to women's careers all along the way; perhaps for men's, too, but men do not usually talk about it as vibrantly as women. In these three phases of career development, what women see as obstacles and concerns changes too.

In 1980, when I entered General Surgery residency, there were three women in my intern class and the first woman Chief Resident finished at UCLA. However, women were in the minority in the field. In one particular interview, the Chair said in his remarks, "Gentleman and, uh, one lady," when he saw me sitting in the audience in a green dress. At that time, I did not care what the ratio or odds were. I just wanted to be a surgeon so badly that I forged ahead. Years later, I found out that at one place I interviewed they had removed all women from their rank list, including me.

I was the sixth woman to finish General Surgery at UCLA, in 1986, the second woman vascular fellow there, in 1987, the fourth woman to past vascular board exams, the first woman faculty on staff at UCSD in 1987 and UCLA, in 1989, and the only woman in the country serving as a Vascular Surgery Division Chief, from 1998 to 2003. I was told by one Dean who interviewed me for his Department Chair of Surgery that he just couldn't give that surgery job to a woman. And he didn't. That was in 2002. I am now one of only three women Department Chairs in Surgery in the country and one of only six ever appointed so far.

The field of surgery is still male dominated. Medical school enrollments, on the other hand, are 50 percent women. When I began my career in 1980, the percentage was 15 to 20 percent. My class at Rush University was 42 percent women, an unusual number for those days. Norma Wagoner, PhD, Dean of Students, was a marvelous recruiter of women. Surgery programs today are attracting about one-third women. We need to do better. Most professions change when more than a third of their constituents become different in nature, age, ethnicity, gender, or other background. However, in order to attract more women to surgery and see a change, we need to actively pursue it. Over the past twenty-five years, the increase in the number of women in surgery has followed a natural selection process of sorts. I love Darwin and find his observations fascinating. However, I feel now we need to alter the environment and actively make raising the number of women in surgery one of our priorities.

How should one do that?

Women faculty members and partners should be asked what they want and need to progress in their careers and practices to make them enjoyable, tolerable, and durable. Most women need and want flexibility and can tell you how they want to work their day. We, as leaders, should not react as if their requests are not appropriate, condemn their requests, or talk about them among others. The environment must be made more amenable for women. We also need to actively recruit female medical students into residency programs and subsequently into our departments or practices. Only then will the numbers increase. And, lastly, we must provide avenues and equal opportunities, so the women we work with can lead. We cannot rely on serendipity to increase the number of women in surgery or the number of women who will lead. There are some who feel only a miracle will allow women to reach their equal representation, not only in surgery but in other fields, such as politics and business. But we create our own miracles with a bit of help from our leaders. And our leaders are you and me.

Surgery and Me

The best reason I can give to those who ask (and even to those who do not!) about why I chose Surgery, is that I really feel as though Surgery chose me. I did Surgery as my first clinical rotation during the third-year of medical school because I wanted to get it out of the way. I could then do Medicine followed by Obstetrics and Gynecology and then *finally* do my Pediatrics rotation—because I thought I wanted to be a pediatrician. I had it all planned out.

During my two-week Orthopedic rotation, I just loved being in the operating room. I met an amazing senior resident—Tom Witt—when I did my General Surgery rotation next. I not only loved the operations but also loved the variety of disease processes and the knowledge and expertise that Tom had as a senior resident. I wanted to be like him. I also saw the passion that the faculty had for their work—the patients, the procedures, the diagnosis, the prognosis, the teaching, the research; their plates were full but they could not wait to take on more! That was me! That was when I discovered that I simply "*fit*" into Surgery—and that Surgery had found me!

I came from a family without physicians or nurses or other healthcare professionals. I wanted to be a teacher like my mother—a high school biology teacher. Because it was thought at the time that there were going to be too many teachers, getting into the education department at the University of Illinois was not available to me. So I chose Biology as a major with a minor in Chemistry. Nursing was another option I considered. The nursing school was in Chicago, and began in my senior year of college. However, I wanted to stay in Urbana for my senior year, so I chose the pre-med program instead. Serendipity—that is how I found my profession as a physician and then as a surgeon.

Or really how Surgery found me!

Reference:
[1] This article was published in *Yale Journal of Biology and Medicine* 2008 December; 81(4): 203–204.

Inspiring Quote:
"Give the world the best you have and the best will come back to you."
— Madeline Bridge

Carol E. H. Scott-Conner, MD, PhD, MBA
General Surgeon

"Long, Strange Trip"

"Lately it occurs to me what a long, strange trip it's been." When I was younger, before all the grey hair and wrinkles, patients would sometimes ask me how long I had been a surgeon. I have always dated my "surgeon-hood" from the start of my residency, in 1976. By that metric, I now look back on thirty-five years in the profession. What have I learned? My path as an academic surgeon has had multiple twists and turns. By keeping my focus consistently upon my goals, and at the same time following the direction that fate took me, I've somehow made it to a position where I'm now invited to write about how I got here. Think of water following the contours of the land as it seeks its path to the sea. Water, gentle as it is, was all it took to dig the Grand Canyon—unsuspectingly powerful.

"When one door closes, another door opens" was a favorite saying of my father. He learned it from his own father, who, as a Methodist minister, had a ready supply of homely sayings applicable to most situations. I would amend this a little bit—sure, look for that other door, but make sure the open door goes into the room *you* want to enter. If it does not, then go back and burrow under that closed door, batter your way through it, or pick the lock if you must. Persistence is rewarded. The first closed door that I encountered was medical school.

I applied to medical school in the 1960s, at the height of the draft. Young men were being sent to Vietnam, and all too many of them came back in body bags. Admission to medical school was one of the few ways the young men could obtain a coveted deferment. I, and other women of my era, competed against a floodtide of men. We were interviewed by (largely male) admissions committee members, who asked, with some justification, "Why should we accept you, when that means we reject a man—a man who may then be sent off to die in Vietnam?" Sometimes the question was articulated, on other occasions it simply hung in the air like a fetid balloon.

"Third Time's the Charm"

It took me three consecutive attempts to get in. Out of fairness, I have to admit that my grades (electrical engineering at Massachusetts Institute of Technology) were not straight "A"s. I was admitted to MIT straight from my junior year in high school. It was tough going almost immediately. I fell in love with a classmate, and that didn't really help my grades either, although I would do it all over again in a heartbeat.

I met this classmate, Christopher Gephart Scott, in October of my freshman year. I was invited, as one of the thirty-some MIT coeds, to "pour tea" at an event hosted for an aliquot of the 900-some MIT male freshmen. As it happened, Chris came to that particular tea. I was free to mingle after all of the tea had been poured. Shy and bookish, I drifted off to a corner bookshelf in a far corner of the room. Chris did the same. We talked. We hit it off. We were married in January 1967.

"When You Come to a Fork In the Road, Take It"

When I wasn't admitted to medical school, I took a job as an engineer. Then the local engineering economy went into a tailspin and my division was eliminated. I didn't see it coming; but clearly two of the senior engineers on the project did, because they found other jobs just weeks before the plant shut down. We were let go with a two-week notice, and the company did make an effort to help us find other jobs in the industry. But there were no jobs. In spring 1971, Chris sustained a massive stroke and a week later he was dead. I was still unemployed. I decided to try one last time for medical school. Later, if a head-hunter asked me about the one-year gap in my resume, I would say that I had suffered a major derailment.

In the midst of this derailment, I went ahead and applied to medical school again. Now I was not only female with mediocre grades but widowed to boot. Admission committee interviews often included a half-hour interview with a faculty psychiatrist. Despite that, New York University took a chance and admitted me.

History repeated itself and, once again, I fell in love with a classmate during my freshman year. Harry Faulkner Conner was just back from his service as a medic in Vietnam. We had a lot in common—his father, like my grandfather, had been a minister in the church. We were both older and had experienced life in ways that our classmates lacked. By the time I began my third year in medical school we were married. At that time married students or residents were distinctly rare. It was fortunate that third-year students often took in-house calls, because dormitory accommodation essentially consisted of a single, shared room with a narrow pull-out single bed, until an apartment building close to the medical center opened up.

"Lead With Your Strengths"

I started my third year with the Surgery clerkship, because I was reasonably sure I did not want to be a surgeon. As happens with many, I found that I not only loved surgery, but that I was actually good at it. When the dust cleared at the end of third year, I had "B"s in everything but surgery— in surgery I got an A. I also scored the highest in that section of the "National Boards'" (a precursor to the USMLE exam).

I stayed at NYU (New York University) for my residency. The first few years of that residency were every other night call, and the residency itself was pyramidal. A pyramidal residency was one in which only one of two, three, or even four entering residents would graduate as chief residents; the rest were terminated, often abruptly. Such residencies no longer exist. I have photographs of my entering class of residents and my graduating class of chiefs. I don't know the exact numbers, nor do I know how many of my fellow interns were destined for neurosurgery or other sub-specialties, but the contrast is stark. NYU at that time was best characterized as an elite and extremely difficult residency that was equally hard for men and women. If there was gender discrimination, I never felt it.

That has been a consistent experience throughout my professional life. It may be hard to get a door open, but once open (in this case, the door to medical school), the great world beyond is largely indifferent to gender. The system is perversely fair; it may take more effort (and hence more preparation) to get somewhere, but that preparation pays off once you get there. There were no women on the fulltime faculty of the surgery department at NYU at that time. I did not lack for mentors, but they were, of necessity, all men (and a few female senior residents). They were all central to my development, and many have stayed in touch since and some continue to do so even now. Incredibly, people—both men and, when available, women—have always stepped forward to guide and help me.

By some miracle, my second marriage survived medical school and residency, and this summer we will celebrate thirty-seven years together. Although it was possible to remain married, we never quite figured out how to have children. I seriously doubt that I could have completed my residency with children, nor do I feel that I could have managed my early academic appointments. And then it was biologically too late. One makes choices, and that was the trade-off that I made. I'm glad it is no longer required.

I completed my residency with no research experience. I never really thought about doing research, and even though I wanted an academic career, I had very little concept of what that entailed. I saw the professors at NYU teach students and residents while caring for patients, and supposed that was all that there was to academic life. So when I went to Dr. Frank Cole Spencer, my chairman, and sought advice about jobs, he suggested that I try the new medical schools that had sprung up around the country to enhance care in the VA (Veterans Affairs) hospitals. It seems ironic now, but the war effort that made it difficult for me to get into medical school may have helped me get my first job!

"Almost Heaven, West Virginia"

I joined the faculty at Marshall University, a new medical school in Huntington, West Virginia. I was appointed as an Assistant Professor; they wanted to appoint me as an Instructor, but NYU (bless them!) had given me the title of Clinical Instructor in Surgery for my chief resident year. I was the third general surgeon as a part of the full-time faculty, and the two senior faculty members, Drs. Kenneth Scher and James Coil, took me under their wing. They pushed me to apply for grants, to write papers, and continue my surgical education. As a member of a three-surgeon group, I did a wide range of surgeries.

I decided that I needed additional training in research, so I enrolled in a PhD program at the University of Kentucky. I commuted once or twice a week to Lexington and operated on Saturdays to make up the time. My thesis advisor was my first female role model after my mother—Dr. Betty Sisken.

"You've Got to Know When to Walk Away; You've Got to Know When to Run"

I was at Marshall University just long enough to attain promotion to Associate Professor, and then things changed. I had completed the course work for my PhD and knew that I could finish it at an even greater distance from Lexington. Suddenly, the mood in the department shifted. I had not been savvy enough to recognize the change in the wind before I was laid off from my engineering job, so perhaps I was especially sensitive to political nuances. I didn't know the cause of their discontent, but I knew something was up when my two senior "partners" stopped talking to each other and started looking for other jobs. Within the year, all three of us left the department. I landed a job at the University of Mississippi Medical School. People have asked me how one knows when it is time to move on; in my experience, the handwriting on the wall has been so clear that it has appeared to be written in letters of fire.

"Be a Surgical Squid. Leave a Trail of Ink"

It was at the University of Mississippi that I discovered that my major scholarly strength was textbook writing rather than research. James D. Hardy, my chairman and mentor there, helped me get an editor at Lippincott for my first textbook. It took years to complete *Operative Anatomy*, but that was just the beginning. I also became bitten by the "chairman" bug. I decided that, since I wasn't going to do ground-breaking research and cure cancer, I would like to leave my mark on the future by leading a department of surgery. Part of my drive to do "something significant" came from a lasting sense of grief over my first husband's death—a sense that all of the promise of his young life had gone unfulfilled, and that somehow it was very important that I do everything that I could with mine. I sought out every opportunity I could find to be on key committees, to lead committees, and to learn as much as I could about how the medical center worked. By the time I left University of Mississippi Medical Center (UMMC), I had been Chief of Staff of the Hospital and acting Chief of Surgery at the VAMC (Veterans Affairs Medical Center). If someone offered me a job doing something, I accepted gladly. It was all valuable experience. I put the word out that I wanted to be a Chair of Surgery. People started nominating me for these sorts of jobs.

"Plan Your Work and Work Your Plan"

At my interviews looking at various chairs, a common comment (despite all the work I had taken on) was "You lack administrative experience." (Translation: "What makes you think you can lead a department of men?") At the same time, many departments at desirable schools were in a sort of "holding pattern" with an interim chair. The departments that were looking all seemed to have problems that I felt ill-equipped to solve.

I decided to go back to school yet again, this time to get an MBA. There happened to be a fully accredited MBA program at Millsaps College, a small but excellent liberal college a few blocks from UMMC. I enrolled and, once again, went to school part-time while continuing to work full-time. Courses began at five-thirty at night, so I would race to finish rounds and head over. I was allowed to advance-place many of the basic entry-level pre-requisites by taking exams. So, for example, I taught myself basic accounting and passed the exam, allowing me to go straight into managerial accounting. One of the revelations of that phase was the realization that you can teach yourself anything. I thought of generations of determined autodidacts studying in the great public libraries of our big cities, and I felt a kinship. By 1995 I was on the home stretch to complete the MBA, and I was offered the incomparable opportunity to become Head of Surgery of the University of Iowa College Of Medicine.

"Grasp the Nettle Firmly"

Many things combined to make that particular position attractive. In contrast to the "problem job" scenario I described previously, University of Iowa was the only medical school in the state. It had a crystal-clear purpose and mission. The first task I was given was to help the development of a state-wide trauma service by attaining ACS Level I Trauma Center status for the hospital. It was a task which I was able to throw my whole heart and soul behind. Less than two years after I became Head, we got our Level I status.

Not everyone was as enthusiastic about this plan as I was. I came into conflict with several faculty members and that conflict led to litigation. The state of Iowa stood behind me and we were able to continue to move forward, but during those darker days I took comfort from the big sign in front of the ER "Level I Trauma Center," and I often recalled the old adage "grasp the nettle firmly."

After five or six years, budget pressures increased for our department, as they did all over. The cumulative effect of conflict and budgetary pressure took their toll. I realized it was time "to walk away," and I was asked to step down as Head. The Dean requested that I remain in place until other key recruitments were achieved. I stayed for just under nine years. I returned to life as a faculty member. In 2010, I entered a five-year phased retirement program which allows me greater freedom to write. I published my first book of short stories, *A Few Small Moments*, a year later. The book is part memoir, part fiction—my attempt to convey my fascination of surgery while respecting the privacy of all the folks involved.

Conclusions

It has, indeed, been a long and strange trip. I've enjoyed every step of the way. The homey adages and principles that I learned from my parents have stood me well. The companionship and support of my husband, Dr. Harry Conner, have been crucial. I could never have succeeded alone. When I needed help, people stepped forward with suggestions and ideas. I wish all young surgeons the same happiness that I have found.

Sources of Quotations

"Lately it occurs to me, what a long, strange trip it's been" — lyrics from a Grateful Dead song, "Truckin'," recognized by the Library of Congress as a National Treasure in 1997.

"When one door closes, another opens; but we often look so long and so regretfully upon the closed door that we do not see the one which has opened for us." — Alexander Graham Bell

"Third time's the charm"—precursors of this popular catch phrase include Elizabeth Barrett Browning and some old Scottish proverbs.

"When you come to a fork in the road, take it." — Yogi Berra

"Almost Heaven, West Virginia" — this motto of the state of West Virginia always comes into my mind on the music of John Denver, whose song "Take me Home, Country Roads" brought it into common usage.

"You've got to know when to walk away; you've got to know when to run." — this paraphrases lyrics from "The Gambler," a song recorded by Kenny Rogers.

"Be a Surgical Squid" — generally attributed to Robert Zollinger.

"Grasp the Nettle Firmly" — this goes back to at least the 1700s, and versions of this adage have been found wherever the stinging nettle is found.

Susan Reid, BA, MD, FRCPSC
General Surgeon

Being a Woman Surgeon

Being a woman surgeon means that in the same day you can be tough as nails and as soft as butter. It suits me just fine. You have to make firm decisions in and out of the operating room, but you can really connect with your patients and their families on a daily basis. All surgeons need nerves of steel and steady hands, but we can also hold the hands of our patients when they need it. A surgical career has allowed me to live my life to the fullest. If I died tomorrow I would be happy that I have led a productive life. I have made a significant contribution to the lives of many people through my work, and together with my husband I have the best legacy: my two wonderful children.

As the first girl in my family, but third in line behind two boys, I had no choice but to develop a keen sense of competition, always trying to keep up with my brothers. As a child, I was determined to climb the same trees, jump from the same heights out of the barn and ride my bike just as far. Although I was a bit of a tomboy and loved to play sports, I also had balance with my girlish side, with interests in clothes and fashion. The sports won out and I completed an undergraduate degree in Physical Education, thinking I might teach. But my interests shifted to medicine and I was delighted to attend medical school at McMaster, for their unique program of Problem-Based Learning. My medical school class was 50 percent female, so by the time I decided to enter surgical training it was no longer even on my radar to think that I could possibly be treated differently because I was a woman. I never felt that my faculty had different expectations for me or treated me differently than my male colleagues. I did work very hard, but that has always been my nature. Luckily I was blessed with technical skill that allowed me a sense of confidence that I think others could sense. Maybe this is why I never really felt I was treated differently.

The timing of my surgical career has been very lucky for me. Although I did not have many female counterparts when I started down this path, the timing has also allowed me to be sitting on that leading edge of women who entered General Surgery in the 1980s. Back in 1984, in a class of 100, I was the only female to choose General Surgery. One of my female colleagues entered the field of Urology, but that was it—out of fifty women, only two of us chose Surgery as a specialty. When I started my residency, I counted only two other female residents in the whole program. When I was finished training, I became the first female General Surgeon in my city. I have many more female colleagues these days, and the number of women entering surgical training in Canada is finally on the rise.

Over the years, I have repeatedly been asked about balance, how to get it, how to keep it, and how to avoid losing it. There have definitely been sacrifices in my life for my career and also sacrifices in my career for my family. Having a wonderful husband and two amazing children has kept me grounded in what is really important in life. That doesn't mean I haven't missed out on family events. I have, but what working woman or man hasn't?

I figure women surgeons are no different from any other working woman with a family. You have to make decisions every day about how you spend your time. Do I head to work early, at six a.m., to catch up on some files that need to be dictated or do I stay back to see my kids off to school? When my kids were in basketball season, I adjusted my schedule to make the Tuesday and Thursday games; when I was a Program Director and it was time for reading application letters, I didn't go to any school events, and it would be Dad's turn to help with the homework at the kitchen table while I did my "homework." Unlike many other professional careers, in surgery you can have some control over your schedule—some days. I learned long ago that you can drive yourself crazy if you mentally try to balance the scales of work and home every day. Once you realize that it is okay for the scales to shift back and forth, and that over time it all does balance out, you can stop making yourself feel guilty for being at work and then guilty for being at home.

I love the variety of my surgical and critical care practice. I have different things to do each day in different areas of the hospital. It is never boring and there is always something new to learn. As my career takes an administrative turn, there is a whole new world of knowledge and skills for me to develop. I feel very privileged to begin this new chapter in my career as a woman surgeon—as the first female in Canada to become Chair of an Academic Department of Surgery. I look forward to working with my colleagues as we strive to bring excellence to all aspects of our Department and our University.

Inspiring Quote:
"Don't let anyone rob you of your imagination, your creativity, or your curiosity. It's your place in the world; it's your life. Go on and do all you can with it, and make it the life you want to live." — Mae C. Jemison, first African-American woman astronaut

Martha Zeiger, MD, FACS, FACE
Endocrine Surgeon

Are We the Only Ones Still Squeegeeing the Glass Ceiling?

My disclosures include the following: Although I can rightly claim expertise in the fields of endocrine surgery and molecular biology, I cannot, in good faith, claim any expertise in the social sciences. What I can offer you, however, is a glimpse into my life experiences and the lessons learned over three decades as a woman in medicine. I will share with you the difficulties faced by others and me, as well as introduce you to some of my wonderful mentors, often oblivious to their incredible influence and belief in my successes. I also confess that I have never publically shared my story.

A housekeeper in a cartoon is certain that a glass ceiling still exists when she overhears the conversation of two female executives in an elevator and says, "Oh, there definitely is a glass ceiling. I squeegee it." The question put forth in this chapter is simply stated: Does gender inequity still exist in the workplace? I would first ask you to consider whether you believe you experience gender inequity in your own department and/or institution. Are the men who hold more senior positions more qualified, more dedicated, more innovative, fairer, or more intelligent than you? Do you receive the same level of support and resources from your department and from your institution? Do you have the same level of support at home and from your community, in terms of household chores and child-rearing responsibilities as that of your male colleagues? We have all experienced inequity. Ash *et al* in 2004 had studied over 1,800 faculty members at twenty-four academic medical schools and reported concerning results: namely, that "female medical school faculty neither advance as rapidly nor are compensated as well as professionally similar male colleagues;" furthermore, "women's deficits are greater for faculty with more seniority."[1] As junior and senior female faculty members, many of us experience this challenge on a daily, weekly basis, and yet it is difficult to sometimes quantify or verbalize without seeming unscientific, without seeming to be a non-team player, without begrudging our male colleagues their own successes.

I grew up in an era when a young girl would have never seen a female doctor or a woman executive, and when most mothers relinquished any designs on a career, in order to become a full time mother and housewife. What I can share with you is a perspective gained from attending medical school when women did not go into surgery, when there were few women doctors, and when there was only one female chair of an academic surgery program in the United States. Fortunately, for me, my mother had worked as a nurse anesthetist for the Neurosurgery Department at New York Hospital and, growing up, I thus became quite familiar with many very exciting and dramatic operating room stories. And in our family medicine closet there was always an endotracheal tube, a laryngoscope, needle and syringe at the ready. Thus, being regaled with worldly stories from a man's world and being surrounded by "powerful tools" I viewed on a daily basis, in a subtle way, I was taught that, indeed, there were more exciting things out there that I might one day be a part of.

I attended Brown University as an undergraduate and applied to medical school in 1975. At Brown I had been on both the Women's Varsity Swim and Tennis Teams for three and four years, respectively, and been captain of the tennis team for two years. At the end of one medical school interview, the admissions officer from a very prominent institution said to me, "If you were a football player with your GPA we would definitely accept you." It took me a few minutes to actually comprehend the implication and naiveté of his statement; words at the time had escaped me. I had not only practiced and competed as much as any football player, but I had played a varsity sport every season with sometimes overlapping seasons transitioning from one sport to the other. As a footnote, our women's tennis team was virtually undefeated in the four years I played for them. Our men's football team that was considerably better funded (they did not have to sell movie tickets or have bake sales to fund their travel south) rarely won a game in the years I attended. With no means to pay for medical school I applied to the Army, Navy and Air Force for scholarship and was accepted by all. I chose the Navy because both my father and uncle had served in the U.S. Navy during World War II. It was not, however, until I was issued my dog tags and a Geneva Convention ID during my Navy internship, nor until I witnessed the entire San Diego Naval Hospital's Surgery and Anesthesia Department be sent to the Mediterranean, within twenty-four hours during the Tehran Hostage Crisis, that I understood the full magnitude and implication of becoming a member of the armed forces; namely, should I be killed in action, my dog tags would positively identify me; should I be captured, in theory, I could not be subject to torture.

During medical school at the University of Vermont, as a way to relax and escape the rigors of studying, I had the wonderful opportunity to play on a women's ice hockey team, aptly named the "Mother Puckers." One evening when our opposing team did not show, I learned how my teammates and I truly played, as we spent the two hours scrimmaging amongst ourselves. There was incredible checking and pushing that I had not experienced from other teams, highlighting for me the Darwinian selection of aggressive women in medical school at the time.

After internship in the Navy, I was then very fortunate to be stationed in Pearl Harbor, Hawaii, as a General Medical Officer. As one of many collateral duties associated with any military duty station, we covered a Navy Station on Midway Island, populated with the famous Gooney Birds or Albatross. There were gun turrets and remnants of fighter planes left over from the World War II Battle at Midway, with Albatross densely populating the landing strip as well as the entire island. Perhaps it was when the ornithologist from the University of Hawaii asked me to help him amputate an Albatross' leg, because it had sustained a compound fracture, that I was destined to become a surgeon. Amputating the bird's leg under local anesthesia was actually my very first operation as the primary surgeon, or, as a one might call it, a Gooney Bird Surgeon. The Navy dentist on the island and the ornithologist were my first assistant and anesthesiologist. We had excellent follow-up, as Albatross mate for life and return to the exact same nesting area every year. This particular Albatross was sighted each year for several years after his operation. Although Albatross are magnificent in flight, they are notoriously clumsy on both takeoff and landing. Apparently, the loss of one leg did not inhibit this particular Gooney bird from either.

After my first internship in the Navy and my stint as a General Medical Officer in Hawaii, I was certainly very proud to have successfully been accepted to and completed a surgical residency at Maine Medical Center in 1988, where I did my second internship. At the graduation ceremony I was celebrated and recognized as the first woman to do so.

Serendipitously, somehow I was given access to or actually given my residency file after graduation and came across the description of me during the original interview as a "29 yo G2 P1 at 30 weeks gestation" (twenty-nine-year-old woman with one child who is thirty weeks pregnant with her second). I found it both amusing and all the more remarkable that I had been able to achieve what I had and, in the end, felt very supported by the attending staff, who clearly had had tremendous prejudices to overcome.

In a man's world, as both a surgeon and a naval officer I have had some extraordinary experiences: I was "the" surgeon on a surgical team in the US Capitol Building—an operating table set up exclusively for George H. W. Bush should he be shot or injured during his inaugural speech January 1989; our operating room table consisted of an oak table; our I.V. pole consisted of a hat stand. President Bush was typed and crossed and we had a trauma, chest, and neurosurgery tray at the ready. I also served on the USS Abraham Lincoln, a nuclear-powered aircraft carrier, as the sole woman and surgeon among 5,000 men. As the surgeon on board, I ran a full-scale disaster drill, from airplane crash to evacuation of personnel. When the armed services decided to run a full page advertisement for several weeks across the entire country in multiple newspapers, they had identified a male Emergency Room Physician in the Air force, a male Family Practitioner in the Army. Only then did they decide they needed a surgeon who was a woman and in the Navy. Well, that would be me—and maybe only me!

During fellowship at National Institutes of Health (NIH), I confess I do not recall experiencing any sexual discrimination, under the guidance of brilliant researchers and mentors Jeffrey Norton and Steven Rosenberg, both world renowned surgeon scientists and both wonderfully naïve to the notion of women being lesser than their male counterparts, as either surgeons or scientists.

With regard to our advancement in society or any lack thereof are we to blame? Is it that we try too hard to fit in, that we have not created our own unique style in the workplace? Or is it that we lack appropriate mentors and examples to emulate? Or are we truly oppressed, with biases, both conscious and unconscious, emanating from not only men in the workplace, but women as well?

Even in the military, where women fight alongside men in combat, there still exist barriers to promotion. In February 2012 it was reported that the "Pentagon took a small step . . . and announced that women would be formally permitted in crucial and dangerous jobs closer to the front lines. But it stopped short of officially allowing women to serve in combat. . . . Nonetheless, many women in Iraq and Afghanistan have served in combat as attachments to infantry foot patrols, and in many cases they have come under fire and fought back. . . . Serving in jobs like the infantry remains crucial to career advancement in the military, and critics of the current policy say that by not recognizing women's real role in combat, women are unfairly held back."[2]

There are many statistics that have been published that suggest that, indeed, women do not fare as well as men. For instance, although early in our careers the NIH (National Institutes of Health) funds research conducted by men and women equally, this funding falls off considerably over time. Women have significantly lower application and funding rates, the reasons being somewhat unclear; but questions arise about the level of support women receive at their own institutions compared to men, conscious and unconscious biases, and child-rearing.[3]

I have shared with you just some of my story only to emphasize the man's world in which all of us have entered, the conscious and unconscious prejudices we all have experienced along the way. I tell you some of my story, not because it is any more remarkable or fascinating than your own, but so that you can reflect upon your own unique journey. Finally, I would be remiss to leave out the most important people in my life: my husband, John Britton, a pediatric anesthesiologist, who has been my unfailing champion since medical school and my two wonderful children, Tenaya and Zachary, who are both my true joy and guides in life.

In summary, we definitely have come a long way over the past several decades, have made significant strides in our roles as surgeons and as leaders. We are fortunate to be surrounded by amazing role models: Julie Freischlag as former Chief of Surgery at Johns Hopkins and Patricia Numann as former President of the American College of Surgeons, to name only a few. Surrounded by role models such as these impressive women, who would not have unwavering faith in our future?

So do I believe there is a glass ceiling? Absolutely and positively, yes! However, with the momentum generated by those who have gone before and who are present in our midst, I believe it will someday be completely shattered.

References:

1. Ash AS, Carr PL, Goldstein R, Friedman RH. Compensation and advancement of women in academic medicine: is there equity? *Annals of Internal Medicine.* 2004;141(3):205-12.
2. Bumiller, Elisabeth. *New York Times* (February 9th, 2012)
3. Pohlhaus JR, Jiang H, Wagner RM, Schaffer WT, Pinn VW. Sex differences in application, success, and funding rates for NIH extramural programs. *Academic Medicine: Journal of the Association of American Medical Colleges* 2011; 86(6):759–67.

Mary Maniscalco-Theberge, MD, FACS
General and Breast Surgeon

You Can Do (Almost) Anything With Hard Work!

As I look back on my life to date, I feel fortunate to have grown up with a very close nuclear family. My father was in the United States Navy, so early in life we moved around a lot. As a consequence of these frequent moves, my brothers and sisters also played the role of my best friends and my mom and dad were my greatest counselors. Throughout my entire life, they have always been there to support and encourage me. My parents taught me that anything can be accomplished with hard work, and that all I had to do was work hard enough to earn what I wanted. This work ethic has served me well in my life and career. Another theme in our home that was guided by a strong faith was to do the right thing—even if it was not popular or more difficult. This mantra has served me especially well as a leader. By approaching each task thoughtfully and fairly, I have always been able to defend my actions. Having a solid sounding-board on which to bounce ideas and decisions allowed me to develop both the perspective and the analytic, critical thinking required to survive my early surgical career as a "solitary woman."

My family is now extended to a wonderful husband and children. Their perspectives are often a little different from the "Maniscalco Way," and have provided me an expanded view of situations, giving me an even greater ability to understand others. My passion for family is a driving force in my life; as long as we have each other, life will be good.

During my five years of general surgery residency, I was the only woman in the program—and being the only woman was an issue almost every day. To this day, I believe my Chief always thought I would make a great surgeon. He just hated the fact that I was a woman! Reflecting back on my residency experience, I believe that he always had my best interest at heart. He knew the world of surgery at that time and understood that being a woman surgeon would not be easy, so he took it upon himself to make me tough. This "toughness" was not in an "act like the guys" way, but to challenge me with a higher standard, to be able to always defend my decisions and hold my ground. This constant challenge on a daily basis is best conveyed by a comment made by one of the residents who graduated with me. On residency graduation day, he came up to me and said, "Mary, if I had had to put up with your experiences in this residency, I would have quit. I am so proud of you!" The acknowledgment from one of my peers, that it really had been harder for me, made me proud that I "survived," and challenged me to live up to the effort that my Chief had invested in me.

My first assignment out of residency was at Frankfurt (Germany) Army Regional Medical Center. Our Medical Center was a regional support center for US military beneficiaries in Europe, the Eastern bloc nations, the Middle-East and Africa. While stationed in Germany, I was a member of both the deployable triage and resuscitation teams that supported the entire theater. The experiences on these teams motivated me to expand my training in Trauma and Critical Care, to better respond to the military medical mission. I believed that no soldier, sailor, airman or marine should die, if preventable, for doing what their country has asked of them, and I wanted to become an even better surgeon.

As my career progressed, I was fortunate to be assigned to Walter Reed Army Medical Center in Washington, DC. At Walter Reed, I was an attending for both the General Surgery Residency and the Critical Care Medicine Fellowship. I was faculty member at the Uniformed Services University of the Health Sciences. It is in this teaching role that the following story took shape.

"Just an Appy"

One day, I was lecturing medical students and one kept falling asleep. When I queried if there was a problem, he said he had been on call the night before. I enthusiastically asked what he saw, learnt or did.

He responded, "Not much, just an appy"—referring to an appendectomy that had been performed.

"Just an appy?" I repeated.

I asked if anyone had ever seen a patient die from appendicitis, and they all said no. I then shared with them the story of a patient whom I had cared for as an intern. A seventy-nine-year-old male was admitted to our surgical service with a history of several weeks of abdominal pain. He had visited outlying clinics several times but had not been correctly diagnosed. That evening he was diagnosed with perforated appendicitis. Despite our best efforts, he developed every complication you can imagine related to perforated appendicitis and eventually died. I told them this story to emphasize that appendicitis can be a deadly disease. I then told them that by making the correct diagnosis of acute appendicitis and performing an appendectomy, his night call team had saved their patient from a potentially deadly course. They had saved his life.

I was sure they understood that saving his life was pretty important to their patient, but I asked if they understood the full impact of the phrase "just an appy." What about his wife? She still has a husband to interact with and share fiscal responsibilities with. What about his two children? They still have a father to love and provide for them. This can expand to his parents, friends and extended family, who all still have him in their lives. Additionally, in a couple of weeks he will be able to go back to work, so his company and colleagues will benefit. Because he can work, he can pay taxes that support his local community, state and national programs. So, by saving his life with "just an appy" they have affected more than just one individual.

I ask again: "Just an appy?"

As a surgeon, it is a privilege and honor that our patients allow us to take their life into our hands and remove disease or relieve suffering, which results in far-reaching effects. I am often asked by associates and friends (who see the long hours, hard work and stress of being a surgeon), "If you could start your career over, would you still become a surgeon?" Absolutely.

Inspiring Quote:

"You have to get up every morning with a smile on your face and show the world all the love in your heart." — Carole King

BEING A WOMAN SURGEON

Kimberly Ephgrave, MD, FACS
General Surgeon

"Why Surgery?"

Editor's note: Dr. Ephgrave passed away in March 2012. I heard about her passing from colleagues. Her husband, Tom Rocklin, Vice President for Student Life at the University of Iowa, assisted with completing the submission process for his wife.

Many people know years before medical school starts that they will do something surgical after graduation. When I started medical school in 1977, I had not even considered being a surgeon as an option, so when my sister, a more advanced medical student, proclaimed that I would love my surgery rotation, it sounded utterly and completely wrong. I thought that might be her code for "I'm having a great time on *my* surgery rotation" (which she was) at Henroten Hospital in Chicago.

I, on the other hand, was slogging through a compressed pre-clinical year, and had no interest in hearing that there would be opportunities for crazy-long hours once I got onto the wards. Plus, it made sense that an oldest child would be a hard-working over-achiever, but I had faith in my own slackness.

I first heard about surgery during our "Introduction to Clinical Medicine" course, run by the Department of Internal Medicine. It was generally ridiculed when surgery was mentioned—apparently surgeons were arrogant, laughable and stupid. So besides not being an early riser or wanting to work extremely hard, I also did not aspire to be arrogant, laughable, or stupid.

My first clinical rotation was three months of Internal Medicine at Cook County Hospital, which was hair-raising, action-packed and seemed it could be completely satisfying. None of the medicine attendings I worked with was female, but I met several bright female interns. One month I even had a female chief resident. One of our patients that month was having recurrent, crescendo-transient ischemic attacks, so we called for a vascular surgery consult. *That* was an eye-opener.

The vascular chief—a fast moving, fast-talking woman who, as a fourth-year resident, had two more years of clinical experience than my own

192

chief resident, was very polite to the patient and the medical team. Her own residents and students looked like they were treating her with kid gloves, but I was too intrigued to worry about that. I said something to her about not knowing there were any women in surgery. "Don't be silly," she snapped back. "The chief of Surgery, Dr. Jonasson, is female!"

I had picked a clinical schedule with the three-month surgery rotation at the end of the junior year, in large part because I was sure I wasn't interested in it, and chose to do it at a small community hospital so that my husband and I could commute together to where he was studying for his PhD in Psychology. The first week, I remember recounting en route all the things that confirmed the clerkship would be worthless: surgeons were indeed arrogant, surgical masks made me hyperventilate and mastectomies in massively obese women were disgusting.

Somewhere around the third week, though, I found the ground was shifting under my feet. Laparotomies and thoracotomies were fantastic. I could not believe how beautiful the viscera were in live patients compared to the formalin-fixed mushy, gray cadavers—though I had enjoyed Histology and Gross Anatomy at the time.

The insides of our live patients were not only colorful but actively moving, as the intestines contracted in peristalsis, the lungs filled and emptied and red vessels pulsated. Disease was clear; even a junior student could see that the hard, white, golf-ball-sized cancer needed to come out of the colon, or the globs of yellow plaque that needed to be removed from the carotid artery. Time pretty much stopped when I was in the operating room. Going to the ED was also fun, especially seeing undiagnosed patients with abdominal pain, and going to the ICU gave me a chance to put to work all the cardiac and pulmonary physiology I could remember from *Guyton and Hall Textbook of Medical Physiology*. Residents argued passionately about concrete issues like use of drains and took us students to the library to help them settle the questions.

Still, when the rotation was over I told myself the instant gratification of being a surgeon was not something I would want or need when I became more mature. I had always wanted a family, too. I hadn't yet met the fabled Dr. Jonasson, but from what I had heard she didn't have children. So I decided to apply for residency in Internal Medicine, but also to sign up for a senior elective in Surgery at the University hospital on the chair's service, to see some really big cases and get the surgical bug out of my system.

Things did not work out the way I planned. I had a good—maybe great—time on the chair's service, and helped with the outpatient adrenergic blocking of a pleasant young woman with a pheochromocytoma. Unfortunately for me, the patient re-scheduled her surgery at the last minute, to a day that I would be gone on my nth interview in Internal Medicine. I came home furious, ranting that evening at my husband's back as he typed at his computer terminal. I had missed the only pheochromocytoma resection I might ever get a chance to see in my entire medical career. For what turned out to be such a mediocre medicine program, I decided I would not even put it on my match list.

"I don't get it," my husband responded, without turning around. "Do you hear yourself? Why aren't you interviewing in Surgery?"

That was late November 1979. In December I switched and started interviewing for surgical programs. Seven years later, our first son was born while I was a junior faculty member at the University of Iowa, not yet on the tenure track. I had completed an internship in Chicago and then five more years of surgery residency in Dallas, Texas, moving because my husband got his first faculty position in nearby Ft. Worth.

Three years after that, when we had a second son, my laboratory was up and running and tenure was in sight, I got a phone call from a former chief resident at Parkland, Mary McCarthy (now Professor of Surgery at Wright State). She asked me to come to a "strategic planning session" for something called the Association of Women Surgeons (AWS), which she had to remind me was the group that hosted a great breakfast attended by women surgeons. Seeing a whole room full of dynamic, good-humored women that were all surgeons at that breakfast had awed me at my first trip to the American College of Surgeons several years ago as a chief resident. "Yes, ma'am" was my automatic response. Mary McCarthy can be forceful, and, besides, I trusted her judgment. And that involvement with AWS provided several pieces that were missing from my life—peer mentors by the dozen, senior mentors like Patricia Numann and opportunities to plan and lead an organization in a supportive atmosphere unlike anything else in my academic surgical world.

I am now in my mid 50s and haven't operated for over a year, so my perspectives on myself and surgery have shifted. I realize now that I am quite impatient compared to friends who pursued Internal Medicine, and nowhere near as nice as the ones who devoted themselves to Pediatrics or Psychiatry. I also realize that although I did not think that I needed any kind of help or support when I started residency, I really do need female peers and mentors. Thank goodness many other women started in surgery at the same time I did. And though we stalled out at approximately 20 percent female residents in general surgery programs before duty-hour reform, improvement in surgery has proceeded rapidly since then.

All three of my sons are done with high school; the youngest (born in 1989) is still in college. After a decade with a female Chair of Surgery, Carol Scott-Conner, my department at the University of Iowa remains one of the strongest in the world in female faculty, which I find thrilling. When I was a resident at Parkland Hospital in Dallas, it made surgeons nervous on the rare occasions when they spotted two female residents chatting. "Are you talking about us?" I remember one surgeon asking nervously—not un-reasonably since there were some grounds for complaint.

Last week-end, by contrast, I heard someone call my name while I wandered at an art fair in Iowa City. It was three great, young faculty members in Surgery, all female. None of them happened to be on call, and they were obviously enjoying themselves.

I am fortunate to have met many great female surgeons: trailblazers like Drs. Olga Jonasson, Kathryn Anderson, Anna Ledgerwood, Karen Deveney, Carol Scott-Conner, Maria Allo and scores of talented women closer to my own age (or younger), like Julie Freischlag, Linda Phillips, Joyce Majure, Barbara Bass, Leigh Neumayer, Myriam Curet, Karen Brasel and Mary Hooks. I am convinced, though, that the newest generation of female surgeons will be the best one yet.

SECTION 8—NARRATIVES FROM THE WORLD OF TRANSPLANT AND TRAUMA SURGERY

Thérèse M. Duane, MD, FACS, FCCM
Trauma/Critical Care Surgeon

Answer Your Calling

It is exciting to contribute to this important work on women in surgery.

My name is Thérèse Duane and I am a Professor of Surgery at the Virginia Commonwealth University Medical Center in Richmond Virginia. My practice is trauma, critical care and emergency general surgery. I have the great fortune of literally knowing that I was going to be a surgeon from my mother's womb. That phrase is really the only way to describe truly knowing that being a surgeon was a core component of my being. My desire and dedication only grew as I continued on with my education. In addition, I realized early on that I was destined to become a trauma surgeon and have been very blessed to have realized these goals.

I have had many mentors over the years, and when I was young I did not even realize who they were because the relationships were so natural. My first mentor was my mother, who along with my father raised seven children, six of whom are girls. My mother was a nurse and my father was a New York City police officer, so my upbringing was very middle class. My mother expressed the fact that she became a nurse because her mother had been a nurse and, in her time, women did not become doctors. She knew that she wanted the best for her daughters, and saved so that we could go to school and to college. Interestingly, when my father would ask my mother why she was saving, and she said it was for the girls to go to college, his response was simply, "Why do they need to go to college? They just need to get married." Interesting how times have changed.

As I got older my mentors included the department of surgery chair, Dr. L. D. Britt. What is interesting about Dr. Britt was that everyone was treated the same: gender neutral. The expectations were the same, the punishments were the same, the accolades were the same and it was all based on merit. It had nothing to do with gender. I look at that as exactly the way it should be, and it has guided me in my career. Once in fellowship, this philosophy remained the same until I joined the faculty of Virginia Commonwealth University. An associate dean pointed out that as a woman in surgery I was somewhat unique. I then reflected that I was only the fourth female faculty member to join the department of surgery, and therefore had a particular responsibility for the women residents.

My greatest mentor continues to be my husband. Despite our busy two-physicians' home, we have been blessed with almost twenty years of marriage and the greatest gift of four children. The children understand our commitments to work and participate in the family responsibilities. One of the wonderful things about what I do, in particular, is my in-house call, because it allowed my husband to learn early on how to be the primary caregiver when I was away. After the birth of our first child, I was back on call within three weeks, second child within two weeks, the third child within one week and the fourth child just within a few days. With each additional child my husband got better and better at simply figuring things out. Because of these experiences, I believe that he developed a relationship with the children that otherwise may not have developed if my presence was there at all times. In fact, as I go off to work now, the children look forward to time spent simply with their daddy; and that time is a wonderful benefit that I don't think people realize is available to them with this profession.

As I have now been on faculty for over ten years, I have seen an increase in the number of female residents and junior faculty. Because of the benefits I have had from mentoring and mentorship, I have aggressively embraced the concept of developing and nurturing the upcoming generations of physicians and surgeons in academic medicine, men and women alike. When mentoring people I emphasize, most importantly, that this profession is a calling; it is truly a gift from God and one needs to know what it is that He wants. If you make the right choice in your career, the balancing component actually becomes easier. The fact is that you will spend most of your time at work, and you need to keep that in mind so that when you are here it is fulfilling. You are a happier person at home. People who make a choice based on their perception that life will be easier often find that this is not the case. They struggle to strike a balance. Hence, when I counsel medical students, I simply tell them this: "If you could find yourself happy doing anything else other than surgery, then do it; and if you cannot imagine yourself doing anything but surgery, then you need to commit yourself one hundred percent." That does not preclude a family, and does not preclude outside hobbies. It allows you to accomplish more in the same amount of time than someone who is approaching work and life with reluctance and an acceptance of mediocrity.

Challenges are a part of life and what does not kill us can only make us stronger. However, I have never felt that I was unfairly treated based on gender. I had struggles because I was a New York girl, now in the south, but it never came from my faculty members. In fact, it often came from nurses who had not experienced a lot of female residents. However, it did teach me that I needed to approach things with more grace and gentleness than was in my nature. So, in actuality, every challenge, every difficulty became a blessing for me and an opportunity for me to improve myself and grow. Although there had been times when I wanted to blame interpersonal conflict on gender, I came to realize that I needed to accept more responsibility. I had to look within myself to determine my role, resulting in more effective interpersonal skills. Blaming gender is useless, as it is not something I can change. Therefore, I focus on what I can change, and it makes all of the difference. I continue to encourage other women to avoid using gender as a crutch as well.

I have wonderful memories and experiences from over the years. I reflect fondly on the people who have loved me enough to talk to me straight and tell me when I have really screwed up and when I have done a good job. Open and honest, albeit gentle, is the type of mentor I strive to be for the people that I am training and the people who look up to me.

For those who are coming after me, I would suggest focusing on how wonderful it is to be a surgeon and not dwell on how tough it is to be a woman in this field. Being a trauma surgeon, and being a trauma surgeon who is also a mother and a wife, is truly a blessing, because I am fulfilled at work and am focused on the positive. I am surrounded by motivated, positive, interesting people. In addition, it allows me to foster outside interests. I am an avid triathlete, which completes my embrace of not only spiritual health, but mental and physical health as well. I have optimized my efficiency and effectiveness in all the roles I have in my life.

This would be the advice that I would give to young people looking to pursue a profession. It is not about how I raise a family and pursue a profession at the same time; it is not about how hard it is. It is about how wonderful it is to be able to bear a child, raise this child, and also go to the operating room and save a life. These gifts are the blessings, and these need to be the focus.

I believe strongly that we need to move away from focusing on gender differences and the presumed problems with disparities in pay and treatment. Let us focus on what is right, what is wonderful, what each of us as individuals can do, if this is what we are called to do. At the end of the day, if you are doing what God has called you to do, you will be wonderful at it, and you will be able to balance other things in your life that are a priority and that are important! Focus on those things; and when you reflect on your life ten, fifteen, twenty years into the practice, I promise you, you will be fulfilled in all aspects. Fundamentally, you are the person who is in charge, and you are the one who is responsible for your choices. Embrace that responsibility and embrace the opportunity.

Inspiring Quote:
"I can sleep when I am dead." — Therèse Duane

Amina Merchant, MD
Trauma/Acute Care Surgery Fellow

Kidney Transplant

How could one ever imagine taking an organ from one person's body and placing it into someone else to change another person's life?! It seemed so bizarre, so unlikely, so out of this world. Yet, the first kidney transplant I scrubbed into transformed my outlook on surgery and shaped the way I value life. This surgery, so brilliant and amazing, makes me proud to be a surgeon. Every late-night shift and every opportunity in residency excites me, when I see how surgery can truly enable people to live life to its fullest.

The kidney transplant sums up the awesomeness in a nutshell and why I love my job. Life goes on, and one organ that can easily be discarded after death has the possibility to completely change someone's life—enable the patient to move beyond her disease and live life to its fullest.

Mr. Martinez lived with long-standing diabetes and hypertension, so disabling it caused his kidneys to fail. Consequently, his arms were slashed multiple times to create fistulas and grafts that could be used for hemodialysis. Each time, it would work for a couple years, and then clot off for us to begin the cycle again: slash, create, dialyze, clot. Unfortunately, this process requires three hours at a dialysis center three times weekly! Many people are unable to work, unable to attend family functions, unable to spend time with their families just to stay alive. It remains a nuisance, yet is vital to their existence.

Finally, one night at eleven p.m., Mr. Martinez's turn came. Someone had donated a kidney that matched his. He had served his time—five years on the waiting list; and now, his life was about to change forever. Instead of being disabled, an organ donation had enabled him to live a normal life again.

He was taken to the operating room, prepped and draped in a sterile fashion. I took a deep breath during the time out, to go over the steps of this surgery. Using a number-10 scalpel blade, an incision was made from two centimeters medial to the anterior superior iliac spine to just above the pubic tubercle. The adrenaline surged; I was about to be a part of this man's transformation. Bovie cautery was used to cut through subcutaneous fat, Scarpa's fascia, and the abdominal muscles.

"Make sure you stay extra-peritoneal," my attending advised. The inferior epigastric artery was ligated for better exposure. I used my hands to easily decipher the planes. They magically opened with a few finger sweeps.

The external iliac vessels were identified. A large right angle was used to dissect and isolate the vessels, first the artery and then the vein. At any moment, I could create a hole in the artery and he could bleed out and die: The power is in my hands and I must respect the human body. Vessel loops were placed and attention was now taken to the midline to identify the bladder, which occurred without difficulty. Angled clamps were placed on the iliac vessels and blood flow was diverted from the right, lower extremity. The donor kidney was placed onto the field—it was cold and grayish-appearing. Efficiency is key or serious damage can occur.

A venotomy was made and prolene was used to suture the donor vein and donor artery to the recipient, Mr. Martinez. The vessels were unclamped and flow was diverted to the new kidney. My eyes sparkled as I saw the kidney gain color and appear well perfused. It was a living and useful organ again! I couldn't believe that such a concept was possible; we were defying basic medical principles by inserting a foreign organ into the body and expecting success, rather than rejection.

The donor ureter was sutured to the recipient bladder with interrupted PDS suture. Hemostasis was achieved.

Anesthesia noted urine in the Foley bag! This man had not urinated in decades; instead, his blood had to be filtered through a dialysis machine. He will now gain his life back and have so much more time and energy to devote to experiencing this world. The fascia was closed with interrupted neurilon sutures. The subcutaneous tissues were closed in two layers.

My face glowed. Transplant surgery is difficult but life changing for the patient and the surgeon. I remain grateful for the opportunity to have been a part of this man's life, and for the technical challenge of the surgical procedure. These kinds of experiences keep me excited about my job and my life. The patient was extubated without difficulty and tolerated the procedure well. All sponge, needle and instrument counts were correct at the end of the case.

Inspiring Quote:

"I've come to believe that each of us has a personal calling that's as unique as a fingerprint—and that the best way to succeed is to discover what you love and then find a way to offer it to others in the form of service, working hard, and also allowing the energy of the universe to lead you."

— Oprah Winfrey

Amy Rushing, MD, FACS
Trauma Surgeon

The Working Couple

Today, women can find a plethora of advice about how to keep a relationship thriving. You can pick up any magazine while waiting to pay for groceries and read about "bonding with your spouse" or "how to reignite the fire." I often look at the titles and smirk, as I have a feeling that the formula they're prescribing has little to do with my life. I work as a trauma surgeon in a busy urban hospital. My husband is a cardiac surgery fellow on the brink of starting his career. I am thirty-four-years-old and my husband is forty. We live in a two-bedroom home with no children. We have a dog named Halsted. It's no secret we live to work.

That's what we were doing one Tuesday evening last September. My husband and I are in the hospital taking care of our respective surgical services. He is trying to tie up loose ends before going home, and I am covering for a colleague who needed to attend a parent-teacher conference. It is relatively early in the evening, and I figure I will be home in time to make the standard nine-o'clock dinner. I am debating the options of leftovers versus frozen pizza when my trauma pager goes off: "Delta Trauma: 30 Y. O. Male S/P multiple GSW," indicating the impending arrival of a patient with multiple gunshot wounds.

I make my way down to the Emergency Department located in the basement of the hospital. When I arrive, I find my residents in the trauma bay gowning up. The patient has not yet arrived, so I take the time to inventory the room. "Do we have the chest-tube trays out? Central-line kit?" I ask. "What about hypertonic saline?"

My questions are answered with quick shuffles around the cramped room. The nurses are setting up IVs and the respiratory therapist checked the oxygen tank and airway equipment. I nod to the Emergency Medicine attending that we are ready. I complete my survey as the paramedics roll in with a young man sitting upright on the stretcher. He is about thirty, African-American and athletic-appearing with large arms. He is clearly frightened as he sits with a non-rebreather (oxygen) mask over his face, his eyes wide and his heavy breathing almost audible. I watch his chest rise and fall as I side-step my way to the head of the bed opposite my chief resident.

"What's your name?" I ask. He answers my question in breathy syllables. By the time I complete the initial assessment, I know there is going to be trouble. He has one gunshot wound to the right shoulder, two to the right wrist and two to the abdomen. Wounds we can handle, I think to myself. It's the trajectory that gets your heart rate going, and I have a bad feeling about this one. His blood pressure flashes on the monitor: 108/95. The small difference between the systolic and diastolic numbers suggests early tamponade physiology. Simply speaking, it means that the heart is having difficulty relaxing to allow blood into its chambers due to blood compressing the heart within its own sac. The blood within the sac is abnormal and, in this situation, translates into a hole in the heart from penetrating trauma.

We quickly obtain the portable ultrasound machine and perform a cursory exam, looking at the heart and the abdominal cavity. There is a black stripe that encases the four chambers of the heart and I know we need to be in the operating room. I instruct one of the residents to call upstairs to let the OR staff know we are coming. Repeat blood pressure: 88/28. The chest x-ray we obtain shows a bullet fragment in the right chest with a one-centimeter pneumothorax and no mediastinal shift. We just need to go upstairs and open his chest, preferably before his heart stops beating.

As we package the patient up for the OR and hang a unit of blood through his large bore IV, I hit the most recent number on my cellphone. "Hey, are you still here?"

"Yeah, what's going on?" my husband replies.

"Why don't you just meet me in Room One," I say. I turn off the phone and continue steering the stretcher with my chief resident leading the way. The patient is still awake, though his level of consciousness is fading. I speak to him in short sentences, encouraging him to stay awake. He nods slightly, his eyes partly open.

The path between the elevator and the operating room seems long and has a serpentine quality. We meet the anesthesiologist at the OR front desk and offer a brief report: "Thirty-year-old male with multiple gunshot wounds to the right shoulder, right flank, and abdomen. Pericardial effusion seen on ultrasound. No known past medical history. No known allergies."

The anesthesia attending nods and introduces himself to the patient. We quickly turn into Operating Room One.

Operating Room One is known in our hospital as the trauma room. It's packed with all types of surgical equipment, chiefly things that are designed to stop bleeding and resuscitate patients. Like many operating rooms, the walls are whitewashed cinderblocks and there are no windows. The light offered is fluorescent in nature, reinforcing the cold, sterile nature of the room. Suture boxes and bins with gloves and gauze line one wall. Off to the side, the scrub tech stands gowned and gloved, counting steel instruments. He briefly looks up to survey the party coming in. In the middle, a narrow operating-room table awaits my patient.

We quickly transfer the patient from the stretcher to the table, in a well-choreographed manner: anesthesiologists at the head of the patient, nurses in the middle and my intern at the foot. The patient remains sitting upright to facilitate his breathing, as monitors and masks are exchanged. Out of the corner of my eye I see one of the hospital perfusionists coming in with a heap of equipment designed to collect and salvage shed blood, so that the patient may receive an auto-transfusion. I frown behind my mask as we do not have the time or the space in the operating room to accommodate the Cell Saver.

"What is this?" I ask, pointing to the equipment. (Of note, it's typical "attending speak" to ask questions you already know the answers to.)

"Dr. Rushing asked for the Cell Saver," the perfusionist replies.

"We don't have room for this," I say, trying to be diplomatic—but *this* Dr. Rushing did not want the Cell Saver.

In the trauma setting we forego auto-transfusion, as it is time-consuming and often yields more headaches than it's worth. The blood is often mixed with intestinal contents and not suitable for recycling. This machine's presence in my already-cramped room is the thinking of a cardiac surgeon. My preference is to rely upon the red and white plastic coolers one often will find at a picnic, coming in with fixed numbers of various blood products. For the sake of maintaining the staff's momentum, I keep quiet and look for my husband, who comes through the door.

I decide that starting the case is more important than arguing about extraneous equipment. I instruct my chief resident to scrub while I prep the patient. In this situation, the plan is to be ready when the patient is induced, so that if he arrests we can promptly open the chest. Our patient is maintaining his blood pressure throughout the induction and intubation. My prep is quick yet thorough, as betadine paint coats the patient from neck to mid thigh. I finish and quickly wash my hands. My husband has already scrubbed and donned his gown and gloves. Meanwhile, I notice the circulating nurse has been kind enough to turn up the room temperature, as I put on my gown and gloves.

With the patient asleep and relatively stable, we finish draping and I hand the scalpel to my chief resident. She makes a long, smooth incision from the sternal notch to the xiphoid process. As we proceed with opening the chest, I start to collect a mental checklist of potential findings and pitfalls. A straightforward ventricular wound? Sure, I could handle that. But an injury to the pulmonary artery or something as equally complex was going to be wrought with technical complexities that I rarely see. My contempt about the cell saver was forgotten; I was glad to have my husband here.

The sternal saw divides the bone with a generous whirring sound. After placing the retractor, we see the sac that encompasses the heart: It's purple and bulging with blood. Typically, this layer of tissue is almost transparent, and one can see the heart skipping freely in place. In this instance, it is clear the patient has cardiac tamponade. I grab a pair of toothed forceps and pick up the full sac, which is similar to picking up a water balloon with tweezers. We open the pericardium to evacuate a large blood clot. It takes about a millisecond to identify the source of bleeding: a small defect in the right ventricle about the size of a pea. While small, this defect continues to spew a pulsatile jet of blood about one-hundred times a minute. I put a finger over the hole and we get sutures ready for the repair. Fortunately, the defect closes with two figure-of-eight sutures reinforced with cloth pledgets. In spite of the successful closure, however, there was still blood welling up from around the heart. Anesthesia continues to keep up with these losses by hanging bag after bag of donated blood. The red and white coolers keep getting exchanged at the door.

"We're picking up the heart," my husband proclaims, and I realize this is a warning to the anesthesiologists as they watch the steady blips on the telemetry monitor whip into an irregular frenzy of spikes. A little ventricular tachycardia (VT or V-tach) always gets your attention. Underneath the heart a pool of blood quickly appears, and constant suction is required to see anything. A small half-inch tear is seen where the superior vena cava empties into the right atrium. The injury is tucked underneath the corner of the heart, with the thin vein threatening to open further with even the slightest turn. My husband and I look at each other and he grabs a stitch. I carefully lift the heart again. He places the needle deftly into the thin tissue and closes the defect by almost half. My finger slides over the remaining hole as he receives a second suture from the tech. He hands it to me.

"You have a better angle," he points out. I take the suture and my forceps and quickly throw another figure-of-eight stitch. Now, I make no qualms about it, my husband makes this look better than I do. I get the tissue together and tie the sutures down. The hole is closed. I then wonder how long I had been holding my last breath.

By now, the patient's intravascular volume is on the upswing; however, he is somewhat cold and consequently oozing blood from even the tiniest needle marks. We irrigate around his heart and inspect the nearby structures. The right lung is injured as a result of the bullet's trajectory, but does not require intervention. We decide to place chest tubes and temporarily close the chest wound with a combination of protective drapes and sterile towels, so that the patient can get to the intensive care unit to be rewarmed and resuscitated.

Once in the ICU, my husband and I stand outside our patient's room and observe the typical commotion that ensues when bringing a critically-ill post-operative patient to the unit. The nurses work at unraveling the spaghetti of IV tubing and monitoring cords, as the patient is tucked in and connected to the unit monitors. I watch the crimson fluid trickling from his chest tubes; fortunately, it resembles fruit punch more than frank blood, signifying that internal bleeding has stopped. At that point, I realize how fatigued I am. My shoulders and calf muscles are tight. My head is slightly pounding from a combination of mental exhaustion and hunger. I really have to pee.

I turn to my husband. "Thank you," I say. Simple and understated as it was, he understands my appreciation for him, his patience, and his skill.

He looks at me and winks. "You're welcome."

That's it. That's our secret. When people ask me how we make our marriage work, I respond with the mere notion that we truly have a genuine appreciation for one another. I met my husband when I was a third-year medical student on my surgical clerkship. It was the very first clerkship of my medical school career—one of the most anxiety-provoking experiences at the time (soon to be surpassed by the first day of internship and completely overshadowed by one's first day as an attending). When we met, my husband was ten years younger and exuded a focused energy on taking care of patients. I was awestruck. Not by his ambition or intelligence, but by his ability to remain warm and humble in an environment that is typically characterized by the Peter Bentons and Derek Shepherds of *ER* and *Grey's Anatomy*. My admiration for him continues to this day, however it is often mixed with exasperation for leaving his socks on the floor and forgetting to empty the dishwasher. Regardless, we make a good team. He claims to love my drive and my ability to stand up for what I think is right. I cherish his patient and kind nature. Ten years in all: surgical residency, my critical care fellowship, another trauma fellowship, his cardiothoracic fellowship, soon to be followed by another year of training in complex aortic reconstruction. In those ten years, we have also endured the passing of my mother, the turbulent grief her death bestowed upon my family, the drifting of friends and colleagues in and out of our lives and the quiet unease about where this lifestyle will eventually lead us. At the end of the day, I realize that the path my husband and I have chosen is not very popular or easy, but it has afforded us the privilege of impacting a lot of lives in a very powerful way. Sometimes, we even get to save a life together. I'll take that over a magazine article's advice any day of the week.

I dedicate this story to those who have supported me unconditionally: my parents, sister, a group of outstanding surgeons from Norfolk to Baltimore and (most of all) my husband.

Inspiring Quote:
"The most courageous act is still to think for yourself. Aloud."
— Coco Chanel

Shannon M. Zielsdorf, MD
General Surgery Resident

From Tragedy Comes New Life: The Bittersweet Night of a Transplant Surgeon

I awaken in the darkness and fumble for the source of beeping. It is neither my phone nor my alarm clock; it is my pager from the hospital that I finally reach. I return the call and receive the news while still in a dreamlike state. It seems they have found an organ donor that matches my patient who is in liver failure. Now *this* is the metaphorical alarm clock that truly wakes me from my slumber! I throw on a pair of scrubs, run out the door, and drive to the airport, excitement vibrating through my body. This moment exemplifies the reason why Surgery is the specialty I have chosen: brilliant anatomy, extensive operations and—most importantly—lives to be improved or even saved.

When I arrive at the airport's private gate, the attending transplant surgeon, Dr. H, and myself—a junior surgical resident—pile into the six-seater plane that serves as our chariot for the night. As we fly to the small town where the donor awaits, my mind wanders to my patient at home. My patient, Ms. T, has a disease called "primary sclerosing cholangitis." Her liver has been replaced by scar tissue and, therefore, has little function remaining. For this reason, Ms. T has undergone an extensive medical and psychological evaluation; and she has been deemed a suitable transplant candidate. Without a new liver her disease would likely take her life within six months; however, this may no longer be her fate if the potential liver is suitable!

Now, stepping into the operating room, the euphoria of the flight is tainted with reality. On the operating table lies a twenty-year-old young man, brain dead after an untimely accident. All the hope and excitement of my patient's future life is overshadowed in this instant by the premature loss of life of another individual. Herein lies the bittersweet truth of transplant surgery: One human being cannot be saved without the ultimate sacrifice of another. I am comforted by the thought that this man's loss will not be in vain. In fact, after seeing various other transplant teams arrive at the hospital as well, I realize it is quite the opposite: Multiple organs such as

212

heart, lungs and kidneys will also be harvested for several patients in need across the country.

As I make the initial incision from xyphoid to pubis I relax, despite the operating room's even chill. Holding a scalpel in my hand makes me feel at home. Proceeding with the operation, the exposure we gain during this liver procurement is second to none. How beautifully the common bile duct travels from liver to duodenum after the dissection is complete. How exciting it is to see that this donor has anatomical variants of his vasculature—both right *and* left aberrant hepatic arteries? Before I realize it, Dr. H is ready to cannulate the aorta and begin the final stage of the surgery. We quickly deposit ice within the surgical field in order to preserve the organs. We dissect out the liver and rush it to the back table in the operating room, to be inspected further and packaged extensively. Dr. H admires the flawlessly smooth organ and puts it eloquently: "Call the team at home. Tell 'em it's perfect."

Upon our return, Ms. T is already in the operating room, abdomen open and ready to accept her new organ. Dr. H and I have the privilege of playing her knights (or heroines) in shining armor; only the fairy tale kiss is in the form of a new, functioning liver. She will be saved!

Finally, when I return home after the long day, my psyche returns to that dreamlike state. However, before I drift into a deep sleep, I place my pager next to my phone and alarm clock as usual. I do not know the specifics of the next page to come, but I *do* know it always brings some aspect of brilliant anatomy, interesting operations and a life to be improved or even saved.

Inspiring Quote:
"The question isn't who is going to let me; it's who is going to stop me."
— Ayn Rand

Hannah Copeland, MD
Cardiothoracic Surgery Fellow

A Unique Night on Call

I was a fourth-year general surgery resident and settled in to another trauma call as the chief resident on the trauma service. We ordered dinner and ate as we always did, in the residents' room, though this night was different from all my previous trauma calls: I was six-months pregnant.

It started out as a regular Tuesday night trauma call. Then at eleven p.m. we received a patient who sustained a gunshot wound and needed immediate resuscitation. We have a unique situation in our hospital, where certain critically ill trauma patients can be resuscitated on arrival in an operating room located in the emergency department. So if a trauma patient needs an emergent operative procedure, any delay in surgical intervention is eliminated.

I reached the trauma operating room as the patient rolled in. He had a gun-shot wound to his right axilla and he lost palpable pulses en-route to our hospital. Advanced Cardiac Life Support protocol was started immediately. Within seconds, my attending made a crucial decision and ordered me to perform a life-saving procedure: "Hannah, open the chest, now!" he ordered.

I performed my first "Emergency Department thoracotomy" and started a cardiac massage. (No matter how calm and cool you may seem while performing this procedure, inside your own body there is an adrenaline surge.) I took a knife across his left chest, opened it, opened the pericardium and started to do a cardiac massage. Then I clamped the aorta.

Inside me, my son began to kick. My belly felt like a slow rhythmic punching bag; and the more of an adrenaline rush I got—it went from kick . . . kick . . . kick . . . to kick, kick, kick, kick to punching and kicking one right after the other. Suddenly, the patient's pulses were back!

Thank God! I started to close the chest. As I was closing the chest, my attending started to open the right axilla, where the second-year resident had been holding pressure. The anesthesiologist was hanging units of blood to keep up with the blood loss. Nurses were running around in the trauma resuscitation area. I moved over to the right axilla with my protruding belly, trying not to get in anyone's way and get bumped—because under a gown no one could tell I was pregnant!

I made it over and we uncovered the wound slowly. There was a clear laceration of the axillary artery greater than 2 cm, and we began to clamp and try to shunt it. The rhythmic kicking started again inside my belly, keeping time to the adrenaline rush; and it became kicking, punching, kicking, punching—over and over. As we gained control of the axillary artery, the vascular attending entered the room and I started to harvest a saphenous vein. The intense kicking and punching subsided to just continuous, slow kicking. We sutured in the vein and closed the axilla.

The patient was extubated the next morning. The next evening, I was at home in bed trying to sleep and at eleven p.m. my son woke me up, kicking and punching. "We have to talk," I said to my belly. "It's not trauma call—let's sleep." It took a little bit for him to wind down.

The patient eventually left the hospital. I learned that operating while being pregnant was going to be a new, unique residency experience. My son was a part of that experience!

Inspiring Quote: "Take life one day at a time!" — Hannah Copeland

SECTION 9—LEADERS IN OTORHINOLARYNGOLOGY SHARE THEIR REMINISCENCES

Kathleen Yaremchuk, MD, MSA
Head and Neck Surgeon

Where Do I Fit In?

It never dawned on me that being a woman would be a problem in medicine, surgery or Otolaryngology. I was an only child raised by parents who taught me that I could achieve whatever I set my mind to. My mother was a full-time nurse and my father worked in the automobile factory. When I was eight years old, I had acute appendicitis; during my post-operative recovery period, I fashioned a nurse's cap out of paper and showed it proudly to my mom when she came to visit. She looked at my handiwork and dropped it dismissively in the trash. "If you are interested in medicine, you are going to be a doctor," she pronounced, and that was that. I saw no reason to argue with her wisdom, and from that point on, whenever anyone asked me what I wanted to be when I grew up, I said, "a doctor."

I lived in a blue-collar neighborhood and went to a high school that reflected the work ethos of an immigrant population. I did well in school and, as all students did at the time, took an aptitude test. My counselor told me I excelled in mechanics and farming. I wasn't sure what to do with that information or how it would fit into a career as a doctor.

As luck would have it, one day I was reading the Sunday paper and an article described a six-year combined undergraduate/graduate medical school program at the University of Michigan. They were interviewing for their first class in 1972. I showed the article to my counselor, who said that it was interesting but nothing more. I wrote the University of Michigan for more information and before I knew it I was filling out the application for an interview. Besides being innovative in the duration of the educational path, the program was accepting 50 percent females in the initial class. I was the first one in my family to attend college, so my parents were not giving advice regarding where I should apply to college.

My application was accepted for an interview, and I was excited to have made the first cut of the selection process, but was completely un-aware of what to expect. I remember wearing a yellow blazer and navy- blue pants to the interview. One of the members of the selection committee exclaimed, "I will remember you, you are wearing Michigan colors—maize and blue." I was accepted to the program and to this day believe my choice of school colors made the difference.

When it came time to decide on residency and my future specialization, it was clear I loved being in the operating room, and felt comfortable in the lifestyle of hard work, long hours and excitement. As a medical student, an intern told me to look into Otolaryngology as a career. He was going into Ophthalmology but felt I would enjoy the broader scope of practice that Otolaryngology provided. Once again, sage advice which I followed.

I did my general surgery internship at Cook County Hospital in Chicago, where there were three other women, two in the program and the Chair. There was never a thought that as a female surgeon I wouldn't fit in. I do remember the woman senior resident lost her keys because both of her winter coat pockets had holes in them, and she bemoaned that she had no time or energy to purchase a new coat. Every other night call would do that to you. Her comment did give me pause.

My Otolaryngology residency was done at the University of Chicago, where I was the only woman resident in the program, although several years earlier a woman from the military had completed the program. Northwestern University in Chicago had a woman resident at that time, and we became friends when we rotated at the same hospitals. It did not occur to me that women in Otolaryngology were a rarity until I finished practice and went to look for a job.

In 1982, when I finished my residency, I couldn't decide between academics and private practice so I interviewed for both. I even interviewed for a fellowship in neurotology at a prestigious hospital, and was surprised to have the fellowship director ask me how I thought a woman would do in neurotology.

As I started attending national Otolaryngology meetings, it became apparent I was an anomaly. I was consistently asked if I was a nurse, office manager or someone's wife. I began to tire of the usual line of questioning and started to give edgy responses. I stopped going to meetings because I didn't feel like I belonged: At that time the specialty of Otolaryngology was an "old boys club" with no room for advancement of women. In the early

1980s the specialty was 98.5 percent male. How that fact escaped me previously is an unknown.

Otolaryngology's specialty journal used to print a picture of the opening ceremony of the society's annual meeting on the cover. In 1991, the photograph showed the stage with two rows of elderly men with gray hair and dark suits and the new incoming president, Dr. G. Richard Holt. I couldn't stand it any longer. I didn't know Dr. Holt from the man on the moon, but I sent a letter suggesting that because there were no women on the stage, the message given was that women were not welcome and would not succeed in academic medicine in Otolaryngology. I described the feeling of being excluded from leadership within Otolaryngology and that the specialty was missing valuable contributions by women. This was decades before there was talk of the values of diversity.

I was surprised to receive a letter from Dr. Holt, and even more surprised to learn that his wife was an ophthalmologist and that all of his four daughters were either in medical school, residency or in practice. He sympathized with my concerns and was steadfast in his support of women in surgery. To change the 98 percent male preponderance in the specialty, however, would take years, because of the slow dilution effect of adding women to the small specialty pool of Otolaryngology.

In the 1990s I decided to accept a position in the Department of Otolaryngology at Henry Ford Hospital in Detroit. It gave me the opportunity to have a clinical and academic practice. More important, it allowed me to develop administrative skills in a medical group practice environment. Although I never believed I would strive to be a chair of a department, I developed skills that would allow me to do so.

Within the Henry Ford Medical Group I accepted administrative positions of increasing complexity and responsibility. The positions tended to be broader in reach and covered all specialties within the practice. There were opportunities where I served as Medical Director for an insurance company and Vice President of Medical Affairs for a hospital that became part of our health system—a result of a joint venture with another health system. Each position added a skill set and knowledge that I hadn't had previously. Many people refer to "additional tools for the tool box" and that is exactly what happened.

In 2009, the Chair of Otolaryngology accepted a position elsewhere and I decided to apply for the position. Although being the Chair of a department was never a life goal, I decided I was as competent as anyone else for the position. There were fourteen applicants for the position and I was selected. At the time, of the 103 academic programs in Otolaryngology, there were only four woman chairs of Otolaryngology in the country. I would be number five, and before I knew it we were back to four when one woman stepped down to move to another institution.

The specialty of Otolaryngology in the past ten years has changed as a reflection of the increase in women medical students and subsequent increase in women seeking residencies in Otolaryngology. Despite this, it is well recognized that women to this day are underrepresented in leadership and academic positions within the specialty.

In 2011, I was awarded the prestigious Jerome C. Goldstein Award for Public Service by the American Academy of Otolaryngology—Head and Neck Surgery Foundation (AAO/HNS). The presentation occurred at the AAO/HNS Annual Meeting Opening Ceremony. I was now on the stage where twenty years previously women had been invisible. I made a point of inviting my adult children and wearing a red dress to receive the award. I was making a statement to myself and everyone in the audience that times were changing and the days of dark suits were in the past.

I look at my career path and recognize that whenever a door appeared to be closed, a window would open that would give me space to grow and express my creativity and ingenuity. I often wonder what would have happened had I allowed myself to continue to look away from the men-only Otolaryngology stage and not dare to push the envelope for women in the specialty.

Inspiring Quote:
"You may be disappointed if you fail, but you are doomed if you don't try."
— Beverly Sills, former American opera soprano

Sujana S. Chandrasekhar, MD, FACS
Otolaryngology—Head and Neck Surgeon

What's a Nice Girl Like You Doing In a Profession Like This?

What's a nice girl like you doing in a profession like this? That was the first line of my personal essay when I applied to ENT residencies. I had heard it, or some version of it, so many times that I figured I might as well start with that issue head-on. Even though I had interviews at ten residency programs, it was really clear once I got to those places that the door was only marginally open to women or any "other" (non-white or non-male) applicant. While others might have been applying for one of four available slots, I was fighting for the zero-to-one slot set aside for the "other." I was actually told point-blank at two of the places that they had already picked "the girl." One was a local program, so I just accepted it. The other had cost me a round-trip airplane flight, which somehow made it more frustrating. It's funny that I never dwelled on the female nonsense during medical school. I just wanted to learn, and I just wanted to move ahead and do what I wanted to do. It is really good, sometimes, to go through life with blinders on.

I did two years mandatory training in General Surgery before my four years of Otolaryngology. There were a couple of women scattered in the five-year General Surgery program, and less than a handful of us doing a preliminary year or two. It was a weird, exhilarating, stressful, fun, fantastic time. The women bonded silently—across religions, backgrounds, beliefs. One day the male residents at one of the hospitals presented three of us with a birthday cake—all three women had December birthdays. It was a dark marzipan cake in the shape of a giant penis and testicles, with a candle at the tip. The female senior resident was encouraged to "blow" the candle out. She took a huge knife and chopped the penis off at its base. I imagine that ribaldry didn't occur again.

The men were a strange lot. There were a few who didn't harp on my gender or make stupid jokes, but most did. When I finally figured out what "on the rag" meant, I was grossed out—for them. I couldn't believe that they would refer so frequently to a soggy sanitary napkin! I spent three months with one surgery chief resident at the VA, doing vascular and general surgery. Well, that chief resident told the sickest jokes. At the end of our three months together, he told me that he had been trying to make me cry every day for three months. I apologized and told him that he should have just told me to cry and I would have taken care of it for him on day one.

I was on call every other night during those two years of General Surgery training. We had a single junior resident on call room—more of a closet, really, with a bunk bed. The men put up *Playboy* centerfolds all over the place. Yuck. So one of the reps came by and I asked him to get me a *Playgirl*. Back in those days, those centerfolds had tight briefs on. I put up two *Playgirl* centerfolds and, miraculously, all the porn came down, and stayed down.

Otolaryngology residents were on call only every third night. We had one woman in every class. The numbers are better now. Women make up 32 percent of residents in Otolaryngology[1] (the percentage is way less for senior faculty). My residency training program was very fair, gender-wise. I also did not see gender bias when I applied for fellowships. I ended up being the third woman fellow ever at a world-renowned fellowship, and, in fact, fellow number two was training alongside with me. She and I have remained the best of friends.

Job searching after training is when I started to see gender raising its head again. I didn't know how to negotiate, and one institute told both my co-fellow and I that we didn't have enough research experience. She had a PhD, and I had done seminal research on AIDS and the ear. They took a guy with less research experience than either of us; but he could, and did, go fishing with the boss, while the wives stayed at the boss' home and baked cookies together. Oh, *that* kind of research. Right.

I climbed up the ladder, still with those blinders on. I started the programs I wanted to start. I did the research I wanted to do. I cobbled to-gether the funds. I was told that I might not be ready for promotion "since you've been out on maternity leave" for the past three months. When I could get a word in edgewise, I pointed out that I had earned nearly as much in nine months than the others had in a year, and that I was the only one doing research and publishing and mentoring students and residents. When I got my promotion, I was told by committee members that I should have applied for tenure, as my CV had had enough for that.

I had three children in a row in my first five years as an attending surgeon. Well, I was getting old, and, *á la* Mariesa Tomei in "My Cousin Vinny," "my biological clock was ticking." I signed all my charts in between learning how to breastfeed my first child. I wrote what remained for a long time the most accessed article in one of our major journals in between nursing and diaper changes for my second child, and started working on my Triological Society thesis during my third maternity leave. I got a Research Award for that. When the baby books advised reading to the baby while nursing, I would read ENT journals or *Time* or *Newsweek* out loud. I found out that my University did not have a maternity-leave policy for faculty, which struck me as very odd, so I wrote one up for myself.

I've worked in two academic medical centers as a full-time faculty member for a total of eleven years. I had a horrible experience ending in my leaving academics, but I have found a happier and more productive place now. I am in solo private practice and have been so for ten years. For the past three years, I've shared space and overhead with three other otolaryngologists. I also work at the VA one day per week. I just negotiated a deal to set up a huge clinical program for one of the large healthcare systems in the area. I maintain my faculty appointment; now it just has the word "Clinical" in front of "Associate Professor." And I'm co-running a biotech startup based on some of my research.

In the ten years of private practice, I've published more; followed my passions to serve on the Board of Governors of the AAO-HNS, including running for and securing the position of Chair of the Board of Governors (BOG); got the Women in Otolaryngology committee to become a full Section of our Academy; and now I'm running for president-elect of the entire 12,000 member American Academy of Otolaryngology-Head and Neck Surgery.

Oh, yeah, and we also had our fourth child, our only daughter, nine years ago. My children are doing well; my oldest is going off to college this fall; my husband and I have a wonderful friendship and deep love and respect for each other; and our families are incredibly supportive of our career choices. If I win this election, the kids and hubby know that I'll have to carve some time away, but I'll do my best to make the best of the times we get to be together.

So, what's a nice girl like me doing in a profession like this? Finding my path, getting up when I've fallen down, teaching myself to be better every day, wearing the blinders when needed, taking them off and fighting when that's needed. In a word: succeeding.

1. Association of American Medical Colleges.2012 physician specialty data book: Center for Workforce Studies. https://members.aamc.org/eweb/upload/2012%-20Physician%20Specialty%20Data%20Book.pdf

Inspiring Quote:
"Life is not easy for any of us. But what of that? We must have persever-ance and above all confidence in ourselves. We must believe that we are gifted for something and that this thing must be attained."
— Madame Mariée Sklodowska-Curie

Cherie-Ann Nathan, MD, FACS.
Otolaryngology—Head and Neck Surgeon

My Journey as a Surgeon-Scientist-Leader

Keeping up with two active boys can be very frustrating and I once asked an anesthesiologist friend at dinner, "How do you fix this problem?" referring to the difficulties I had with my sons. My husband, a critical care pulmonologist, interjected, "Stop approaching this like a surgeon, honey! Sometimes you just have to let the *disease* evolve." If being a woman surgeon is not fun and challenging enough, being married to an internist takes it to another level.

It is a well known fact that surgeons are all about action and internists love to analyze and decipher a problem and manage chronic conditions. I am married to one of the most astute clinicians. So whenever a relative called with medical problems, I would immediately say to them, facetiously of course, "Hold on a minute, let me get the *real* doctor." Little did I know that my son, then a toddler, had been listening to all these conversations, until I got a call from his kindergarten teacher. "Dr. Nathan," she said sounding concerned, "I was a little disturbed in class today. We were working on a project in which the students were asked what their parents did for a living. When it was little Sean's turn to talk about his parents he said, "My mom is only a surgeon, but my dad is a real doctor!" I put the teacher at ease and assured her that my husband was not brainwashing my kids. It was I who was to blame with my flippant comments to relatives on the phone.

On the contrary, success of most women surgeons who have families is dependent on their spouses, and it certainly is so in my case. You have to marry a man who is supportive of your career, as traveling and networking are very important for flourishing in the academic world. Not only does a woman surgeon spend long hours in surgery, but if one has a research career with NIH (National Institutes of Health) funding, one tends to bring work home and wake up early in the morning to find that extra time. I did try to keep the evenings free after work for the family, and got into the habit of an early four a.m. start, to work in peace before the kids woke up.

My career path was set very early, as I recall saying as a third-grader that I wanted to be a "cancer surgeon." My role model was a family friend who was an outstanding Surgeon-Scientist and Chairman of the Department of Surgery at the renowned Tata Cancer Hospital in Mumbai. I was a fun-loving child with numerous extra-curricular interests, such as piano, track & field, ballet, drama, debate etc. I was socially gregarious (euphemism for loved to party) and my good grades were mere footnotes to my extracurricular prowess. I don't think many of my friends took me seriously when I said I wanted to be a cancer surgeon, not just because I did not fit the mold of the nerdy bookish student but I was also a girl! But the desire to be a cancer surgeon never wavered in my heart, and I am living proof that no goal is too lofty if one perseveres.

I also had to learn while very young the art of juggling so many activities and interests while working towards the career path I had chosen. Looking back, I realize now that I had subconsciously learnt the important lesson that one needed balance in one's outlook to succeed. Being a concert pianist, I had a head start in my quest to be a surgeon, thanks to my dexterous hands. My journey had many twists and turns and serendipity often played a big role, as I went through graduate research, residency and Head & Neck fellowship onto full-time academic staff, before becoming Chair of the Department at age forty-seven.

The satisfaction of being a woman surgeon, Chair and a mom is tremendous; but it is important to multi-task efficiently to be able to spend plenty of time with family on returning from work, so the kids never miss out. It really is more about quality than quantity when it comes to family time. I realized, when I was on maternity leave, that I spent more time with my kids during a work day than I did when I was on maternity leave, as I often took things for granted and ended up spending precious little quality time, although I had the entire day with them. By necessity one is forced to learn to prioritize when time is a premium.

One of the important ways to capitalize on every precious moment is to have help for chores by having a baby-sitter or caretaker take care of the routine jobs, shopping, cleaning etc. It is also important to have the kids do homework, music practice etc.—things they can do on their own before one gets home. Then time at home can be spent doing fun family activities. This worked well for me as my boys are wonderful musicians, one a violinist and the other a cellist. I loved accompanying them on the piano for all their competitions and playing duets and trios with them. We played for multiple fundraisers, cancer research, Sci-Port, etc., and this helped introduce my boys to the fun side of medicine.

There are some other pointers that I learned from experience that make a woman surgeon's job raising a family easier. A smaller town with shorter distances and less traffic definitely helps. In addition, slow OR turn-around times that we all complain about can also be a blessing!! I was able to run over to my kids' school between cases to attend an event, if only for a brief moment, show them my face and wave vigorously, so they knew I was in attendance. Little did the kids know that I was not there for the entire event, but all they remembered was that you were there! The rest of the time they are too busy having fun with their friends to even notice you! As the kids grow older and become more independent, the time constraints relax somewhat, and there are opportunities to take on additional leadership responsibilities, both in academics and the community at large.

I am often asked if it has been challenging being a woman surgeon. No, but it certainly has been very special. I realized earlier in my career as a resident that if one has a strong work ethic and integrity one can never lose. Let me explain that statement. I started my residency in a program where I was going to be the first woman resident surgeon to graduate. The first day on service the chief resident said, "What are you doing in this program? This happens to be an all-male Jewish program." Now not only was I a woman, but an Indian woman who had not grown up in the US. I worked hard and never complained, and it seemed like all was going well. A couple of months later, this same chief resident was walking back from lunch with our team and there was a puddle of water on the ground. Before I knew it, this strapping man had picked me up and held me above his head saying, "I cannot let my Indian princess walk through this puddle of water" and carried me across. I knew right then that there was something special to being a woman surgeon, and even the harshest critics can be won over if one carried one's share of responsibilities with dedication and fortitude.

A general surgeon once said to me in my preliminary general surgery year in Michigan, "Cherie-Ann, remember your success here has been noted because you have retained your womanly traits and don't find it necessary to compete with the men by being one of them." At that time, twenty-eight years ago, I thought that it was a strange comment, but later realized its truism, because many women surgeons felt it was necessary to hide their feminine traits to survive. I believe that is not the case, and as long as we are hard-working we are recognized for our efforts.

I feel fortunate to have been promoted to professor at the age of forty, and went onto become one of only four women surgeon chairs in Otolaryngology/Head and Neck Surgery in the country. In fact, I believe many "feminine" traits are an asset. The feminine intuition and the ability to read body language helps me during history-taking, and I believe I am a better diagnostician for it. The feminine ability to connect with people and read interpersonal dynamics has helped me avoid many minefields in my dealings with patients/families, residents and colleagues. The motherly ability to multi-task, think on one's feet and deal with chaos to get anywhere with her offspring comes in real handy in the OR! And, of course, the maternal instinct can be channeled into mentoring students, research associates, residents, fellows and junior faculty. In fact, I truly believe that the best thing that can happen to a department or a program is to have a Mother at the helm: There is nothing better than a "Tiger Mom" to bring out the best in a ward!

I personally believe that I owe all my fortune and achievements in medicine to the powers above. A strong faith is an important asset and as critical and invisible as the keel is to a sailboat. As a medical student in India, I volunteered at Mother Teresa's home for the disabled and destitute in Mumbai, known as "Asha Daan" (translation: "Spreading Hope"). Every year in January, Mother Teresa (now Saint Teresa) visited this home, and during one such visit I had the opportunity to pray beside her. She held my hand, asked me what I did, and then prayed that I become a good doctor. I feel fortunate to have been blessed by a saint, and believe my successful career is in large part due to that special power above, all the wonderful mentors I have had, my parents—who instilled in me the work ethic needed to be successful—as well as a supportive husband and kids who keep me grounded.

Inspiring Quote:
"Invention, it must be humbly admitted, does not consist in creating out of void, but out of chaos." — Mary Wollstonecraft

Marion Everett Couch, MD, PhD, MBA, FACS
Otolaryngology—Head and Neck Surgeon

How It Happened

Lately, I have been reflecting on how it happened that I became a surgeon. I was born in 1960 and grew up in a rural area just outside of Ithaca, New York. It occurred to me a few years ago that I did not know a single female physician while I was growing up. I didn't know any surgeons, and certainly no female surgeons. In fact, I never knew a single female professor, lawyer, business owner, police officer, fire fighter, or politician. There were no female role models in many fields, including medicine, for many of us who grew up in the 1960s and 1970s.

But I had a father who was a Cornell professor and a mother who was a nurse. They instilled in their children a love of education and a belief that you could do anything you wished. I can only conclude that this was enough to give me the confidence to pursue my dream of being a physician.

And now, when I reflect upon my time as a medical student, I can't recall a single female surgery faculty member, and certainly no female leaders such as a chief or chair or professor. So, again, I am left wondering why I thought it was possible to become a surgeon, since I had never, ever met a single female surgeon.

The answer resides in the powerful impact that individual people can have in your life. First, my husband has always been hugely supportive of my aspirations. We married when I was twenty-four years old and he has, for over thirty years, been a constant source of support and encouragement. In many ways, we grew up together, having met in the eighth grade. Second, I have had wonderful friends who have been steadfast and true to me. Because I am in a male-dominated field, many of my friends are male, but these friendships are enduring, and I have found my friends to be fiercely loyal. We have enjoyed watching our families and careers grow. Finally, I recall the importance of working with a single female chief resident during my surgery rotation. She was so competent and professional. Thanks to her, I finally believed that I could succeed in surgery—and I applied for a residency program in a surgical subspecialty.

I was fortunate to have worked with a few female Otolaryngology residents during my residency training. One took me aside and explained that as a new mother, she would not be the best surgeon, nor would she be the best mother, but that it was still worth the compromise needed to have children. I never forgot that and am now able to reflect upon her words. Now that I am a mother myself, I have to admit that I disagree with her. I am the best surgeon that I could possibly be and the best mother I could be. But I'm a different mother in that I rarely get to volunteer during the day. My twins know that I contribute in different ways. I take pride in quietly forging a new definition of a good mother.

Now, as I progress in my career, I still enjoy taking care of my patients. I still love operating. For me, there is no greater joy than training residents and medical students. But now I get to think about how to make healthcare systems better. Part of that is to look at how women are participating in shaping the future of surgery. I don't think we have made enough progress in terms of women becoming professors or chiefs and chairs. I hope more women pursue leadership roles, and I hope that they are able to get the support, such as mentoring and sponsorship, needed to succeed. I also hope that we never forget how important each individual can be. You can change someone's life.

There is probably no greater calling than to help others. And in surgery, you get to do that in a myriad of ways, each and every day.

Inspiring Quote:
"Watch your thoughts for they become words. Watch your words for they become actions. Watch your actions for they become habits. Watch your habits for they become your character. And watch your character for it becomes your destiny. What we think, we become." — Margaret Thatcher

SECTION 10: ONE WOMAN'S QUEST TO START A TRANSPLANT CENTER

Linda Wong, MD, FACS
Transplant Surgeon

Acute Transplant Center Rejection: Starting Over

Being a doctor used to be fun. It was a lot of work but gratifying nevertheless. We could save lives, prolong life and ease suffering. Patients trusted doctors. Nurses trusted doctors and worked together to care for patients. Third-party payers trusted doctors and paid them a reasonable proportion of what was requested. Medicare paid for those patients who worked hard and saved for the "golden years." The government stepped in and helped those who could not afford care. Being a transplant physician was the ultimate in gratification, because we could do life-altering surgery to replace damaged organs and give people a second chance at life.

In the last few decades, medicine has transformed into a business—a highly-regulated entity, filled with rules, regulations, protocols and bureaucracy. Never has this reality been so apparent to us until a small medical center in Hawaii, Hawaii Medical Center (HMC), went bankrupt, and the only transplant center in the state needed to close. Fortunately another medical center (Queens Medical Center) came in and rescued the transplant program.

What follows is my diary, my account of what happened in this transition and what it took to save the transplant program in Hawaii. I could go on in this editorial fashion and sound like I am complaining, but the play-by-play version of this will stick with you longer. Keep in mind, I did not embellish. All of this is true.

August 9, 1969: Hawaii Medical Center (HMC)

Honolulu. A surgeon from Hawaii went to a meeting on the mainland and watched how other surgeons were performing kidney transplants from living donors. Surgeon gets permission from hospital administrators to do this. Dr. David Hume, a famous transplant surgeon, comes to assist with the first living kidney transplant. (Apparently, Dr. Hume liked to surf, so it was easy to get him here.) First transplant was a success. Newspapers reported the story. A transplant program is built.

January-May 1993

That surgeon who did the first kidney transplant twenty-four years ago is still here at this program. He is also my dad. (This, in itself, is a recipe for potential disaster and the subject of an entire book, which I have yet to write).

Although I grew up in Hawaii, I have been away on the mainland in various schools and training programs for fourteen-and-a-half years; but I have now returned to Hawaii and joined this transplant program.

I am entering practice with my dad—who thankfully paid a lot of my tuition, but also thought that women physicians should probably be pediatricians instead of surgeons. If they had to be surgeons, then perhaps they should be ophthalmologists because they could "have a normal life and family." I tried to fulfill his dream, but somewhere along the line I told him that I could not dedicate my life to the eyeball, and that all I ever saw in those operating microscopes were my own eyelashes reflecting back on me. He was secretly hoping that my brothers would go into medicine and surgery instead, because boys should do this; but, well, they had other things to do.

So entering practice with Dad after almost fifteen years of being away from home, entering the "wrong career" and having to start a liver program 2,500 miles away from the nearest one, when I had just finished fellowship (I was tasked with building a liver transplant program), was met with much skepticism by all. In spite of the odds, we successfully perform the first liver transplant in May 1993. Over the years we have been able to successfully maintain a small liver transplant program in the middle of the Pacific and serve the needs of the people of Hawaii.

Liver transplantation is a life-saving procedure done for patients with end-stage chronic liver disease or acute liver failure for various reasons. Most patients who are waiting have chronic liver disease, most commonly due to hepatitis B and C viruses. Potential candidates are placed on a list at a local transplant center but are also registered on the national candidates list. Those patients with acute or fulminant liver failure, who have an estimated seven days to live, are placed on the list as a Status 1 and have the highest priority. All other patients are given a score—the Model for End-Stage Liver Disease (MELD) score—and these scores range from 7-40 based upon several blood tests that measure liver function and the severity of illness. The highest MELD score patients are transplanted first.

Hawaii Medical Center: Friday, 4 p.m., December 16, 2011

I am sitting in the office on the campus of our transplant center at HMC, a center that in the last four years has declared bankruptcy twice and has continued to struggle along. We are wondering if the medical center will be sold, and there are innumerable trips with administrators and lawyers to bankruptcy court. We have had years of oscillating between "the new rock-bottom" and "a glimmer of hope." Potential buyers have come: some that have "turned around distressed hospitals;" some with a religious focus— Catholic healthcare groups, Adventist healthcare groups; some with a shady business approach ("we'll make all the doctors rich"). All of them eventually walk away—shaking their heads and moving on to another opportunity, as they leave us here like poor kids in an orphanage who didn't get picked by the latest potential parents.

Then a phone call comes in:

"HMC is closing. No more surgeries as of 5 pm today and you need to close the transplant program."

Forty-two years of transplants with more than 1,300 transplant patients, and we are done with a single phone call. We needed to close our kidney, pancreas, heart and liver transplant programs. Our small medical center had no potential buyers, due to neglected buildings, many semi-retired staff and financial difficulties, and finally had to close its doors.

Transplant centers are required to notify people when they close their program. The instructions for this were in very fine print somewhere, but no one really has read these in any great detail. It would be like a policy on hurricane insurance. You would just keep the policy in the drawer and then try to figure out where it is and what it said when the hurricane comes.

Friday, 6 p.m., December 16, 2011

So I dig out the United Network for Organ Sharing (UNOS) transplant policies and actually read the fine print: "Written notice should be provided at least 30 days prior to the anticipated date of withdrawal or termination by a method that can be tracked and that provides proof of receipt. . . ." (UNOS Appendix K4)

Well, it's too late for this.

"Written notice must be provided no later than 7 days following withdrawal or termination. . . ."

So here we are. We have to now notify 424 patients that they will be inactivated on the transplant list. We're also supposed to notify all "Transplant Program's potential candidates and living donors currently receiving care." Great. This is probably at least another 500 patients. We have seven days to do this, two of which are weekend days and the other five days are the last five mailing days before Christmas. We get the nurse coordinators to sacrifice the last five shopping days before Christmas in order to get these letters out. Phones are ringing off the hook as panicked patients wonder who will care for them, and desperate renal patients anguish at the prospect of being on dialysis until eternity.

Friday, 7 p.m., December 16, 2011

I read more policies as the night goes on: "For liver candidates, all Status 1 candidates must be transferred within 7 days of termination followed by all active candidates in descending MELD score order with all candidates whose MELD score exceeds 25 to be transferred within 30 days." (UNOS Appendix K5)

How do I break it to patients' families? Their loved ones are desperately waiting—some in the hospital, hoping for a liver, the ultimate Christmas gift. It was worse than finding out that there was no Santa, for there is no gift here and no possibility of receiving a gift, even if I had it in my hand. Nothing in my medical training had prepared me for having to tell a patient, "I'm sorry, I can't give you a transplant because my hospital just closed. I will need to fly you to another center on the mainland 2,500 miles away. I can't guarantee you will survive this flight, but if you don't go you will definitely die. I'm not sure if your medical insurance will cover transplant on the mainland yet. It will cost $50,000-$60,000 to take this flight and, by the way, insurance may not cover this part either."

Now how different is this from a robbery in a bad neighborhood? ("Gimme all your money or I'll shoot.") The difference is that death might be long and painful, and I was asking not just for the money in their wallets but, potentially, in all of their savings accounts too.

One patient had waited for several months in the hospital but never seemed to get the right donor—always wrong blood type, wrong size liver, or something else. He was in the intensive care unit (ICU) by this point and, as the hospital began to transfer patients and wind down services, there was the worst of all ironies. There were only two ICU patients left: my desperately ill patient and, next to him, a potential donor of the same blood type. At the very moment that we had a reasonable donor—and sitting a bed away—we were banned from doing any operations and we were no longer a transplant center. Shakespeare couldn't write a tragedy like this one.

Queens Medical Center (QMC)—Opening a New Transplant Center: Saturday, December 17, 2011

In another galaxy, two miles away, a new transplant center was trying to come to life.

In order to open a new transplant program, UNOS had a lengthy application to make sure that all of the transplant physicians, nurses and operating room staff were properly trained and competent, especially in a new hospital that had never seen these transplant patients previously.

They needed to have properly trained pharmacists, dietitians, social workers, financial coordinators and medical consultants. A transplant program manager had to be hired. Equipment needed to be purchased, and this included surgical instruments and monitoring devices. The applications had to show that everyone was properly credentialed, educated and committed to this new program.

Week 1: UNOS Application for a New Program

"Please attach current CV, letter from credentialing committee, commitment letter, formal training, formal training log, transplant experience, transplant experience log, letters of recommendation."

Sure, that seems simple enough to UNOS—just do it for each of the surgeons, each of the physicians and the ancillary services for each of the programs. Make five copies with original signatures from all of the physicians that are spread around in many offices, half of whom are gone during the holidays, and then Fed-Ex everything two days before Christmas. The frantic phoning began:

"I know it is two days before Christmas and you are currently shopping, but do you think you can update your CV before tomorrow?"

"Happy Holidays! I need a letter of recommendation."

"Where are you? I need your signature. *Now!*"

"I know you have been through this data file fourteen times already, but I need to know all of the dates and hospital numbers of all the kidney transplants I've done since, um, say 1997."

"There are no medical record numbers on this file. Does this mean I have to go through every single chart in our office computer to get them?"

"What time does Fed-Ex close?"

Week 2: The Paparazzi

No drama would be complete without the media. We make the headlines:

Hawaii Medical Center Closes Emergency Rooms

Transplant Patients Desperate For a New Center

HMC's Closure Leaves Hundreds of Transplant Hopefuls in Limbo

Patients Counting on Transplant Clinic to Stay Open

Queens Medical Center Applies for Organ Transplant Program

Phones are ringing: "The Star Advertiser wants a statement." "Line 3 is some guy that wants you to be on Hawaii Public Radio."

They want a statement. They want a comment. They want answers. They want you to go to the legislature, the governor, the Feds, Obama, and, if necessary, Oprah. Why won't anyone do anything? And what are you doing about bone marrow transplant? There are blogs of people blaming others for why this happened. Everyone has a theory and some advice. People were trying to help—a lobbyist, a lawyer, a doctor, a patient who wanted to hold signs to help protest—but all of these people could not possibly help me with what really needed to be done to move on.

It was at this point that I changed the ringtone on my phone to a popular line in a Lady Gaga song: "Stop calling. Stop calling. I don't want to think anymore!"

Week 2-4: UNOS Application for a New Program

The application gets sent in, but not before Christmas. It is just not humanly possible to fill out the whole UNOS application in less than two weeks.

Not since sixth grade English has my paper been turned back for corrections so many times. The UNOS analyst had daily rebuttals:

"We need an original signature on this."

"We need a letter of the overall transplant director assessing the liver director, the liver surgeon assessing the liver physician, the liver physician assessing the liver surgeon."

"If you're going to be a single physician transplant program, you need to have a policy on this and a means of letting all the patients know this. You have one physician listed at the top and two at the bottom."

"The requirement is that the physician has participated in 45 kidney transplant patients but there are only 44 listed."

"We want all of her transplant cases not just the last 3 years."

And the final blow was, *"Her commitment letter didn't sound committed enough."*

Week 4: We Move From Tragedy to Irony

So a month of drama goes by and this is what we have accomplished: We moved the staff. We marvel at how little time it took to submit the UNOS application, oblivious to the number of times UNOS has sent it back for revisions. Administrators at the new hospital (QMC) proudly have hired our entire transplant staff and are marching them through endless orientations, physical exams, potential office space, computer training and the ID badge headquarters. The operating room is hunting down equipment, buying things, picking eager volunteers to join the ranks of the budding "transplant team." A mock transplant is planned in preparation for the real operation. The lab is ordering new tests, making changes, and making protocols. There are meetings and meetings and still more meetings to make protocols, policies, forms, computer templates, training sessions. It's new. It's bold. It's going to put this hospital in the news and be the talk of the town.

News for everyone: There are more than a thousand transplant patients out there waiting to be cared for. They call HMC transplant and the phones have been disconnected. They call QMC transplant but no one is there yet and they don't have an office much less a phone. There are no functioning transplant nurses, no transplant staff. So with no one to turn to, they call me . . . because "we saw her on TV." *She's* still there.

Phones ring again:

"I got this letter saying that there's no transplant center, so what do I do now?"

"I was told to get my chart. Where do I do this?"

"Do we still have clinic? I have an appointment tomorrow, where do I go?"

"I had my transplant five months ago and I want to know if I can have a cat."

"When do you open again?"

"I ran out of medicine and no one answers the phone anymore."

"I know I haven't seen you in three years, but I'm going to the dentist and I want to know if I need antibiotics."

"No one is answering the phone at medical records, so now what do I do?"

"My insurance doesn't cover this medication, what do I do?"

No one can help me. My nurses, social worker and financial coordinators no longer work for HMC, and they are still in computer training and hunting for ID badges at QMC. I am left with all of these patients, office visits, clinic and phone calls.

"Stop Calling. Stop Calling. I Don't Want to Think Anymore!"

Week 5: The UNOS Phone Call

Several weeks after turning in our homework to UNOS, we had a very serious call involving UNOS, CMS and assorted people with long important titles. UNOS had received our applications and were giving us an expected starting date for our program. This phone call felt more like the final meeting between the pastor and a prospective couple to be married—with the couple being the transplant team and the new hospital.

UNOS wanted QMC to understand that they were taking this transplant team with all of its prior patients, and that they would be held responsible for all the past patients and their follow-up data and whatever pending audits and infractions that had occurred at HMC since the beginning of time. So there we sat, transplant team marrying QMC. QMC would take us and our one-thousand-plus orphaned patients and their families, in-laws, idiosyncrasies, and baggage—to have and to hold, for better or for worse, in sickness and in health until death do us part (provided that death is recorded in the UNOS computer). In turn, the transplant team would accept whatever the medical center requested—all of the meetings, committees, planning and future audits. I almost said "I do" at the end of the phone call.

Week 6: Queens Medical Center. So You Want to Be a Transplant Center?

At the end of the sixth week, UNOS approved the liver transplant program. (The revisions on my commitment letter must have brought tears to their eyes.) We are happy and the community would think that we are ready to flash the neon "OPEN" sign on our transplant center. UNOS tells us that any time we're ready, they can just "flip the switch" and all the waiting liver candidates will come over electronically to the new center. Again, that sounds simple from the UNOS standpoint.

We were a new center but were not a "Medicare-approved" center, and without Medicare approval we could not participate in Medicaid. So the system is set up to fail. We cannot obtain Medicare certification until we submit a year's worth of transplant data with good outcomes. So either we don't do transplants on Medicare patients or we do them, don't get paid and the program cannot survive financially. If we don't transplant Medicare patients, these patients will have to travel 2,500 miles to the next center or they just die. It doesn't matter that our entire team has worked together on Medicare and Medicaid patients for the last twenty years; this was technically a "new" transplant center. Somehow this all seemed wrong.

It's a no-win situation. I feel like we have been thrown out of the tree house of the exclusive boys club and the rules to get back into the club are impossible.

However, there may be a loophole as we find out that we may be able to ask for "Mitigating Circumstances" and get earlier Medicare approval. Another application is in the works. I write yet another letter, but by this time I have earned a PhD in the literary composition of the ultimate sob story. There is not enough tissue to go around and even the financial staff is crying at this letter. Surely there must be a limit on how many times I can say "save the people of Hawaii," "prevent racial disparities in transplant," "geographic disparities in an underserved area," and "financial burden."

Week 9: Queens Medical Center: Progress, I Think

We meet every week, we have an agenda and we have an outside "Transplant Consultant" that they've hired to give us advice. A quality assurance meeting is established to discuss outcome measures, complications, performance improvement measures. There are plans to check statistics on organ survival, patient survival, hospital length of stay, complications, reoperations and infections. They want to collect data and more data, make graphs, make charts and compare everything to be sure that we are up to UNOS standards.

I remind them, of course, that we have done no actual cases, so it's tough to really have any outcome measures. We have a liver transplant program now, but only a handful of patients are listed because they cannot get past the Medicare conundrum. We have no actual kidney transplant program because UNOS says we need "a board certified nephrologist who has been involved in forty-five kidney transplants in the last five years." We have a board certified nephrologist who has forty-three cases and another nephrologist who forgot to turn in the last part of his board certification, who has fifty-four cases.

Week 10: Queens Medical Center: False Alarms

I guess we are ready: We have potential liver transplant patients and calmly await potential donors. We are as ready as we can be, considering we have no Medicare approval and we have a list of patients—90 percent of whom are blood type O. Everyone is on edge, "amped up," newly trained and with an enthusiasm that is palpable.

On the first weekend, we get two potential donors—but both of them fall through. The next weekend, we have another potential donor. This one is in QMC. The donor has some medical issues and my potential recipient has to fly from a neighboring island to get here. This will be a logistic adventure.

Do I call the operating room and alert everyone now? At two a.m.? Should I send them all into a frenzy? What if it doesn't really go? Is it better to get them all prepared early for potentially nothing or tell them a little later and have them worried about whether they can get everything done in time? At two-fifteen a.m., I decide to test the operator.

"Please find me the transplant nurse on call."

Operator shuffles a lot of papers and takes my number. She has never heard of a transplant coordinator. This has never been one of the people she has had to find. I stare at the ceiling wondering if she will find the coordinator and how I got myself into this entire predicament. In the meantime, the transplant nurse apparently reads my mind and calls me.

I decide to wait until seven a.m. because I cannot deal with the panic that I will create at two a.m. So, I call the operating room to schedule the liver transplant. There is an apneic moment on the phone, and when the charge nurse regains consciousness, I repeat, "I'd like to schedule a liver transplant, perhaps around five p.m., but this is a tentative time."

The charge nurse and her staff have been fully trained, but all memory of that has been lost in this brief phone call.

She blurts out, "Is this the same patient and room that has the procurement?"

Sigh. "No," I explain calmly. "There is a donor and one surgeon will be taking out the organs. There is a separate room with a different patient, the recipient, where I will be trying to put in a liver."

Another pause, then the charge nurse responds in pressured speech, "I don't know if I can do this, I don't know if I have the staff or the rooms. I need help. Well, maybe I'll get one of the nurses who is on the transplant team, because I just don't know . . ."

Sigh. Unfortunately that liver was not suitable, so I cancel the case. I send the patient back to his house from the airport. I reason that these false alarms are a good way to test the system.

March 6-8, 2012: Queens Medical Center: Longest Days Ever

Eighty-two days have elapsed since our program closed. It is a dark and stormy day. There is thunder, lightning, flooding and it rained seventeen inches in twenty-four hours in parts of Hawaii. There was even hail in a few spots and hail has never been seen in Hawaii before. Roads are closed, flights from Neighbor Islands have been cancelled and the city is paralyzed. This is the day we have two organ donors and have to open this fledgling transplant program.

The first liver is suitable but a mainland team has decided to take the lungs. They have to fly six hours and time the operation so that they are removing the organs as close to the return flight time as possible. They get an ambulance and a police escort back to the airport to accomplish this. As if there wasn't enough drama.

I put on my good-luck shoes, have two diet cokes and try to forget the last eighty-two days. I concentrate only on the operation and try not to look around the room. My old operating room was a large rectangle and this room was very square. Things were in different places, the lights were different and half the staff had expressions of fear, apprehension and anxiety. I tell myself that I've done this operation 180 times before, and as long as I concentrate and zone out the rest of the noise, I will be OK. I turn the disco music on louder so I don't have to deal with anything but the operation.

The transplant goes fine and we are done in four hours. We move the patient to the ICU where most nurses are on edge. The nurse caring for the patient was hired from HMC, had seen many transplant patients and was unaffected by the hysteria. Other nurses looked through the glass as if we just delivered a baby panda in the zoo.

I stay with the nurses to ease their anxiety although the patient was perfectly fine. I had another diet coke and even fixed the ICU printer, before I decided to venture out of the hospital at three-thirty a.m. for a short nap.

As if this first transplant, the lung procurement, and the rainstorms were not enough, we actually have to do a second liver transplant the following day. The team is feeling better about the situation, but the electricity goes out for a split second during the operation—thanks to the thunder storms. Emergency generators kick in.

Both patients had flown in from Neighbor Islands and one of the surgeons had to fly to another island to get the second liver. We send another surgeon downstairs to the emergency department to get the liver from the procuring surgeon, who is driving from the airport. He goes downstairs, gets lost in this large hospital, goes out the wrong door and gets locked out. A nurse gets the liver and we cannot find this other surgeon for fifteen minutes, as he is so horribly lost in various hallways, loading docks and dead ends in this large hospital. We eventually find him and finish off the operation.

I am sitting in the ICU again, with less than two hours of sleep in the previous forty-eight hours. I have been through eighty-two days of applications, policies, meetings, statistics, endless phone calls, conference phone calls, the media, stealing instruments, moving charts, trying so hard to care for all the patients and make them last until we re-open.

I have opened two liver transplant programs in my career and I am relieved to be able to continue. I know we have a long way to go before we can get the kidney program open, but at least we are on the way. I am completely exhausted from this entire experience, but glad to be here. I turn on my BlackBerry where 120 new messages are waiting. The most recent is from the hospital Public Relations department:

"Congratulations on the first liver transplant. We would like to have a press conference."

I almost fell out of my chair.

Inspiring Quote:
"Well-behaved women seldom make history." — Laurel Thatcher Ulrich

SECTION 11—INTERVIEWS: CONDUCTED BY
DR. PREETI R. JOHN

Debrah Wirtzfeld, MD, MSc, FRCSC, FACS
Surgical Oncologist

In the following interview, Dr. Wirtzfeld shares some insights into her role as surgeon and mother.

When did you first realize you wanted to train as a surgeon?

I originally wanted to be a Gastroenterologist. In fact, I did my surgery rotation after my Internal Medicine application interviews had been completed. I was asked by surgery to consider applying late, as they thought "I had what it takes to be a surgeon." The wording was not as politically correct, but I took it as a compliment. This was in line with what I had been feeling and thinking. I remember the exact day I knew that I wanted to be a surgeon. We had taken somebody with Crohn's disease to the operating room for a small bowel resection. I remember the room, the people in the room, and the operation, vividly. I ended up applying to Surgery at the University of Calgary, and was awarded my first choice. It remains my first choice to this day.

What are your thoughts on mentorship?

I have only truly understood what it means to have mentors more recently in my career. I certainly have had people ask me my thoughts about what I wanted to do and where I wanted to go, but very few took a vested interest in providing advice and/or guidance.

I trained nearly fifteen years ago; it seems like an era away. There were still not many female residents, and there were even fewer female staff. On one occasion when I was still a junior resident, I was seeking support from the only other female resident. She replied, "I cannot speak with you right now about your wanting to quit, because I am on my way to speak with the program director about my desire to quit!" We are now both surgeons practicing in an academic environment.

I have found mentors must useful in helping me obtain (or try to obtain!) balance between my personal and academic lives. When I finished my Fellowship in Surgical Oncology at Roswell Park and had been recruited to work there, the Chair of Surgery said to me, "You need to formulate both professional and personal goals. You must work hard, especially as a woman, to ensure that your professional goals do not take over your personal goals." I thought this was very forward thinking for a man in his fifties. I have always been very goal oriented, but I appreciated the emphasis on personal goals.

Interestingly, until recently, most of my mentors have been male surgeons in their early to mid fifties. They have inspired me and have motivated me to move forward.

I have received undying support from several of my mentors. When Dr. William Pollet, former Chair of Surgery at Memorial University of Newfoundland, found out I was pregnant, he commented, "Just let me know what I need to do to make it work."

It is only within the last five years that I have recognized female mentors. This has been mostly through my involvement with the Association of Women Surgeons and my recruitment to the University of Manitoba, where the Assistant Dean of Academic Affairs, Heather Dean, has taken an interest in my advancement. Dr. Wally Temple, Chair of Surgical Oncology at the University of Calgary, is also a strong supporter of women in surgery.

I think there is an appropriate environment for mentorship in this field. However, we need to seek out the people whom we want to mentor and communicate this to them. Although we tend to think of mentor-mentee relationships as "just happening," they do not. I advise my residents and medical students to seek out those people whom they wish to emulate. They need to approach these people and advise them that they want to have these people as mentors.

What do you think is remarkable about surgical training in Canada?

Until recently, I was a member of the Executive Council of the Royal College of Physicians and Surgeons of Canada (RCPSC). In Canada, we have a Royal College which demands excellence at a National level. I think the variability within Canada is less than that seen in the US, having worked in both countries. We have seventeen programs that train surgeons to a nationally accepted standard. I have had people I have worked with in the States comment that when you work with someone trained in the Canadian system you get a consistent, good product. At the RCPSC, we are working with other countries to bring the best of the Canadian system to them.

What hobbies do you have outside the hospital and do you feel you have enough time to pursue these?

I work out for approximately thirty-sixty minutes, five-six times per week. This includes aerobics, strength training and some yoga. I also enjoy movies, getting together with friends and family, dining out and attending the theatre/galleries.

I have two children, Eric, who is ten, and Ryan is six years old. I have had them on my own, and I remain the single strongest adult involved in their lives. They have seen me at my best and my worst. They will grow up knowing what a strong woman is and with the knowledge that they must work hard to get what they want. There is no room for whining or complaining in our house, without recognizing that the solution is part of the process.

I think, like most people, that on average I have time for everything I want to do. It requires balance, planning and a firm commitment to what is important. The plans I make with my family are as important as work obligations. In medicine we tend to let our families slide as a consequence of "requests" from our profession. This does not foster physical or psychological health. It can be best summed up by the principles of the Covey time management system, which has as its two axes importance and urgency. Most physicians/surgeons deal with urgent, highly important issues. However, this is stressful. One's personal obligations cannot be met this way—they need to be met as important issues in a less urgent manner. A well-planned-out life leads to less urgency, less stress. Emphasis on being a good surgeon has made me better in my personal life, just as emphasis on health and well-being in my personal life has made me a better surgeon.

I have many career and personal goals. I write them down and re-evaluate them annually. Personally, I wish for my children to be happy. I believe the best way to do this is for them to see their mother as healthy and to be given the opportunity to experience the most of life. Although I recognize that I have no ultimate control over this, I attempt to listen to them, react to what they are saying and give them as much responsibility as possible for their own decisions.

For myself, I have personal goals related to travel, health and maintenance of my friendships. I try to see all my friends, spread out over North America, at least once every two years.

Have you ever experienced difficulties in your personal relationships related to your professional training?

My answer is mostly speculation. I think that many of my personal relationships have ended or have been seriously altered because I wanted to become or have become a surgeon. I was once engaged to someone who thought I was going to be an internist. When I applied to and was accepted to the surgery training program, I feel that this was not acceptable to him. He could not figure out how we were going to find time for family. I think that there was an expectation that I would be the primary caregiver for someone with a very busy surgical practice. Ironically, I am very involved with my children.

I am not willing to compromise who I am or what I do. I am good at what I do. I have had other relationships over the past ten-fifteen years, but there was never the feeling that I could become a better person through the relationship or that I was accepted for who I am without there being some form of request for change.

Have you had to juggle your job requirements with raising children? What are some of the difficulties you have had to face and how do you deal with them?

Yes, definitely, it's a constant juggle. One of my favorite quotes is "Nothing worth doing is simple." When I was pregnant with my second son, I lost my childcare. I was living on the East Coast of Canada at the time, with my parents on the West Coast. I had to fly my son out to Calgary to live with my parents until I found someone else. My parents have come out at various times to live with me for several months at a time as required. I have had to face the fact that some weekends I do not have childcare, and thus my children round with me. I have a lot of help and accept my nannies as being fabulous and integral players in my children's lives. I speak with them regularly and get their input on what they think about my children— about my children's wants and desires. I do not try to control what goes on at home. I'm with my children a lot and they recognize that I appreciate them.

I believe that if we work really hard we can coordinate our lifestyles. There are those times where you spend a lot of time in the hospital, but I structure my life such that this is limited. Members of the department are aware that I will spend no more than two nights, on average, away from my children, in any given week. This includes any activities that extend beyond six p.m. I accept the premise that a good meeting can be run in an hour, and I also accept that if a committee cannot move forward within a year, it needs to reexamine its mandate. I limit all the meetings I chair to one hour and I reevaluate all committees that I am on annually. If there is not progress with regard to the latter, I speak with the Chair and ascertain where the committee is going and whether my input is still necessary. There is a lot of wasted time that needs to be better managed. Perhaps this needs to start with training our residents on the important principles of time management.

You have to be who you have to be. I have spoken with some people who had tried to take a career path that is not ultimately a good fit, such that they can have a good work-life balance. You have to be true to yourself and look for opportunities. You have to look for and accept help wherever you can find it.

My oldest son is now ten. I live for the day when he is twelve, such that if childcare falls through once in a while he will be old enough to baby-sit. He is an amazing individual, as both my children are.

Have you experienced unfairness during your training/career?

Certainly, I think we have all experienced unfairness from time to time. At one hospital I worked at for a short time, I felt that the OR nurses were being unfairly harsh on me. I subsequently moved to a different hospital. One of the staff surgeons at the initial hospital said to me that he had never seen the nurses be so hard on somebody. He wanted to let me know that I had handled it well and that it was not all in my head. It is sometimes difficult and not always related to gender. Ultimately, if you are confident and good at what you do, it will get you through.

I remember one time, when I was a senior resident, all the members of the team from the medical student to the attending were male, except for me. They would go into the locker room and discuss the patients, such that I was out of the loop. I gave the attending two options, either come out of the change room to discuss the patients with me or I will come into the change room with you. He chose the former. I sometimes think female nurses in the OR and on the ward are harder on female residents. I am not sure what this represents, but apparently we are not yet at a point where we can be completely supportive of each other.

When I was a junior resident, I heard one of the staff orthopedic surgeons say to another orthopedic surgeon during rounds, "It will be a cold day in hell before we let women into this program." A cold day in hell happened the next year. Otherwise, I have not heard any other comments. I have had many female colleagues, especially from American programs, confide in me with regard to this issue.

What kind of advice would you give a medical student/resident about balancing work and personal life?

I would say go for it, define your resources and define who you are. You need to know what it is you want in life. You need to have the professional and personal goals. You need to look for people who have done those things you want to do and speak to them. Define them as mentors. Make them aware that they are a mentor for you.

Women who are currently surgical trainees will do what they want— more so than what we did! There is no right time to have children as it is an individual decision. If I had a student ask me for advice about pursuing a career in surgery, male or female, I would advise them that if they felt a passion for the field, they should think of pursuing it as a career. Seeing the strength of some of my patients, especially those who are dying young from a malignant disease, has been a great source of inspiration to me.

Inspiring Quote:

"You gain strength, courage and confidence by every experience in which you really stop to look fear in the face. You are able to say to yourself, 'I have lived through this horror. I can take the next thing that comes along.' You must do the thing you think you cannot do." — Eleanor Roosevelt

Taylor S. Riall, MD, PhD, FACS
Hepatobiliary and Pancreatic Surgeon

In the following interview, Dr. Riall shares some of her thoughts on surgical training, mentorship and life.

When did you first realize you wanted to train as a surgeon?

I wasn't sure what I wanted to do after my first two years of medical school. My first rotation was ob-gyn. I wasn't given much direction and it was, overall, a bad experience. I was concerned that I had chosen incorrectly—perhaps medicine wasn't right for me. However, this was followed by pediatrics. The residents and faculty were so nice and I was given clear direction and I loved it. I was convinced I was going to be a pediatrician.

Then I did surgery. I remember the moment I knew I was going to be a surgeon. We were in the OR (room 1 in the old Blalock 7 ORs at Johns Hopkins Hospital) operating on a patient with a gunshot wound to the leg. The surgeon fixed the superficial femoral artery injury. Then he handed me the needle driver and taught me to close the incision. I was hooked. I never looked back.

What are the advantages of surgical training in the U.S.?

Excellent resources, unparalleled talent, opportunity.

What do you perceive is lacking in surgical training in the U.S.?

Continuity of care and personal responsibility. With work hour restrictions, residents don't get the same continuity. For example, if they operate on a patient on Friday, a different resident may round on Saturday and Sunday. And likely a different one sees the patient preoperatively and postoperatively. Even more concerning, if that patient required reoperation—a significant learning opportunity—a different resident would perform the operation. Much is lost in transitions, and residents have lost "ownership" of patients and have transitioned into shift-like thinking, which is not the ideal way (in my opinion) to take care of surgical patients.

What do you think of the work-hour restrictions for surgical trainees?

As above, they severely limit quality and continuity of care and resident learning, by actually taking care of patients and learning the pattern recognition one cannot obtain from a book. In addition, with the new restrictions, I think surgery is attracting people who don't have "surgical personalities" and, as a result, we are seeing more attrition.

How do you balance your personal and work life?

You have to make time for yourself and the people who are important to you. If I waited until I wasn't tired to do things, I would never do anything. You need to set priorities and do the things that are really important to you. I love to run—I started in the lab during residency. I have run four marathons and qualified for Boston—now twice! I love to swim and bike and just did my first triathlon in May. We travel to beautiful places and enjoy the outdoors on these trips.

My time is limited and I feel that I made decisions along the way to make my life as I want it to be. I am extremely busy, and Charlie and I made a conscious decision not to have children. This is not necessary and not the right decision for everyone, but was the right one for me.

What are your goals in life?

I want to be happy. And I have achieved that. I turned forty today and reflected on my life. I am successful in my job—both in the OR and in my research. I love my job.

I have an incredible husband, Charlie. (I always say I won the husband lottery!) He makes my time away from work incredible. I live comfortably and have paid off my medical school loans. I am in good shape.

I have career goals as well and I constantly re-evaluate them with my mentors. These goals change if they interfere with my primary goal of being happy. I feel that I live my life such that when the time comes, hopefully a long time from now, I will not feel cheated. I do all the things I want to do.

Do you ever wish you had more time to enjoy life outside the hospital setting?

Always. But I wouldn't change my life for anything—there is nothing I would give up.

Have you ever experienced difficulties in your personal relationships related to your profession/training?

It was difficult as a resident. I felt that many men were intimidated or turned off by what I did. I had nearly resigned myself to being alone when I met Charlie. While I was in the lab I took ballroom dancing lessons. I am very self-conscious and don't like to do things I am not good at—so this was a stretch for me. I met Charlie dancing—he is a great dancer—so I am certainly glad I left my comfort zone.

Do you think it takes a special kind of person to be the spouse of a surgeon?

It certainly does. When people ask what Charlie does, I tell them he is an engineer, but I am his fulltime job.

What does mentorship mean to you?

Mentorship comes in all forms. I do not seek "mentorship" and I think young surgeons often try to do this. I feel that mentors present themselves based on your efforts and interests. It is a relationship that cannot be forced.

I have been fortunate to have unbelievable mentors, whom I greatly admire for the following reasons:

Charles J. Yeo, for his immaculate attention to detail in patient care and his unsurpassed operative skill. I model my patient care after him. An excellent mentor to me throughout my career.

Keith D. Lillemoe, for his dedication to mentoring young surgeons. He has mentored me since medical school and continues to do so from a distance, since we both left Hopkins. He never ceases supporting the careers of people he trusts. He always lets me know he is proud of my accomplishments and supports me nationally. He gives me advice whenever I need. And he does this for so many people like myself. In addition, he is an excellent surgeon and clinician.

Courtney Townsend, Jr, a man of his word. An excellent clinician and chairman. He has strongly supported my academic career as a junior faculty member and allowed me get where I am today. I am grateful every day for our relationship.

What advice would you have to young women who choose to pursue a profession and start a family at the same time?

It can be done. But you can't do everything. You need to carefully evaluate what you want. Define your priorities. You will always have to give and take, but that will be okay if you are doing the things you truly want.

Surgery offers many paths and you need to decide what your priorities are—and these may change along the way. You also need to realize that you cannot do everything and every decision comes with a tradeoff. Having kids may mean less time dedicated to research and clinical care. As such, academic promotion may be slower. Conversely, not having kids may allow you to advance faster, but then you miss out on all the special things that come with having children. I may become full professor quickly but who will take care of me when I get old?

I always tell students that I love my job and wouldn't trade it for anything. Having said that, if there is something else they'd be happy doing, they should do that. You have to love it more than anything else.

Kristy Weber, MD
Orthopedic Oncologist

Born in St. Louis, Missouri, Dr. Weber lived there through high school. After initially planning a career in veterinary medicine at the University of Missouri-Columbia, she changed her mind and pursued a medical career. In this interview, she shares some of her thoughts about life and training in the field of Orthopedic Surgery.

Why did you choose Orthopedic Surgery?

Although I was attracted to both Oncology and Pediatrics, Surgery fit my personality best. I like the ability to "fix" problems and have an immediate impact on patients. I didn't decide to go to medical school until my last year in college. Once I started medical school at Johns Hopkins, I prioritized surgery as my initial interest.

I liked how happy the orthopedic surgeons and residents were, and I initially wanted to specialize in sports medicine. I had the idea that there was only one orthopedic sports doctor that took care of the U.S. Olympic team, and I decided I wanted to be that doctor. Once I started my ortho-pedic residency at University of Iowa, I was drawn to the patients with cancer, and particularly admired the orthopedic oncologist there. I felt that I could make a bigger difference in these patients' lives than in the lives of elite athletes.

Have you faced difficulties in your career?

I've worked for and with some men who are insecure and threatened by both men and women who excel. It is important to surround yourself with extremely competent people who may be smarter or more effective than you are. It is important to mentor younger faculty members, and not everyone does that well.

My philosophy is "Be nice and work hard," and this will go a long way toward success. Yes, I have experienced and watched women treated in-equitably, and this will change as we educate people at all levels about conscious and unconscious bias. I don't think there is a place in the twenty-first century for surgical leaders who are not courteous and respectful to both men and women in the field.

What are your thoughts about mentorship?

I have been extremely fortunate to have many outstanding mentors in all stages of my career. They have essentially all been men as I did not come into contact with many senior orthopedic women leaders. I continue to seek out mentors at every stage of my career, even now.

Mentors for women surgeons do not need to be women. I have learned a great deal from my male mentors in the field. It is important to seek out mentors, not wait for them to find us. Now it is my obligation and responsibility to mentor younger women and men in the field.

I have had wonderful mentors—too many to list. During my residency training, I admired Jody Buckwalter, orthopedic oncologist, and Stuart Weinstein, pediatric orthopedist at U. Iowa. Also, Frank Sim, an orthopedic oncologist at the Mayo Clinic was instrumental in my academic progress. They continue to support my career and have become friends.

What is your advice to aspiring orthopedic surgeons?

I would say it is an outstanding field. There are great opportunities to help people with musculoskeletal injuries or diseases. I think women make particularly good orthopedic surgeons. The numbers of women in this field are increasing over time.

Make clear choices as to how you'd like to structure your life and where you want to be in five and ten years. In most academic settings it takes extra effort to advance up the promotion ladder and be in leadership roles. You can't do that easily or quickly working eight a.m.-five p.m. However, if you can find a more flexible environment, it may be possible to work toward promotion more slowly while raising a family. Given the intensity of work as a surgeon, it is important to identify tasks that you are comfortable outsourcing, in order to prioritize what is most important to you.

You can decide to work in an academic setting versus private practice, to work full time versus part time, to be involved in extra-curricular orthopedic organizations/committees or not.

How would you describe your personal life?

I enjoy outdoor activities: camping, backpacking, skiing, canoeing, climbing, traveling, gardening. I also enjoy reading about environmental/conservation issues and try to make time each year for active outdoor vacations. Sometimes it is difficult to balance life on a daily basis. My philosophy is "Work hard, Play hard," and hopefully life will balance in the long term. At the end of the day, it is our "choice" how to spend our time.

I don't have my own family so I prioritize my parents as well as my brother's family (with two nieces, ages four and nine).

I think the concept of a "legacy" is important both personally and professionally. I would like to make a difference in the field of orthopedic surgery. Personally, it is my relationships with family and friends that are the most rewarding parts of my life.

Do you have any final thoughts you would like to share?

I am grateful for the following in my career: great surgical cases—removing cancers and reconstructing limbs; long relationships with patients over many years; and opportunities to work with true giants in the field of orthopedic surgery.

I am humbled by patients' appreciation of the care provided to save their lives/limbs and improve their quality of life. They teach me to "seize the day" as life is both short and unpredictable.

Inspiring Quote:

"Real leaders want to do the right thing more than they want to be popular." — Kristy Weber

Deborah A. Geer, MD, FACS
General Surgeon

In the following interview, Dr. Geer shares her thoughts about her love for surgery and is candid about her regrets.

Why did you choose to become a surgeon?

My first rotation in the third year of medical school was surgery. I loved it—the idea of doing something for a patient and really seeing the results of your work. Also seeing patients get better, not just endure chronic problems. I then spent a year trying to convince myself that another specialty would be better, knowing the time constraints of surgical training, but I found nothing else that compared.

I love working in the OR. It is an environment unlike any other. We build such deep relationships with our teams. I treasure the friendships that I have made by working in the OR environment.

What do you feel about mentorship?

I had no real mentors while training as a surgeon. I feel that mentorship needs to be encouraged more in the field.

Whom do you admire in the field of surgery?

Patricia Numann—I have heard she is always kind, fair, and feminine.

What advice would you have for young women who choose to pursue a profession and raise a family at the same time?

It can be done, but hopefully you find your soul-mate before you are too far into your training, so that you can go through this together.

What advice would you give a medical student who comes to you, asking for advice about pursuing a career in surgery?

Surgery has changed so much since I was in training. I think balancing surgery and the rest of one's life is going to be easier in the future, as no one is expected to give round-the-clock care to patients anymore.

Interestingly, my daughter is a medical student interested in pursuing surgical residency. It seems that the mindset of students now is much more oriented to their personal life, with everyone seeming interested in employed positions and hourly work requirements.

In addition to being a surgeon, you have qualifications in other fields. What motivated you to obtain a Masters in Practical Theology?

I had been doing some medical mission work in Third-world countries (Papua New Guinea, Kenya, Jamaica, Panama, El Salvador) with church-based organizations. Many mission organizations require you to have some formal bible training. With much work now being done about spirituality and medicine, I decided learning about it could help my current medical practice, as well as possibly prepare me for future medical-mission work. I was able to do this while continuing my surgical practice through an on-line degree program, which took three years. At the same time, I pursued Clinical Pastoral Education to fulfill requirements to be a chaplain. Although I thought I could "wear two hats," I have not really acted as a chaplain in my primary hospitals. It has, however, made me much better at listening to my patients and really trying to get to know them as people!

You are a certified music practitioner— how did this come about?

Music has always been important to me. I started flute and piano in junior high school. My dream was to be a professional flutist, but a wise professional flutist once listened to me and shared sage advice: "Keep the flute as your avocation and find something else for your vocation"—hence, medicine!! My son started harp at age twelve. With such a beautiful instrument in the house, I could not leave it alone and have now been playing for fifteen years. The harp is a perfect instrument to play for patients during their time of need. Becoming certified as a music practitioner about ten years ago helped me to see how music could affect patient care. I have used harp music in a psychiatric hospital to soothe very disturbed patients, in nursing homes, and at an Alzheimer's facility. Although there are hospitals where harp is used in the OR, I am busy enough thinking about my patient's upcoming surgery not to be playing harp at the same time.

Do you feel satisfied with what you have achieved in life?

I think I have achieved what I set out to do—have a wonderful husband, kids, and a good practice. I would like to do more medical mission work in

Third-world countries. I have learned to be a very practical surgeon, trying to make do with the best that you have available.

Do you think it takes a special kind of person to be the spouse of a surgeon?

Absolutely!! I have that special person. A man must be very comfortable with himself to take on such a role. There is always the potential for difficulties in relationships when one spouse works so many hours.

Currently my husband and I work together - he is the practice manager. I could not function without his expertise.

Do you feel satisfied with the amount of time you have had to spend with family?

No, I missed so much when my kids were growing up. I am so fortunate to have a husband who stayed home with our kids for sixteen years. My kids had wonderful opportunities being with their dad; but, selfishly, I felt such a loss to have missed so many precious moments.

During chief residency, I lost six weeks due to a complication with a pregnancy. We were only allowed four weeks of time off during the year. At the end of residency, I had to make up those two weeks of time lost. Despite great ABSITE scores and recommendations, I was forced to do an extra three months of residency training. (It was highly unfair, but ultimately gave me a great assignment out of residency with the Army.)

What do you think about the work-hour reform in the United States?

I think it is dangerous. Most mistakes and miscommunications occur during hand-offs. No one sees a patient through their crisis anymore. People seem to be clock-watchers rather than focusing on the needs of the patients. I observed this with my own daughter and her friends when they were in the third year of medical school. They hardly ever had a night of call, and if they did, they had the next day off.

What do your children say about mommy being a surgeon?

Over the years, they have said things like, "You don't act like a doctor!" (Really, it was meant as a compliment.) "Are you a real doctor, or just a surgeon?" "Mommy, can men ever be surgeons like you?"

SECTION 12—POEMS

"Surgeons must be very careful
When they take the knife!
Underneath their fine incisions
Stirs the Culprit—Life!"
— Emily Dickinson

Adriana Laser, MD, MPH
Vascular Surgery Fellow

Nursing Solace

Her sleepy smell
Kneading hands
Warmth
Kitty tongue encircling, coaxing, lapping
The NICU neonate with pneumatosis, on the oscillator.

Stress fading away.
My body curling around hers
Arms wrapped
Darkness
Welcomed pleasant fatigue washes over
The SICU octogenarian who passed this morning, unrelenting carcinomatosis.

Guilt drifting away.
Our private intimacy
Mutual comfort
Silence
Gentle synching rhythms
The MICU mother's upset family, unexplained sepsis without a surgical source.

Words melting away.
Real exhaustion sets in harshly
Pager goes off
Interruption
She looks up, graciously smiling
Forgiving my waking her for this stolen moment.

Christine Rohde, MD, MPH, FACS
Plastic and Reconstructive Surgeon

Out of the Mouths of Babes

Why do you have to work so late again?
Can someone else do it?
I want you home with me.
I miss you when you are at work.
Will you be home early today?
Why do you have to go back?
Can you help ME?
Can you stay home today?
Come home now!
Of course you are tired, you work all day and then come home and take care of us.
My mommy makes yummy food that is good for us too.
My mommy fixes people and makes them better.
My mommy is a surgeon.
I want to be like Mommy when I grow up.
I love you.

Deborah A. Kuhls, MD, FACS, FCCM
Critical Care Surgeon

Daydreaming

Moral grounding, a great beginning.
In church we learn that all the world's children are God's children.
Who are these children, yellow black and white?
I dream of traveling far, being destined in some way.
A Doctor, I want to be a doctor!
My earliest memory, but simply impossible.
Don't know how but the answer's not here.
Searching to find my way, lost, hopeless, and deadened.
Pain of the heart, a branch in the road.
Finally, an answer before it's too late:
"Today is the first day of the rest of your life."
A doctor, a surgeon, home at last.
Good people, yellow, black and white
They helped me a lot.

Deborah A. Kuhls, MD, FACS, FCCM
Critical Care Surgeon

Jacobi Nights

Peds ER. It's still early.
Traumas rolling in . . . one, two, three, four.
My God, the worst, number five.
Little kids perfectly still, strapped to oversized backboards.
Frolicking just moments before,
chased by demon dogs,
falling from windows,
an innocent ramble on a new bicycle.
The family car, a vehicle of terror.
Smashing heads, innocence gone.
Never to be the same, never ever again.
Advance notification.
Thirteen, bicycle versus auto, head injury, unstable, abnormal breathing.
Quiet brave children, terrified wailing parents.
"You must tell me she's going to be okay."
The safe children sleep, safe until drawn. Quiet.
Adult Trauma Level 2.
Elevator stat, six to one, trauma.
Thirty, jumper, female . . . no he's male.
Blonde, lipstick, still, sad, red fingernails, HIV, suicide.
Head, bones, blood, no hope, sad.
Female, car versus pole, tattoo name Nicole.
Crying, no ear, brains, OR.
Never to cry again.
So tired, can't go on.
Code 126 in Ward 1.
"Mrs. P, you were just talking."
Wake up, wake up. Flat line. No hope.
Horrified patients, afraid to sleep again.
Tired, dark, can't go on, briefest rest.
Dawn, beautiful day, safe.

Rounds, must give hope to the living.
Happy people in Ward 1?
Gideons, kind smiling faces.
Hundreds of beautiful white books.
Distraught after 126,
their bedmate now gone,
searching for comfort in the Word.
Doctor, would you like one?
Me? Well, yes!

Joan Huffman, MD, FACS
Critical Care Surgeon

Catch and Release

Shot, he flounders,
thrashing in a sea of blood,
mouth gasping for air.
We toss the lifeline,
encircle with care,
reel closer.
He struggles,
leaking life,
sinking in an acid pool.
We lift him from the brink,
bubble oxygen,
flush plasma,
pack, stitch, pray . . .
Despite all, he fades,
paling,
failing.
We cease efforts,
free the hook from his lip,
liberate to the River Styx.

Joan Huffman, MD, FACS
Critical Care Surgeon

Honest Sweat

OR Room One,
exsanguination and evaporation
chill the dying victim
hasten the spiral of collapse.
We ramp up
the thermostat to eighty
to delay the journey
to the coroner's cooler.
Hermetically sealed,
in mask and cap,
gown and gloves,
we labor in the trauma sauna.
Intertriginous zones awash,
in sweat-soaked scrubs
and brine seared eyes,
I speak to the survivor's family.

Marie Crandall, MD, MPH, FACS
Trauma/Critical Care Surgeon

Two Hundred Forty-Two

Consecutive days in the hospital
Kind of a blur, but some things stand out
HELLP syndrome, caval injury from hepatic rupture
Husband told to "go home," came back the next morning with flowers,
now a single father
Clamshell thoracotomy, pancreas injury, duodenal injury, IVC injury
Walked out of the hospital forty-six days later
Sweet young man with hepatitis C cirrhosis, waiting patiently in the ICU
We passed on a liver for him, it looked a little old, a little fatty
He slipped into a coma the next day and never recovered
The man who was found torturing an eleven-year-old girl in his apartment
Jumped out a seventh-floor balcony, bounced
First time I ever saw femur fractures reduced without pain medication
Golden child, maybe two or three, raced up to me for a hug
I noticed her tracheostomy
Her foster mother told me it was courtesy of her father
I could not hold that little girl tight enough
Learning by immersion in surgery, somehow exhaustion underscoring the
important
Clues
Meaning
Lessons
I learned the language and how to pass it on

Sylvia Ramos Cruz, MD, MS, FACS
General Surgeon

A Place of Our Own

We gather in my living room in Riverdale
above the dark still waters of the Hudson
for dinner in a space devoid of men;
a space where we can sit relaxed
free of male clothing and attitudes donned
each time we go into OR, ICU, Emergency;
a space where we can let our guard down
re-arm for the battles of another day.
Spread around the spacious room
eating takeout food (my culinary talents
undeveloped, more lack of interest
than lack of time), the few who inhabit
this man's world are as different
from one another as we are from them.
We are the tough-as-nails woman, the one-who-cries-
the-fattest-tears-ever-seen woman, the flaky woman,
the much-too-soft woman, the maybe-too-old woman,
the pretty plump woman, and I, the one-who's-been-
through-the-whole-process-and-still-stands woman—
so I've heard us called.
Occasionally, my nine-year-old daughter wanders in
drawn by the jokes and laughter, clinical anecdotes,
sobering stories and, yes, ranting and ravings of women
who chose to take the knife against all odds.
To her, we're all just fine.

Sylvia Ramos Cruz, MD, MS, FACS
General Surgeon

Crossing Borders

The patient, her husband and I
crowd the tiny examination room.
She folds into the chair by the wall.
He stands uneasy by the door.
She from Guadalajara, he from Texas
have crossed *fronteras* of marriage
and children many times *sin* interpreters.
Now they're here for me to say in Spanish
what another surgeon told them in English
sobre el cáncer in her breast, the need for
una operación, quimioterapia, radiación.
He says, "I understood every word the doctor said.
It's just, I couldn't drop the heavy sentence on her."
Ella dice en español, "I know my husband will tell me all that's said.
It's just, he doesn't know medical terms and
what if he misses something?"
She asks, *¿Doctora, perdiré mi pelo bello?*
He wonders if he will lose his wife.
Their thoughts resound in the silence
like trees falling in a far-off forest
I sit enveloped in the language of their fears,
caught on a barbed wire of translation.

Zeenat Hasan, MD
General and Minimally Invasive Surgeon

Dumb Luck

She was in the hospital about every other week
with her memory-foam pillow and pearly white teeth.
Every morning on rounds she'd pleasantly oblige,
lifting her hospital gown to show you her underside.
"For fifty-two days I haven't had a bite!"
"And boy what I wouldn't do for some Boston cream pie!"
We had removed her colon, scooped her insides out,
to stop a cancer that had already spread throughout.
Every time we tried to get her home in peace
her failing body would force a hasty retreat.
She had bad genes or bad luck or a bit of both;
she fulfilled our cynical myth that the good die too soon.
Next door there was a young man with no will to live
who thought to end his misery with a single bullet to the head.
Bright metal carelessly pierced delicate neurons on CT,
lighting up like supernovas where grey matter should be.
We put our expert heads together and swiftly predicted his demise,
only to find him functioning as before, to our scientific surprise.
He was discharged from the hospital metal still in his head,
she watches the food channel dying in her bed.

Sarah N. Cross, MD
Obstetrician-Gynecologist

Teaching Surgery

When she has lain down,
all five feet of her
and drifted to sleep
I place the scalpel in your hand,
try to make you see
the same lines I see.
Here is how you cut flesh
so that it can be repaired. Almost
as if we were never here.
Press with gentle firmness until skin
splits and blood comes forth.
Make movements precise,
purposeful. Always respect
what the body shows
and what it is hiding.

Now you are unlocking mysteries,
shining light into the dark sea
of the pelvis. Here are the fleshy pearls
of her ovaries. And here is a fallopian
tube bulging with pregnancy,
trying to bloom, threatening to burst.
Hold firm on it until you can see
its underbelly. Ligate it all the way
down to its connection to the uterus.
Each bite of fire focused.
When you have loosed it
and its wayward pregnancy,
which never made it to its destination,
place it in this small bag and remove
it from where it threatened to do harm.

SECTION 13—GLOSSARY OF TERMS

Abscess: An abnormal collection of pus/fluid that accumulates in tissues as a result of an infectious or inflammatory process.

Academic career/Academic surgeon: After residency training is complete, a surgeon can choose a position at a teaching hospital and/or medical school, or enter into private or community practice. Academic posts generally require taking care of the most complex of patients while also conducting research, teaching residents and students and taking leadership in local and national societies. Community or private practices usually involve much more hands-on patient care and somewhat less teaching and research.

Academic supervisors: Those in positions of leadership in an academic training program, e. g., Chair/Chairman /Chairwoman, Residency Program Director.

ACS (American College of Surgeons): A scientific and educational association of surgeons, founded in 1913, that sets high standards for surgical education and practice. It has established professional, ethical and moral standards for every practicing surgeon. There are strict requirements for the designation "FACS" (Fellow of the American College of Surgeons).

Anastomosis: Created while suturing together tissues; a surgical connection between two tubular structures, e. g., blood vessels, intestines.

Appendectomy: Surgical removal of vermiform appendix, a tubular structure that opens into the cecum, near the beginning of the large intestine.

Atelectasis: Partial or complete closure or collapse of lung tissue.

Attending: A fully-licensed physician who has completed training ("consultant").

Auto-transfusion: The process whereby a person receives his or her own blood for transfusion instead of banked-donor blood. Blood can be collected from the patient before surgery or during the surgery, by an intraoperative blood salvage device such as a Cell Saver.

AVF (Arterio-venous fistula): A connection between an artery and vein that can be surgically created for the purpose of hemo-dialysis.

Axilla: Armpit.

Balfour retractor: An instrument used to hold open abdominal walls during surgery.

Betadine: The brand name for an iodine-containing solution with antibacterial activity. Used as antiseptic for skin.

Blebectomy: Surgical removal of a bleb. (see Thoracoscopic Blebectomy) A "bleb" is an abnormal, blister-like air pocket on the lung surface, within layers of the lung lining (pleura). When these blebs rupture, inhaled air is able to travel from the airways through the lungs and into the thoracic cavity, creating a pneumothorax with collapse of lung tissue.

Board-like abdomen: A firm and rigid abdominal wall that is a sign of inflammation and infection inside the abdomen.

Bovie cautery: An electro-cautery device used to control bleeding from vessels and tissues.

CABG (Coronary artery bypass graft): A type of surgery that improves blood flow to the heart.

Call/On call: Being on call essentially means being available to provide services to patients when needed. For example, a surgery resident doing "in-house call" has to remain in the hospital and hold a pager. He/she may get paged at any time to deal with patient-related issues.

A physician is on call when he/she is responsible for dealing with patient issues. "Call" can be taken either in-house, when the physician has to stay in the hospital, or from home, when the physician may be required to come into the hospital to deal with issues. 'Post-call' refers to the period after being on call.

Call room: A room within the hospital used by house staff who are "on call"/have clinical duties.

Cardiac tamponade: An abnormal collection of blood/fluid around the heart that restricts its mobility and ability to pump blood. (See Pericardial Effusion)

Carotid endarterectomy: Surgery that involves removing atherosclerotic plaque from the wall of carotid artery.

Case: The term used for an operation (e. g., scrubbing into a case).

Castro: A surgical instrument used to handle blood vessels.

"Cath her/him": Medical jargon that refers to performing a cardiac catheterization procedure which involves passing a thin flexible tube (catheter) into a chamber of the heart, usually through a blood vessel in the groin or the arm.

Cell saver: An intraoperative blood salvage device. (see Auto-transfusion) During surgery, a patient's blood can sometimes be collected using a sterile procedure, then transfused back into the body if needed. In this manner, the blood that is lost from the body can sometimes be salvaged or "saved."

Central line, Central line kit: An intravenous access device/catheter that is placed into a large "central" vein. A sterile kit/tray is available that contains instruments necessary for placement of this central line.

Chairman of Surgery/Chair: Chief of the Surgery Department; oversees the department of surgery and all clinical, research and educational activities.

Chest tube set: A chest tube is a flexible tube that is placed into the chest/pleural cavity to drain air/fluid from around the lung. A chest tube set refers to a sterile tray containing the instruments necessary for placing a chest tube into a patient's chest. (See Pleurovac suction device)

Chief: Depending on the context, "chief" refers either to Chief of the Surgery Department or Chief Resident.

Chief resident/Chief years: A "chief resident" is in the final year(s) of surgery residency training. "Chief years" refers to the final years of training.

Cholecystectomy: The surgical removal of the gall bladder, an organ that stores bile and is located under the liver.

Circulating nurse: In the operating room (OR), this individual is part of the OR team. Examples of some responsibilities of the circulating nurse are helping to move the patient onto the operating table and obtaining surgical instruments, gloves, devices, etc. that are required by the surgical team for the procedure.

Clerkship: Clinical rotations in the 3rd year of medical school.

CMS: Centers for Medicaid/Medicare services.

Cochlea: The structure within the inner ear that plays a role in auditory function.

Code/Code blue: A medical emergency related to the patient losing blood pressure and pulse. A "code" situation may require cardio-pulmonary resuscitation.

Compromised airway: When a patient is not able to maintain an airway to enable passage of air into and out of lungs.

Consult: A medical query posed by one specialty service to another. For example, a team of medical doctors may ask surgeons to evaluate a patient with a potential surgical problem, such as severe abdominal pain. Related terms are **Surgery consult**, a patient-related question that is posed to surgeons; and **consult resident**, a member of the surgical team who usually holds a pager and is assigned to be the first person to go evaluate a patient when a consult from another specialty service is requested.

Couple's match: A couple can request a university training program to consider their residency application together, so that they can both be at the same institution during residency training, even while training in different specialties.

CPCC: Certified professional co-active coach.

"Crack her/his chest": Medical jargon that refers to opening the chest wall and doing direct cardiac massage on someone whose heart stops beating with resultant loss of blood pressure. This phrase could also refer to the breaking or cracking of ribs during cardio-pulmonary resuscitation (CPR)/chest compressions.

CRNA: Certified registered nurse anesthesiologist.

Crohn's disease: An inflammatory bowel disease that may affect any part of the gastro-intestinal tract.

Echocardiogram/Echo: A type of ultrasound test that can be used to assess heart function and structure.

ED/ER: Emergency Department / Emergency Room.

Eighty-hour work week/Duty hour reform: Regulations to limit resident work hours in hospitals. The Accreditation Council for Graduate Medical Education (ACGME) duty hour standards went into effect in July 2003. These standards include an eighty-hour weekly limit, averaged over four weeks.

ENT: Ear Nose Throat.

Extra-peritoneal: The outside of the peritoneal lining of the abdominal cavity.

Extubate/extubation: The removal of a breathing tube from the airway/trachea. The breathing tube is connected to a ventilator, a machine which assists with breathing. Extubation is done when ventilator support is no longer required or desired.

Fellow: (1) After basic surgery residency training, if one obtains further fellowship training, during that period of advanced training, one is referred to as "fellow;" (2) A Fellow of the American College of Surgeons is a board certified, fully licensed surgeon who has met requirements for obtaining the FACS title (see Appendix).

FEV1: Forced expiratory volume in 1 second; the volume of air exhaled in 1 second.

"Flash it": Medical jargon that refers to sterilizing an instrument or device.

Foley bag: A bag used to collect urine that is connected to a urinary catheter called a Foley catheter, which is passed through the urethra and into the bladder.

Gastrostomy tube: A tube placed into the stomach, usually for the purpose of feeding (from the Greek word *gaster*, pertaining to "belly").

Guidewire: A thin, usually flexible wire that is inserted into the body through the lumen of a needle and used to guide placement of a prosthetic device into a blood vessel or hollow organ (e. g., intra-vascular catheter placement). The "Seldinger technique" (named after a Swedish radiologist) is a generic term used for this kind of guidewire procedure.

Halstedian surgical training programs: William Halsted, who worked at The Johns Hopkins Medical Institutions in the late 1800s, is generally recognized as the pioneer of formal, structured residency training programs in the U.S. In addition to training surgeons to be technically competent, he laid emphasis on using scientific evidence for making clinical decisions, and strove to train outstanding scientists and surgical educators. His original model established that surgery was learned in an hierarchical program that required complete personal dedication. House surgeons provided 24/7 service to the hospital, where room, board and training were provided. Early residents literally resided at the hospitals. During his time, trainees spent the majority of their time in the hospital, hence the terms "housestaff." Hospitals also functioned as "houses" for them and "residents," who literally resided in hospitals.

HELLP syndrome: A life-threatening obstetric complication characterized by hemolytic anemia, elevated liver enzymes and low platelets.

Herniorrhaphy: Repair of a "hernia." Hernia often refers to the abnormal protrusion of an organ or tissues through a defect in the surrounding wall that normally contains it.

HIPAA: The Health Insurance Portability and Accountability Act passed by the U.S. Congress in 1996. "HIPAA Privacy Rule" refers to a set of national standards for the protection of individually identifiable health information or "protected health information."

Hypertonic saline: A concentrated saline (salt) solution.

ICU: Intensive care unit.

ID: Infectious disease.

Incentive spirometry: The use of a medical device called "incentive spirometer" to help with breathing exercises after having surgery under general anesthesia.

Intern year/Internship: The first year of residency training is referred to as the intern year.

IV: Short for "intravenous," a term sometimes used for the device that is placed into peripheral veins to enable "intravenous hydration," or infusion of fluids into the vascular system.

Level I trauma center/Level I status: Level I designation for a trauma center means it provides the highest level of specialty expertise and meets strict national standards for trauma-related care. It is a tertiary care facility with specialized teams, facilities and equipment that is available around the clock, 365 days a year, to provide total care for every aspect of injury, from injury prevention through rehabilitation. Lower levels of trauma care are provided by trauma centers that have Level II, Level III and Level IV designations.

Loupes: A magnification device sometimes worn by surgeons, to better visualize small blood vessels and fine structures while operating.

MASH surgeon: MASH is an acronym for "Mobile Army Surgical Hospital," or a temporary hospital in combat areas.

Match/Match day/Match list: Application to post-graduate medical training programs/residencies is done through a competitive process known as "the Match," conducted by a centralized matching service: the "National Resident Matching Program" (NRMP). Medical students apply to residency programs, programs review applications and invite selected candidates for interviews. After the interview period is over, students submit a "rank-order list" to the NRMP. Similarly, residency programs submit a list of their preferred applicants in rank order to this same matching service. The two parties' lists are combined by an NRMP computer, which creates optimal matches of medical graduates to residency programs using an algorithm. On the third Friday of March each year ("Match Day") these results are announced in Match Day ceremonies at the nation's medical schools.

MCAT exam: Students take the Medical College Admission Test (MCAT), the required standardized exam that medical schools use to identify qualified candidates.

Mediastinum, Mediastinal shift: The mediastinum is the central compartment of the chest/thoracic cavity. Located behind the breast bone and in front of the vertebral canal, with the lungs on either side, it contains important structures such as the heart, large blood vessels, trachea and esophagus. A "**shift**" of the mediastinum may be caused by injuries and can result in life-threatening consequences such as low blood pressure.

MELD: Model for End Stage Liver Disease. A score based on blood tests that measure disease severity is derived (7-40) and is used for allocating livers for transplant. The higher the score, the greater the priority for transplantation.

Mid-level providers: (see Physician Extender) Health care providers with a more restricted scope of practice than medical doctors, e. g., advanced practice nurse and physician assistant.

Morbidity and mortality conferences: Weekly conferences conducted at academic centers where specific surgeries with complicated outcomes are analyzed and discussed.

MRI: magnetic resonance imaging.

Neonatal arterial switch: An operation to reverse/correct transposition of the great arteries. Some babies are born with a congenital heart defect called transposition of the great arteries, where the two great arteries carrying blood out of the heart (the pulmonary artery and aorta) are switched in position.

Neuro-ICU: The intensive care unit that treats patients with neurologic disorders relating to the brain and spine.

NIH: National Institute of Health.

Non-rebreather mask: The mask used in medical emergencies to supply a high concentration of oxygen to patients who can breathe independently. **It** covers both the nose and mouth of the patient and has an attached reservoir bag that connects to an external oxygen tank. Exhaled air is directed through a one-way valve in the mask, which prevents the in-halation of room air and the re-inhalation of exhaled air.

Nurse practitioner: An advanced practice nurse.

Ob/Gyn: Obstetrics / Gynecology.

OR: Operating room.

PACU: Post anesthesia care unit.

Pancreatectomy: The surgical removal of the pancreas, an organ in the abdomen which has digestive and endocrine functions. **Distal** pancre-atectomy refers to the removal of the distal part of the pancreas.

Partial bowel resection: The surgical removal of part of the intestine.

Patient hand-offs: A process whereby information about a patient is passed on ('signed out') to the incoming physician, who will then assume care of the patient. (see Sign Out).

Perfusionist/Cardiovascular perfusionist: The person who operates the "heart-lung machine," which helps maintain blood circulation during some surgeries that require cardio-pulmonary-bypass. The heart-lung machine op-erated by the perfusionist maintains circulatory and respiratory functions of the patient, which has a great effect on his or her systemic condition. During open-heart surgery, the surgeon may decide to stop the patient's heart, and a heart-lung machine is used to keep the patient's blood flowing until the heart can be restarted. The perfusionist also collects and processes blood drawn from the patient's own body, referred to as "autologous blood."

Pericardial effusion: The abnormal collection of fluid around the heart that may or may not affect its ability to pump blood. (See Cardiac Tamponade.)

Personal statement: An essay written by an applicant that is submitted as part of the application process for residency training programs. It allows the candidate to introduce him/herself and usually explains his/her rationale for choosing a particular specialty.

Pfannensteil: A lower abdominal horizontal incision.

Pheochromocytoma: A tumor of the adrenal gland that secretes vasoactive hormones into the blood.

Physician extenders: This term is commonly used to refer to highly trained, licensed health care professionals, such as physician assistants and nurse practitioners, who work under the direct supervision of physicians, and are able to perform medical activities typically performed by a physician.

Pleurovac suction device: A three-chamber, compartmentalized chest tube drainage system. A chest tube, once placed into a patient's chest, is connected to this device, which is connected to wall suction and provides negative pressure. This enables evacuation of abnormal collections of air and blood from the pleural cavity. (see Chest tube set).

Pneumothorax: The air between the lung and chest wall that compresses lung tissue.

Post-call: After being on-call (see "Call").

Pre-eclampsia: A life-threatening medical disorder that may occur during pregnancy, characterized by high blood pressure and a large amount of protein in the urine.

Pre-medical program/Pre-med program: Optional educational track that enables students to satisfy medical school admission criteria.

Program director: Person in charge of a residency program.

Pubis/Pubic bone: One of the bones that forms the pelvis.

Pulse oximeter: A non-invasive device that monitors oxygen saturation levels in a patient's blood.

Pyramidal programs: These are residency training programs used to select residents in a pyramidal fashion, i. e., they would start off with more residents than would graduate, eliminating several each year. In the past, some programs (especially in surgical fields) ran pyramid structures that only graduated a few of the trainees each year. Residents could be eliminated at the end of an academic year, and continued progress in the program was not assured. This system used to be used in US teaching hospitals to limit the number of specialist physicians graduating from highly-selective residency programs.

Residency: A post-graduate training program in a particular specialty after medical school.

Resident: While doing residency, a medical school graduate is called a "resident" ("house officer" in some countries). He or she practices medicine under the supervision of attendings.

Rounds/rounding/making rounds: These terms refer to medical professionals walking around in the hospital from room to room/bed to bed checking on patients.

Scarpa's fascia: The membranous part of the superficial fascia of the abdominal wall. The superficial fascia is located under the skin and above the first muscle layer. It is named after the Italian anatomist and surgeon, Antonio Scarpa.

Scrub tech: An operating room assistant who also scrubs into a case, and hands over instruments to a surgeon during the operation.

Scrubbed into a case: Medical jargon that refers to a surgeon being "scrubbed"—or having washed the hands carefully—with soap/water/sterilizer, and donning a sterile gown and gloves prior to a surgical procedure.

Sentinel lymph node biopsy: The surgical removal of a lymph node so that it can be examined under the microscope by pathologists for cancer.

SICU: surgical intensive care unit.

Sign out: A process by which the physician who is leaving the hospital tells the in-coming physician who will assume care of patients about all patient issues before leaving the hospital. Signing out effectively means you are handing over patient care to another incoming physician as you leave the hospital. (See "patient hand-offs.")

Staff cases: Supervise surgeries in the operating room.

Sternal notch: The notch at the upper part of the breast bone/sternum (in the front of the chest).

Sub-internship: A rotation done in the fourth/final year of medical school to gain more experience in a specialty. A medical student has more patient responsibility during a sub-internship than during an "elective."

Surgical service: A team of surgeons and trainees.

Suture types: Different types of sutures used in surgeries for different purposes, e. g., 6-0 prolene, 5-0 PDS SVC (superior vena cava, the large vein that carries blood into the right atrium of the heart).

Tamponade/(See Cardiac Tamponade): The restricted movement of heart, often caused by abnormal accumulation of blood around the heart.

Thoracoscopic blebectomy: A "bleb" is an abnormal, blister-like air pocket on the lung surface within layers of the lung lining (pleura). When these blebs rupture, inhaled air is able to travel from the airways, through the lungs and into the thoracic cavity, creating a pneumothorax or lung collapse. Blebectomy refers to removal of a bleb. "Thoracosopy" refers to surgery on the chest/thorax using minimally invasive technique with small incisions and a camera placed into the thoracic cavity.

Tracheostomy set: A set of instruments that enable placement of a tube directly into the trachea through the skin of the neck, which can be connected to a ventilator to assist with breathing.

Train wreck: Medical jargon for describing a patient with multiple significant medical problems.

Trajectory of gunshot: The path that the bullet takes within the body.

Transient ischemic attacks: A transient episode of neurologic dysfunction caused by temporary reduction or loss of blood flow to part of the brain.

Ultrasound: A type of imaging that uses high-frequency sound waves to look at organs and structures inside the body.

UNOS: United Network for Organ Sharing. A private, non-profit organization that manages organ transplant systems in the US. It is a regulatory body that assists with managing the national transplant waiting list, maintains a database on all organ transplant data, and centralizes organ allocation. It maintains various policies on how transplant centers operate in order to assure quality.

USMLE exam: United States Medical Licensing Exam.

VA: Veterans Affairs hospital.

Venotomy: A hole in a vein.

Ventricular: That which pertains to the ventricle, a chamber of the heart.

Ventricular tachycardia: An abnormal rhythm causing sustained contractions of the wall of the heart, adversely affecting the ability of the heart to pump blood.

Xiphoid/xiphoid process: The small, ossified cartilaginous extension of the lowest part of the breastbone/sternum.

SECTION 14—APPENDIX

Becoming a Board-Certified Surgeon and a Fellow of the American College of Surgeons In the United States

Board Certification by the American Board of Surgery (ABS)

The ABS is one of twenty-four member boards of the American Board of Medical Specialties (ABMS), a governing body for determining specialty fields of medicine suitable for certification.

ABS is a private, autonomous non-profit organization.

ABS has established a comprehensive certification process and is the national certifying body for individual surgeons practicing in the US.

Board certification is voluntary.

ABS requires "attestation of the residency program director that the applicant has completed an appropriate educational experience and attained a sufficiently high level of knowledge, clinical judgment and technical skills as well as ethical standing to be admitted to the certification process." (For more details see http://www.absurgery.org/)

Qualifying Exam

A computer-based exam composed of multiple choice questions with a duration of eight hours.

Certifying Exam

An oral exam conducted by different examiners. Upon successful completion of the qualifying examination, as well as the certifying examination, the candidate is deemed board certified in surgery and becomes a diplomate of the ABS.Reference: http://www.absurgery.org/xfer/BookletofInfo-Surgery.pdf

Fellow of the American College of Surgeons (FACS) Designation by American College of Surgeons

Attainment of certification in the appropriate surgical specialty does not, of itself, entitle a surgeon to Fellowship in the ACS.

Requirements include: Board certification; active, unrestricted medical license; one year of surgical practice after completion of all formal training; surgeons are required to submit the most recent twelve-month summary listing of all surgical procedures they have performed after completion of all formal training; current appointment on the surgical staff of the applicant's primary hospital with no reportable action pending; five references who are themselves Fellows of the College and who practice surgery in the same geographic area as the applicant.

Each Fellow named as a reference will be asked by the College to furnish a statement about the applicant's qualifications as a surgeon, as well as the applicant's professional and ethical standing in the community. The chief of surgery at each applicant's designated primary hospital(s) is required to provide a letter of reference for the candidate. (For more details see http://www.facs.org/)

SECTION 15—ACKNOWLEDGMENTS

ACKNOWLEDGMENTS

I could not have compiled this anthology without the generosity and grace of many individuals and remain deeply grateful to those who helped make this book publication possible.

Carol Scott-Conner's enthusiasm gave me the courage to transform an idea into a distinct reality. She provided encouragement for this project when I myself hardly believed that it would ever come to fruition. She also took the time to read the draft manuscript and write a blurb.

My editorial reviewer Jaya Bhattacharji Rose recognized the potential in my idea, even in its incipient stages, and offered critical, insightful comments that helped mold the early manuscript. Her support and feedback were invaluable during the initial stages of this project.

This book would not have been completed without the wonderful and sensitive guidance of Joan Cassell, whose suggestions for revisions added clarity and focus to certain essays. I am thankful to her for writing the foreword section and for providing input for the title of this book.

I remain indebted to the following four extraordinary individuals who graciously agreed to review the manuscript and write blurbs for me despite their own impossibly busy schedules. Abraham Verghese—family friend and role-model—whose enthusiasm for this project and advice to stick with the traditional publishing route were invaluable. Pauline Chen was kind enough to chat with me on the phone and suggested I ask Joan Cassell to write the foreword. Atul Gawande agreed to write a blurb despite never having met me, which was incredibly generous of him. I met Marty Makary while I was a junior resident and am ever so grateful for his ongoing support.

I want to thank Richard and Jane Altschuler of Gordian Knot Books for recognizing the importance of this manuscript and for believing that these women's voices need to be heard. Thank you Richard, copy-editor extraordinaire, for painstakingly fixing all the little details and adding the final polishing touches.

A big thank you to photographers Tom Jemski (University of Maryland) for the profile photo and to Jordan Denner (Baltimore VA) for the cover photo.

I am very grateful to the following who spread the word about this book project and helped me get contributions: Elliott Haut, William Chiu, Robert Sawyer, Sonya Malekzadeh, Devinder Singh, Amiel Bethel, Chris

Porter (OnSurg.com website), Christina Frangou (General Surgery News). The Association of Women Surgeons disseminated the initial call for submissions via e-mail.

Patients entrust surgeons with their bodies and I am always humbled by the trust and confidence that they bestow upon us. It is the patients who make this all worthwhile. The interns, residents, medical students and fellows I have worked with over the years have taught me invaluable lessons about life, more so than they will ever know.

I have a wonderful, supportive 'work family' within the Surgery department at the Baltimore VA Medical Center. Individual names are too numerous to mention, but thank you especially to Douglas Turner and Brajesh Lal for believing in me and to Pamela Johnson and Michelle Bland for continued support and friendship.

I need to acknowledge a few surgeons who gave me opportunities and guidance over the course of my training. I met Dr. Keith Lillemoe soon after graduating from medical school, and as residency program director at the time, it is he who gave me the opportunity to start training at The Johns Hopkins Hospital. Keith Lillemoe, Edward Cornwell III, Elliott Haut and David Efron were my role models there. In New Jersey, I met several outstanding surgeons and am grateful to everyone I trained with, especially Edwin Deitch, Massimo Napolitano, Anne Mosenthal, George Machiedo, Alicia Mohr, Alan Beitler and Douglas Benson.

I discussed this project with only two family members who offered encouragement and gave me emotional support along the way. My cousin Ravee Kurian, a talented writer, took time to read the manuscript draft and help with the introduction. My aunt, Ammu Joseph, journalist and author, introduced me to Jaya and put me in touch with several published authors who offered their advice.

My father, Dr. Alexander John, worked for 30 years as a cardiovascular surgeon in Germany and retired in 2014. His dedication to work and devotion to his patients has had a profound influence on me. This book will be a (surprise) retirement gift for him. My mother, Sarah, has always stressed the importance of pursuing a meaningful life. I thank them both for their unconditional love and support.

I am deeply indebted to the fifty-nine women who embraced the opportunity to tell their stories, some of them very personal, so that others may benefit from them. Thank you for taking the time to write from your heart and for entrusting me with your wonderful contributions. Thank you to Carol Scott-Conner and Julie Freischlag for providing me with the first two essays that motivated others to contribute. I am honored to have Kimberly Ephgrave's essay in this collection. Even though I will never have the opportunity to meet her, I hope that her family will be satisfied with the end result of this project.

The greatest reward from compiling this book so far has been the new friendships with women surgeons from around the country. These extraordinary individuals touch lives on a daily basis and with this book I hope we can touch many more.

SECTION 16—ABOUT THE CONTRIBUTORS

Kathryn Anderson, MD, FACS, FRCS (Hon: Eng; Ire; Edin.), Pediatric Surgeon (Retired)

Former Titles: President of American College of Surgeons (first elected woman President); Secretary of the American College of Surgeons; President of American Pediatric Surgical Association; Chief, Children's Hospital, University of Southern California. Among other honors, Dr. Anderson was elected to Fellowship in the Royal College of Surgeons in England, and was granted Honorary Fellowship in the Royal College of Surgeons of Ireland and Edinburgh, along with honorary memberships in the Canadian and Australasian Associations of Pediatric Surgery. The American Academy of Pediatrics awarded her their highest honor in Pediatric Surgery, the William E. Ladd medal, in 2007. She was given the Nina Starr Braunwald Award by the Association of Women Surgeons for service to women surgeons, and was celebrated in the National Library of Medicine Exhibition "Changing the Face of Medicine: Celebrating America's Women Physicians." A lectureship in her name has been established in the Department of Surgery, Georgetown University, Washington, D. C. She served as Visiting Professor at academic institutions all over the world, and was longtime Consultant to the United States Army at Walter Reed Medical Center, Washington, D. C. and the National Institutes of Health, Bethesda, Maryland. She retired in 2004.

Nia D. Banks, MD, PhD, FACS, Plastic and Reconstructive Surgeon

Plastic, Reconstructive, Craniofacial and Aesthetic Surgeon, Beaux Arts Institute of Plastic Surgery, Prince George's County, Maryland. Dr. Banks is a board certified Plastic and Reconstructive Surgeon in private practice in Prince George's County, Maryland. She is the owner of the Beaux Arts Institute of Plastic Surgery in Lanham, Maryland, which provides reconstructive and cosmetic surgery services to men and women in the Washington, D. C., metropolitan area. Dr. Banks completed the M.D/Ph.D. program at the Johns Hopkins University School of Medicine in 2002. She trained as a general surgery resident and then completed the residency program in Plastic and Reconstructive Surgery at the Johns Hopkins Hospital in Baltimore, Maryland, in 2008, and is the only African American woman to complete this program. After her residency, she completed a Cranio-facial fellowship and an Ear Reconstruction fellowship in Paris, France. Dr. Banks is an Instructor at the Johns Hopkins Division of Plastic Surgery, a member of the Alpha Omega Alpha medical honor society, a fellow of the American College of Surgeons, a diplomate of the American Board of Plastic Surgery, and a member of the American Society of Plastic Surgeons. Dr. Banks lives in Baltimore, Maryland, where she enjoys food, wine, and the water.

Maria Basile, MD, Colon and Rectal Surgeon

John T Mather Memorial Hospital; St. Charles Hospital; North Country; Colorectal Surgery, PC, Port Jefferson, New York; Clinical Assistant Professor of Surgery and Preventive Medicine, Stony Brook University School of Medicine, Stony Brook, NY. Dr. Basile is a colorectal surgeon in private practice in Long Island, NY. She graduated with an MD from Georgetown University School of Medicine, Washington D. C., in 1991, and thereafter completed her general surgery residency at this same institution. Her fellowship training in colon and rectal surgery was at Saint Vincent Medical Center, Erie, Pennsylvania. She is a member of the research and teaching faculty at Stony Brook's Center for Medical Humanities, Compassionate Care, and Bioethics (www.stonybrook.edu/bioethics), where she teaches courses in the Medical Humanities. She is co-director of "Astonished Harvest," a multi-disciplinary group of poets interested in the interface between poetry and medicine. Dr. Basile's poetry has been published in the *Journal of the American Medical Association*, in *Touch: the Journal of Healing*, and anthologized with writings by physicians and other healthcare professionals. A chapbook collection of her poems was published by The Lives You Touch Publications in fall of 2011, entitled *Minimally Invasive: Poems From a Life in Surgery*. Most recently, her poems were featured in *Paumanok II*, an anthology of Long Island poetry and photography. She lives in East Setauket with her husband, two children, and her father, a retired general surgeon.

Barbara Lee Bass, MD, FACS, General Surgeon

Chair, Department of Surgery, Houston Methodist Hospital, Houston, Texas; Professor of Surgery, Weill Cornell Medical College. Dr. Bass is a general surgeon in practice in Houston, Texas. Since 2005, she has served as the Bookout Distinguished Endowed Chair of the Department of Surgery at The Methodist Hospital and Professor of Surgery at Weill Cornell Medical College.

She chose surgery as a career before she ever met a woman surgeon. Dr. Bass graduated with an MD from the University of Virginia School of Medicine in 1979 and completed training in general surgery at George Washington University. She served as a Captain in the US Army Medical Corps during a fellowship at the Walter Reed Army Institute of Research. She was honored to provide surgical care to veterans in the VA Health Care system for over 20 years. She has provided years of leadership service to the American Board of Surgery and the American College of Surgeons. She is particularly proud of her contributions to birth the National Surgical Quality Improvement Program in the VA and the American College of Surgeons. She loves her two sons beyond all measure and is a fierce maker of home for her husband and their immediate and extended families. Dr. Bass relishes all living things, the beautiful outdoors, human-created art of all forms and spiritual culture. She is an avid gardener, keeper of many beloved animals (and cannot live without dogs), joyous world traveler, and pretty good sailor. This panorama of joys outside of the hospital provides abundant and complete relief from the rigors of her very satisfying but demanding career.

Kerry Bennett (nee Gallivan), MD, MPH, FACS, CPCC, Breast and General Surgeon

Attending Surgeon, High-Risk Breast Specialist, Reliant Medical Group, Worcester, Massachusetts; Director, Outlook Wellness Center, New Bedford, Massachusetts. Dr. Bennett graduated with an MD and MPH from Tufts Medical School, Boston, Massachusetts, in 1993. She then did General Surgery residency training at Tufts-New England Medical Center, Boston, including a one-year Pediatric Surgery Trauma fellowship. She is a high-risk breast specialist with diverse roles, including surgeon, life coach, medical director, re-searcher, yoga instructor, health care advocate, mom, daughter, wife, writer, and teacher. She loves outdoor and athletic activities. She also loves quiet activities such as practicing mindfulness, reading and writing. She cares deeply and adores surgery, learning and teaching. She is a third-generation surgeon with a sister who practices ENT in the Boston area. She has authored two editions of *The Little Pink Book: What I Say Every Day to my Patients* and is currently working on *Stress Less: Tools for Health and Healing*. She volunteers in surgically underserved areas where she practices her

Spanish. She teaches students and residents from the following institutions: Harvard Beth Israel Deaconess Medical Center, University of Massachusetts, Ross University and Massachusetts College of Pharmacy and Health Sciences. For more information please visit www.drkerrybennett.com.

Sarah Blair, MD, FACS, Surgical Oncologist

Clinical Professor of Surgery, Division of Surgical Oncology, University of California, San Diego. Dr. Blair wrote her story based on her experience during General Surgery Residency at the University of Massachusetts in the early 1990s. She graduated with an MD in 1992 from State University of New York Health Science Center at Syracuse, following which she completed general surgery residency training. In the middle of residency she took off two years from clinical duties to complete a research fellowship at Memorial Sloan Kettering in New York. During this time she had her daughter Eva. She also completed a clinical fellowship in Surgical Oncology at City of Hope National Cancer Center. She is now a Professor of Surgery at the University of California San Diego (UCSD), where she has a busy clinical practice and a lab. She primarily focuses on the surgical treatment of breast cancer and is interested in translational projects in using new technology such as nanoparticles to improve localization of cancer. At UCSD she is head of the Women in Surgery initiative. Her hobbies include Yoga and she is a voracious reader.

Helen Cappuccino, MD, FACS, Surgical Oncologist

Assistant Professor, University of Buffalo Department of Surgical Oncology at Roswell Park Cancer Institute. Dr. Cappuccino graduated with an MD in 1988 from SUNY (State University New York) Buffalo School of Medicine, and then completed General Surgery Residency training at Monmouth Medical Center, New Jersey. In addition to her surgical practice, she runs a film production company "'Vertebra Films" with her husband Andy and son Mac. Her company has had movies screened at the Toronto International Film Festival, and also movies that have featured Oscar winners (Colin Firth) and nominees (Emily Blunt, Jesse Eisenburg), as well as Eli Roth. Dr. Cappuccino is a writer and editor for a national culinary magazine, *Gastronome*. Her husband Andy is an Orthopedic Spine surgeon, and they enjoy operating together, especially on medical missions. They have six children:

Jacqueline, thirty-two; Andrew, twenty-five; Mac, twenty-four; Jake, twenty-one; Nick, twenty; Elizabeth, eighteen; and a wonderful dog, Mocha, a Weimaraner.

Christina (Tina) L. Cervieri, MD, Orthopedic Surgeon

Chief of Orthopedic Surgery, Department of Veterans Affairs, VA Medical Center Martinsburg, WV; Clinical Professor, West Virginia University. Dr. Cervieri works for the Department of Veterans Affairs, practicing Orthopedic Surgery with a specialization in Sports Medicine and Arthroscopy. She is honored to be serving United States Veterans. She holds leadership positions at Martinsburg and regionally in Veterans Integrated Service Network (VISN) 5 of the Veterans Health Administration (VHA). She also serves as volunteer Team Physician to U.S. Figure Skating. She earned a B.A. in Philosophy at Yale University, and flirted with the film business before finding her calling in the field of medicine and returning to college for a post-baccalaureate education in the sciences. She graduated from UCLA School of Medicine in 1998 and completed a General Surgery Internship at UCSF East Bay before returning to the East Coast for an Orthopedic Surgery Residency at Lenox Hill Hospital in New York City. She received her specialty training in Sports Medicine and Arthroscopy at the American Sports Medicine Institute, Birmingham, Alabama. She worked in private practice for two years following training, prior to joining Uncle Sam and the federal government. Tina spends most of her free time with her husband and two children, ages two and one. She enjoys food and wine, gardening, biking, skiing, music, dance, and travel. One of these days, she hopes to have time again for these hobbies!

Anees B. Chagpar, MD, MPH, FRCS (C), FACS, Breast Surgeon

Associate Professor, Department of Surgery, Yale University School of Medicine; Director, The Breast Center—Smilow Cancer Hospital at Yale-New Haven; Assistant Director for Diversity and Health Equity, Yale Comprehensive Cancer Center; Program Director, Yale Interdisciplinary Breast Fellowship. Born and raised in Canada, Dr. Chagpar completed her MD with Honors in Research at the University of Alberta, and her general surgery residency training and MSc at the University of Saskatchewan. She went on to complete a Breast Fellowship at the University of Texas M. D. Anderson Cancer Center, an MPH at

Harvard School of Public Health and an MA in Bioethics and Medical Humanities at the University of Louisville. After fellowship, she joined the University of Louisville as Assistant Professor of Surgery, rising rapidly through the ranks to Associate Professor with tenure and Academic Advisory Dean. She built the first nationally accredited Breast Center in Kentucky, prior to being recruited to Yale in September 2010, where she led the effort for Yale to become the first NCI-designated Comprehensive Cancer Center in the Northeast to have a nationally accredited breast center. She is a busy breast surgical oncologist who participates in investigator-initiated and cooperative group clinical trials as well as translational and clinical research. She enjoys teaching and mentoring medical students, residents, fellows and junior faculty, and is currently pursuing an MBA in Leadership in Healthcare. Her hobbies include travel, reading and exercise.

Sujana S. Chandrasekhar, MD, FACS, FAAO-HNS, Otolaryngology—Head and Neck Surgeon

Director of New York Otology, Director of Neurotology, at the James J. Peters Veterans Administration Medical Center; Medical Director of the Vestibular Disorders Evaluation Clinic at the Bronx VA Hospital; Otologist/Neurotologist at the New York Head and Neck Institute. Dr. Chandrasekhar completed her residency in Otolaryngology-Head and Neck Surgery at New York University Medical Center in New York and her fellowship in Otology and Neuro-otology at the House Ear Clinic and Institute in Los Angeles, California. She served on the full-time academic faculty of both UMDNJ-New Jersey Medical School and Mount Sinai School of Medicine before entering private practice in New York City in October 2004. She now serves as voluntary faculty at Mount Sinai. She is at the clinical forefront in management of disorders of hearing, balance, tinnitus, facial nerve, and lateral skull base, as well as cochlear and other hearing implants. She has also written on, and is funded for, gender research in otolaryngology. She is a founding member of the Women in Otolaryngology section of the AAO-HNS. Dr. Chandrasekhar was honored with the AAO-HNS's Distinguished Service Award in September 2006 and 2012. She is Past Chair of the American Academy of Otolaryngology-Head and Neck Surgery Board of Governors, and has been selected by the Academy's Nominating Committee as one of two candidates running for President-Elect of the AAO-HNS in 2014. Her other main interest is in humanitarian outreach. She has led five groups of practitioners on medical/surgical missions to Nicaragua, and has delivered lectures and performed surgeries on several occasions in India, Brazil, Mexico, Colombia, and Venezuela. She is married and has four children.

Jeannie Chun, MD, Pediatric Surgeon

Assistant Professor of Surgery, Division of Pediatric Surgery, University of Maryland Children's Hospital, Baltimore, Maryland. Dr. Chun obtained her undergraduate degree from Brown University and her medical degree in 2000 from Brown University School of Medicine in Providence, Rhode Island. She completed her general surgery training at University of Wisconsin in Madison, Wisconsin, and her pediatric surgery training at University of Louisville, in Louisville, Kentucky. She is married to a colon and rectal surgeon, Jonathan, and has two children ages six and four.

Hannah Copeland, MD, Cardiothoracic Surgery Fellow

Loma Linda University, Department of Cardiothoracic and Vascular Surgery, Loma Linda, California. Dr. Copeland completed medical studies at University of Missouri-Kansas City School of Medicine in 2006, after which she did general surgery residency at University of California in San Diego. She is now training to be a cardio-thoracic surgeon at Loma Linda University. She has a wonderful husband and two beautiful boys, ages two years and nine months, as well as a cute dog named Pete. During her free time she enjoys going to parks, attending swimming classes with her boys and playing sports-ball.

Marion Everett Couch, MD, PhD, MBA, FACS, Otolaryngology—Head and Neck Surgeon

Professor and Chair, Dept. of Otolaryngology—Head and Neck Surgery, Indiana University. Dr. Couch is Chair of Otolaryngology—Head & Neck Surgery at Indiana University. She is also the Director of Surgical Services for Indiana University Health Physicians, a faculty practice of over 1,700 physicians. Dr. Couch is past president of the Society of University Otolaryngologists and former interim Chair of Surgery and Chief of Otolaryngology at the University of Vermont. She completed a residency in Otolaryngology at Johns Hopkins Hospital and obtained her MBA with a concentration in health sector management from Duke University. She has been married for thirty years and is the mother of fourteen-year-old twins. They enjoy skiing, running, and traveling together.

Marie Crandall, MD, MPH, FACS, Trauma/Critical Care Surgeon

Associate Professor of Surgery, Northwestern University, Feinberg School of Medicine, Chicago, Illinois. Dr. Crandall is an Associate Professor of Surgery and Preventive Medicine in the Division of Trauma and Critical Care at Northwestern University, Feinberg School of Medicine. She is originally from Detroit, Michigan, a product of Head Start and local public schools. Dr. Crandall obtained a Bachelor's Degree in Neurobiology from U. C. Berkeley in 1991 and completed her M.D. in 1996 at the Charles R. Drew/U. C. L. A. program in Los Angeles. She finished her General Surgery residency at Rush University & Cook County Hospital in 2001, and in 2003 completed a Trauma & Surgical Critical Care Fellowship at Harborview Medical Center in Seattle, Washington. During her fellowship, she obtained a Masters in Public Health from the University of Washington. Dr. Crandall performs emergency general and trauma surgery, staffs the SICU, and is an active health services researcher. Dr. Crandall loves travel, triathlons, hiking and is a passionate animal rights activist. You can follow her on Twitter @vegansurgeon.

Claire Cronin, MD, FACS, MBA, General Surgeon

Clinical Associate Professor of Surgery, Tufts University School of Medicine; Clinical Director, Auerbach Breast Center, Newton-Wellesley Hospital, Newton, Massachusetts. Dr. Cronin is a full time general surgeon at Newton-Wellesley hospital. She graduated with an MD from Tufts University School of Medicine in 1995 and thereafter completed surgery residency training at New England Deaconness Hospital and Beth Israel Deaconness Hospital. She obtained her MBA in 2009 to strengthen her position as the Clinical Director of the Auerbach Breast Center and as a Trustee of the hospital. It was during a course on leadership that the professor wrote in the margins that he liked her writing. Having chosen a career in medicine because she was a math and science type, and not an English type, this abstract comment opened a whole new world of possibilities to her. She has been published in the *Worcester Medical Magazine* and *General Surgery News*. Her writing incorporates the daily challenges of practicing medicine that surgeons face, like dirty belly-buttons in a laparoscopic case. Claire is an entrepreneur and helped develop "Under Johnnies," which are a disposable paper undergarment designed to be worn under hospital gowns for patient modesty. Her biggest success to date is that she has been married for twenty-five years and has two wonderful children. Claire is an average golfer and skier, but this could improve if more hospitals invested in her Under Johnnies.

Sarah N. Cross, MD, Obstetrician-Gynecologist

Clinical Instructor/Maternal Fetal Medicine Fellow, Department of Obstetrics, Gynecology & Reproductive Sciences, Yale University School of Medicine & Yale-New Haven Hospital. Dr. Cross is an Obstetrician-Gynecologist completing sub-speciality training in Maternal-Fetal Medicine at Yale School of Medicine in New Haven, Connecticut. She earned a B.A. in psychology from Swarthmore College. Dr. Cross completed her medical degree at the University of Chicago Pritzker School of Medicine. She graduated with honors and was elected to the Alpha Omega Alpha Honor Medical Society as well as the Gold Humanism Honor Society. Dr. Cross completed her residency in Obstetrics & Gynecology at Yale-New Haven Hospital. She worked for a year as a generalist before pursuing sub-speciality training. She has worked in the Dominican Republic as well as Rwanda. In addition to being a physician, she is a poet. She has won several awards and is one of the poetry editors for the *The Journal of Medical Humanities.* She lives on the sound in Connecticut with her husband.

Therese M. Duane, MD, FACS, FCCM, Trauma/Critical Care Surgeon

Professor of Surgery; Vice-Chair, Department of Surgery for Quality and Safety; Associate Program Director, Surgical Critical Care Fellowship; Division of Trauma, Critical Care, Emergency General Surgery ; Director of Infection Control STICU; Chair, Infection Control VCU Health System; Virginia Commonwealth University (VCU), Richmond, Virginia. Dr. Duane earned a Bachelor of Science degree from Cornell University, Ithaca, in New York and a Doctor of Medicine degree from the State University of New York, Buffalo. She completed an internship and residency in general surgery at the Eastern Virginia Medical School in Norfolk, Virginia under the tutelage of L. D. Britt, MD. She went on to complete a surgical critical care fellowship at the R Adams Cowley

Shock Trauma Center in Baltimore. She serves as Vice-Chair of Quality and Safety for the Department of Surgery. She is a member of the Acute Care Surgery committee for AAST and currently serves as the chair of the Acute Care Surgery Committee for EAST as well as being a member of the EAST Board of Directors. She is chair of the Membership committee for the Surgical Infection Society and serves on the Board of Governors for the American College of Surgeons. In her spare time she spends time with her four children, Luke John, Xavier, Lila and Sebastian and trains for ironman triathlons with her husband, Jeffrey.

Kimberly Ephgrave, MD, FACS, General Surgeon

Former Titles: Emeritus Professor of Surgery at University of Iowa Carver College of Medicine; Chief of Surgery at Iowa City VA (Veterans Affairs Medical Center); Associate Dean for Students and Curriculum at Iowa University; President, Association of Women Surgeons. Dr. Ephgrave passed away on March 6, 2012. At the time, she was Professor Emerita of Surgery at the University of Iowa Carver College of Medicine. She graduated from Loyola University Stritch School of Medicine in 1980 and completed a general surgery internship there before moving to the University of Texas-Dallas Parkland Hospital and completing a general surgery residency in 1986. In addition to her work as a faculty member, Dr. Ephgrave served for many years as Chief of Surgery at the Iowa City VA (Veterans Affairs Medical Center). She was Associate Dean for Students and Curriculum at Iowa University for five years and served as president of the Association of Women Surgeons. In 2009, after being diagnosed with cancer, she began work toward a Bachelor of Fine Arts in painting at the University of Iowa. Dr. Ephgrave enjoyed painting, writing short fiction and personal essays, traveling, hiking and spending time with her husband, Tom Rocklin, three sons, Dan, Noah and Zeb, and dachshund.

Nicole Fox, MD, MPH, Trauma/Critical Care Surgeon

Assistant Professor of Surgery, Cooper Medical School of Rowan University. Dr. Fox received her combined MD/MPH degree from UMDNJ-New Jersey Medical School in 2005. Dr. Fox completed her residency in general surgery at Christiana Care in Newark, Delaware, and her surgical critical care fellowship at Cooper University Hospital in Camden, NJ. Following fellowship, she joined the faculty at Cooper, an American College of Surgeons-verified Level 1 trauma center, as a trauma/acute care surgeon and surgical intensivist. She is active in clinical research, with a specific focus on long term outcomes of trauma patients as well as performance improvement and patient safety. Dr. Fox is extremely proud of her family. Her husband, Richard, is a physician in Philadelphia, Pennsylvania. They enjoy spending time with their daughter, Isabella Ana, on their horse farm in southern New Jersey.

Julie Ann Freischlag, MD, FACS, Vascular Surgeon

Vice Chancellor of Human Health Services; Dean, School of Medicine, UC Davis (University of California); Former William Stewart Halsted Professor and Chair, Department of Surgery, The Johns Hopkins Hospital, Baltimore; Chair, Board of Regents, American College of Surgeons; President of the Society for Vascular Surgery. Dr. Freischlag was the first female to head the Department of Surgery at The Johns Hopkins Hospital (JHH). She is also the first female President of the Society for Vascular Surgery and the first woman Chair of the Board of Regents of the American College of Surgeons. She studied medicine at Rush Medical School, Chicago, Illinois, in 1980. Following this, she completed both General Surgery Residency as well as Vascular Surgery Fellowship at the University of California, Los Angeles (UCLA). She previously served on the faculty at the Medical College of Wisconsin and the David Geffen School of Medicine at UCLA. While in Baltimore, she worked part-time at the Baltimore VA Medical Center. She has served as principal investigator on several major studies, is editor of *JAMA Surgery* and serves on the editorial boards of *Annals of Vascular Surgery* and *Journal of the American Medical Association.* She is involved with the American Medical Women's Association, the Association for Academic Surgery, the Association of Women Surgeons and the Society of Surgical Chairs. Her hobbies include reading, running, swimming, crafts and watching boys' sporting events. She has three sons, Matthew (thirty-three), Paul (thirty-two) and Taylor (eighteen) and a daughter-in-law, Gretchen. Her five-year-old cockapoo is called Brett.

Amy Friedman, MD, FACS, Transplant Surgeon

Chief Medical Officer and Executive Vice President, New York Organ Donor Network. Dr. Friedman did her undergraduate studies at Princeton University.

She graduated from SUNY Downstate Medical School in 1983, and after general surgery residency at SUNY Downstate completed fellowship training in Transplant Surgery at the Hospital of the University of Pennsylvania. She has held faculty positions at Yale University School of Medicine, the University of Pennsylvania and the SUNY Upstate Medical University where she was Professor of Surgery and Director of Transplantation. As a surgeon, she specializes in live donor kidney transplantation, laparoscopic kidney donation and pancreas transplantation. She has served as principal investigator for numerous drug trials and led a $1.5 million AHRQ-study (Agency for Healthcare Research and Quality) on using the Web to educate kidney transplant recipients on drug regimens. Dr. Friedman has been editor in chief of the *Journal of Patient Safety and Adherence* and serves as an article reviewer for *Archives of Surgery, American Journal of Transplantation, American Journal of Kidney Diseases and Transplantation*. Hobbies include photography, quilting and writing.

Fatima Garuba Wilder, MD, General Surgery Resident

UMDNJ, Newark, New Jersey. Dr. Garuba Wilder graduated from The Ohio State University College of Medicine with a medical degree in 2011. She is a general surgery resident in training at UMDNJ University of Medicine and Dentistry in Newark, NJ. She is taking time off from residency to complete a research fellowship at the Memorial Sloan Kettering Cancer Center, investigating targeted therapy for liposarcoma. Fatima enjoys cooking, traveling and spending time with family and friends in her free time. She hopes to incorporate academic work/research into her career-long term and do medical mission work in the future.

Deborah A. Geer, MD, FACS, General Surgeon

Solo private practice. Dr. Geer is a general surgeon in private practice, and has privileges at Auburn Community Hospital, New York. She attended University of Rochester medical school and subsequently completed her surgical training at Tripler Army Medical Center (a military surgical residency program) Honolulu, Hawaii in 1986. She trained in an era where there were no work-hour restrictions and few female role models. Her husband spent sixteen years at home raising their kids while she worked. He is practice manager in her solo general surgery practice, located in a rural community in Auburn, New York, In addition to training as a general surgeon, Dr. Geer obtained a Masters in Practical Theology, and is an ordained chaplain. She plays the harp, flute and piano and is a certified music practitioner who is involved with therapeutic music.

Madison Griffin, MD, General Surgery Resident

Mercer University School of Medicine, Georgia. Madison Griffin was a fourth-year medical student at University of Texas Medical School, Houston, when she submitted her essay. Growing up as the daughter of a geologist and a lawyer, Madison had never experienced life as a surgeon. After graduating from University of Texas with a BA and BS in 2010, she entered medical school at the University of Texas with an open mind, determined to find something she was passionate about, that would allow her to make a difference in the lives of others. She eventually decided that surgery is the specialty for her. Madison is currently training at Mercer University School of Medicine's general surgery residency program. She chose general surgery for its broad scope of procedures and patients, as well as the different options one can pursue after residency. Madison is also currently a second lieutenant in the United States Air Force (USAF) and plans to serve wounded warriors and their families either as a resident in one of the USAF programs or after residency as a board-certified general surgeon. Hobbies include playing and watching sports and traveling.

Zeenat R. Hasan, MD, General and Minimally Invasive Surgeon

Dignity Health Medical Group; St. Francis/St. Mary's Hospitals and Clinics, San Francisco, California. Dr. Hasan completed fellowship training in Minimally Invasive Surgery at Stanford University in June 2013. She graduated with an MD from University of Missouri-Kansas City in 2007. She has been writing poetry since the age of eight, continuing the long tradition of surgeons as authors. Dr. Hasan grew up in the Midwest, but plans to settle in the Northern California area. Hobbies include tennis, reading and theater. She finds great pleasure in a finely brewed cup of coffee.

Amanda V. Hayman, MD, MPH, Colon and Rectal Surgeon

The Oregon Clinic, Portland, Oregon. Dr. Hayman graduated from Oregon Health and Science University with an MD and MPH in 2006. She completed her general surgery residency training at Northwestern University's Feinberg School of Medicine in Chicago and began a Colon and Rectal Surgery fellowship at the Mayo Clinic in Rochester, Minnesota in July 2013. She enjoys cooking and gardening. Her husband is an internist, and their daughter, Simone, was born in 2009. They also share their home with two cats, a dog, and an au pair.

Joan Huffman, MD, FACS, Critical Care Surgeon

When Dr. Huffman was growing up in small town Ohio, a victim of child abuse, then domestic violence, she imagined a life of wide experiences and travel. Over the years her life evolved, as she became an LPN (licensed practical nurse), then graduated summa cum laude from undergraduate and went on to medical school. Her next journey was surgical residency and trauma-critical care fellowships. For fifteen years she practiced as an Acute Care Surgeon, first at a community hospital in the Philadelphia suburbs and later at the University of Florida in Jacksonville, Florida. Her professional life expanded with interests in Palliative Care, Organ Procurement and Wound Care. She edited Northeast Florida Medicine, published and spoke locally, regionally and nationally. Her soul work included Domestic Violence prevention and medical missions to Haiti. Rising to an unexpected opportunity, she staffed an international medical repatriation and circumnavigated the world in five days. Life broadened and deepened as she travelled abroad to Europe, New Zealand, Africa, Central/South America, and Asia. She has now limited her practice to Critical Care and lives high atop a bluff in Montana, with her partner, Roberta, a retired Nurse Practitioner, where she writes looking out over the plains and mountains.

Imani Jackson Rosario, MD, Urologist

Assistant Professor of Surgery, Urology, Rutgers New Jersey Medical School; Attending Urologist, University Hospital, Newark NJ. Dr. Jackson Rosario obtained her undergraduate degree from Cornell University. She obtained her MD from Georgetown School of Medicine in 2004. As a medical student, she was very involved in community outreach and received an award for humanism in medicine. She completed her Urology Residency at UMDNJ (University of Medicine and Dentistry of New Jersey, now Rutgers New Jersey Medical School) in 2009. Dr. Jackson Rosario has special interest in working with underprivileged and medically underserved communities and prostate cancer in African American men. In her practice she treats a wide range of urological conditions, including sexual issues, in both men and women. She enjoys participating in medical missions to underdeveloped nations around the world. She is a native New Yorker but has learned to love her new life in New Jersey. She lives with her husband, Ramon, who sells roller coasters, their twins, Jackson and Addison, and their dogs, Oliver, a wonderfully behaved French bulldog, and Carlos, a Chihuahua who is not so well behaved. She enjoys cooking and falling asleep on beaches all over the planet.

Preeti R. John, MBBS, MPH, FACS, General Surgeon/Critical Care Surgeon

Acting Director, Surgical Intensive Care Unit, Baltimore VA Medical Center; Clinical Assistant Professor, University of Maryland Medical Center, Baltimore, Maryland. Dr. John graduated with a medical degree from St. John's Medical College in Bangalore, India, following which she traveled to the U.S. to pursue further studies. After obtaining an MPH degree from The Johns Hopkins Bloomberg School of Public Health in Baltimore, she completed a post-doctoral research fellowship at The Johns Hopkins division of Gastroenterology. She then trained as a surgeon at The Johns Hopkins residency training program in Surgery and the Rutgers-New Jersey Medical School Surgery program, where she stayed to complete a trauma and surgical critical care fellowship. This was followed by a year as trauma surgery fellow at The Johns Hopkins Hospital. She is board certified in General Surgery and Surgical Critical Care. While working as an attending surgeon at the Baltimore VA, she developed an interest in Geriatric Surgery and Palliative Medicine, and obtained additional board certification in Hospice and Palliative Medicine—one of only sixty-two surgeons in the U.S. to do so. She loves children and animals, volunteers for animal rescue organizations and shares her home with Coco-Puff, an adopted poodle, and Pumpkin, an adopted cat. Hobbies include cooking, reading and learning about voice-over narration.

Kate Khalifeh, MD, Colon and Rectal Surgeon

Associate Surgeon at Fairfax Colon and Rectal Surgery, Fairfax, VA. Dr. Khalifeh worked for ten years as a nurse in the Cardiac-Surgery ICU at The Johns

Hopkins Hospital before returning to medical school at Johns Hopkins, where she also completed her general surgery residency training. She then moved to Washington, D. C., to complete her colorectal surgery fellowship at Washington Hospital Center. She joined the practice with Fairfax Colon and Rectal Surgery and is currently working to build her practice in Northern VA, working through the challenges of her first years in practice and trying to strike the work-family balance. She is the proud mother of two wonderful little girls who are the highlight of every day. Her husband is a busy plastic surgeon, and in their free time they enjoy spending time with their girls and extended family, swimming and exploring all that the nation's capital has to offer.

Fatima Khambaty, MD, General Surgeon

Mid Atlantic Permanente Medical Group (Kaiser Permanente), Washington, D. C. Dr. Khambaty is a California native transplanted many times over, who now lives in Washington, D. C. She finished both medical school (2000) and surgery residency training at Howard University (Washington, D. C.). After residency, she ended up as a staff surgeon on the Navajo reservation in Four Corners of New Mexico, where she actually had the opportunity to call a medicine man once for a pre-operative consult. A bit bewitched by the desert, she then moved to Eritrea (the Horn of Africa) to work for a Virginia-based, non-profit organization, Physicians for Peace. In Eritrea, she was a staff surgeon at two public hospitals in the capital city, Asmara, and helped to start and run the first general surgery residency program in the country. She subsequently returned to the U.S. to complete a fellowship in Minimally Invasive Surgery at George Washington University (Washington, D. C.). She now works for Kaiser Permanente and squeezes in surgical mission work and generalized globetrotting to feed her ever-growing gypsy when possible. Aside from her love for surgery, she keeps balanced by swimming, cooking and spending time with friends and family.

Deborah A Kuhls, MD, FACS, FCCM, Critical Care Surgeon

Associate Dean for Academic Affairs, Chief Academic Officer, Las Vegas Campus; Associate Program Director, Critical Care Fellowship Program; Professor of Surgery; Chief, Section of Critical Care, University of Nevada School of Medicine. Dr. Kuhls is Associate Dean of Academic Affairs and Professor of Surgery at the University of Nevada School of Medicine. She was born and raised in rural Wisconsin, the eldest daughter of a prominent farmer. Her medical career followed a career in financial product development, after which she followed a lifelong dream of becoming a physician and found her passion in trauma and critical care surgery. She was inspired by her family physician in rural Wisconsin, who cared for her entire family and became a close friend in adulthood. She attended a post-baccalaureate program before entering medical school at the Medical College of Pennsylvania. Following residency and fellowship training at Albert Einstein University and the R Adams Cowley Shock Trauma Center at the University of Maryland, she has spent her clinical career at the University of Nevada School of Medicine caring for injured patients. Academically, she was the Surgery Clerkship Director until she became Assistant Dean, then Associate Dean of Academic Affairs. She has been an active researcher, focusing on injury and care of critically injured patients. Dr. Kuhls remains active in several professional organizations, focusing on medical education, trauma surgery and critical care. In 2012 she assumed the role of national chair of the American College of Surgery Committee on Trauma's Injury Prevention Committee. In 2013 she completed the Executive Leadership in Academic Medicine (ELAM) Program at Drexel University School of Medicine.

Anjali S Kumar, MD, MPH, FACS, Colon and Rectal Surgeon

Washington Hospital Center, Washington D. C.; Assistant Professor of Surgery, Georgetown University. Dr. Kumar is an attending colon and rectal surgeon at MedStar Washington Hospital Center and Director of Research and Education for the Section of Colon and Rectal Surgery. As an Assistant Professor of Surgery at Georgetown University, she is the site director for a medical student core rotation in surgery. Dr. Kumar received her M.D. in 2001 and two B.S. degrees in 1996 from the University of Washington in Seattle, and a Master of Public Health from Harvard University in Boston. She completed a general surgery residency at the University of California San Francisco-East Bay in Oakland, California, with a two-year research fellowship at University of California San Francisco. Following her residency, she trained with world leaders in laparoscopy during a Colon and Rectal Surgery Fellowship at The New York Presbyterian Hospital of Cornell and Columbia Universities. Dr. Kumar has won many awards and grants for women's health research and activism, and has published numerous scientific articles on early cancer detection, treatment and prevention. She has served on the Executive Council for the Association of Women Surgeons—Metropolitan Washington, D. C. Chapter for the past three years.

Adriana Laser, MD, MPH, Vascular Surgery Fellow

University of Maryland Medical Center, Baltimore, Maryland. Dr. Laser was a general surgery resident at the University of Maryland Medical Center (UMMC) when she contributed to this book. She completed undergraduate studies at Wesleyan University and subsequently earned an MPH at Tulane University in International Health and Development. She then graduated with an MD from University of Maryland School of Medicine in 2007 and stayed on at this institution for general surgery residency training. Adriana completed a two year research fellowship at University of Michigan in the Jobst Vascular Surgery Laboratory. She is currently training to be a vascular surgeon at UMMC. She lives in Baltimore with her husband and two children, Zachary and Madelyn. Cooking, building and bouncing with them are her favorite hobbies.

Barbara E. Lazio, MD, FAANS, Neurosurgeon

Providence Medical Group, Olympia, Washington. Dr. Lazio is a practicing neurosurgeon with a focus on brain tumors and stereotactic radiosurgery. After undergraduate studies at Miami University, she received her MD from the University of Cincinnati College of Medicine in 1995. She completed Neurosurgery training at University of Maryland in Baltimore in 2001. Dr. Lazio enjoys spending time with her husband, Matt, daughters, Dahlia and Mia, and their two Weimaraners, Louis and Gracie. She enjoys music and is learning how to play the piano. She loves to be outdoors doing her favorite activities: riding her bike, walking in the woods, exploring pebbly beaches around her Pacific Northwest home. She wishes more operating rooms had windows.

Heather Lillemoe, MD, General Surgery Resident

Vanderbilt University Medical Center, Tennessee. Heather Lillemoe was in her fourth year of medical school at the University of Maryland School of Medicine when she submitted her essay. Growing up as the daughter of an academic surgeon, Heather saw firsthand "the good and the bad" of life as a surgeon. (Her father, Keith Lillemoe, is Chief of the Department of Surgery at Massachusetts General Hospital, Boston.) After graduating from Vanderbilt University with a BA in 2010, she entered medical school at the University of Maryland, unsure of what specialty she would pursue. Eventually, Heather discovered that she shares the same passion as her father. She is currently training to be a surgeon at Vanderbilt University Medical Center. Hobbies include playing and watching sports, music and baking.

Mary Maniscalco-Theberge, MD, FACS, General Surgeon/Critical Care Surgeon

Deputy Medical Inspector, Professional Services Office of the Medical Inspector Veterans Health Administration; Attending Breast Surgeon, Walter Reed National Military Medical Center, Bethesda, Maryland; Associate Professor of Surgery, Uniformed Services University of the Health Sciences Bethesda, Maryland. Dr. Maniscalco graduated with an MD from Eastern Virginia Medical School in 1981. She completed general surgery residency training at Eisenhower Army Medical Center, Fort Gordon, Georgia, and thereafter specialized in trauma and critical care, training at The Washington Hospital Center, Washington, D. C. and Walter Reed Army Medical Center. Dr. Maniscalco served for twenty-six years in the U.S. Army, and was the Chief of Surgery at Walter Reed Army Medical Center from 2001-2006. She was the first and only female Chief of the Department of Surgery at Walter Reed in its 102 year history. She is active in many regional and national associations. She is the past-President of the Metropolitan Washington, D. C. Chapter of the American College of Surgeons (ACS) and the Association of Women Surgeons' Metropolitan Washington, D. C. chapter. She is a surgical educator with the ACS and has chaired and taught the "Surgeons as Educators: Principals and Practice" course for over sixteen years at the ACS Clinical Congress. Her hobbies include knitting and spending time at the lake with her husband, two children, two dogs, and the rest of her extended family.

Patricia Eubanks May, MD, FACS, General Surgeon, Surgical Oncologist

Assistant Chief of Surgery, Department of Surgery, Kaiser Permanente Santa Rosa, California. Dr. May is a board-certified General Surgeon who has been actively practicing surgery since 1997. She graduated as an Alpha Omega Alpha Honor student from Chicago Medical School in 1990, and completed her general surgery residency and surgical oncology fellowship at Harbor-UCLA Medical Center in Torrance, California. She served as Associate Professor of Surgery at University of Nevada School of Medicine, and started the UCSF-East Bay Surgical Residency program at Reno VA Medical Center (VA Sierra Nevada Health Care System). She also became board-certified in Hospice and Palliative Care Medicine with the encouragement of her partner Geriatrician as co-recipient of the Geriatrics for Specialists Initiative Grant. (She is one of only sixty-two surgeons in the U.S. who are additionally board certified in this specialty.) She recently relocated to Santa Rosa, California, and works at Kaiser Permanente. She serves as coordinator of Medical Student Surgical education at Kaiser Santa Rosa and continues as Assistant Clinical Professor of surgery at UCSF. With a heart of compassion and love of surgery, Dr. May continues her active surgical practice, focusing on general surgery, laparoscopy and oncologic surgery. In her free time, she enjoys spending time with her family, which includes her husband, three children, one dog and a lizard.

Amina Merchant, MD, Trauma/Acute Care Surgery Fellow

Vanderbilt University, Nashville, Tennessee. Dr. Merchant is originally from Rockford, Illinois. She graduated from University of Illinois medical school in 2007 and was a general surgery resident at Rush University Medical Center/Cook County Hospital, Chicago, Illinois until June 30, 2013. She is currently pursuing fellowship training in Trauma/Acute Care Surgery at Vanderbilt University. Hobbies include running, hiking and travel. She also enjoys going to the symphony, reading and discussing politics and policy.

Cherie-Ann Nathan, MD, FACS, Otolaryngology—Head and Neck Surgeon

Professor and Chair, Department of Otolaryngology/Head and Neck Surgery, Louisiana State University Health Science Center (LSUHSC), Shreveport, Louisiana; Director of Head and Neck Oncologic Surgery and Research at the Feist-Weiller Cancer Center, Shreveport. Dr. Nathan completed her Otolaryngology/Head and Neck Surgery residency and head and neck fellowship in 1995 at University of California, San Diego. In addition, she was a post-doc fellow at Johns

Hopkins University. She is a surgeon-scientist with a busy practice treating head and neck cancer patients, thyroid and parathyroid diseases and voice disorders, and leads an active clinical and basic science research team. She has an active translational research program funded by the National Cancer Institute, focusing on targeted therapy for head and neck cancers. She is nationally and internationally recognized for her seminal work on molecular analysis of surgical margins. She has published extensively and has over 150 publications in peer-reviewed journals and has authored textbooks and encyclopedia chapters. Dr. Nathan serves on many National committees, including the NCI Task Force, board of directors for the Head and Neck Cancer Alliance, Academy of Otolaryngology/HNS and the American Head and Neck Society, and is a member of many societies, including Alpha Omega Alpha. The Board of Regents in Louisiana established the "Cherie-Ann Nathan Endowed Professorship in Otolaryngology/Head and Neck Surgery" initiated by grateful patients, to honor her dedication and expertise; and she received the Leonard Tow Humanism in Medicine Award presented by the Arnold P. Gold Foundation 2012. Cherie-Ann on the piano and her two sons—one a violinist and the other a cellist—perform as the "Nathan Family Trio" in multiple fund raisers in their hometown, while her husband, a critical care pulmonologist and a music lover, appreciates their performances.

Patricia J. Numann, MD, FACS, FRCPSG (Hon), FRCSEd (Hon), General Surgeon with Special Interest in Breast and Endocrine Surgery (Retired 2007)

Lloyd S Rogers Professor of Surgery Emeritus; SUNY Distinguished Teaching Professor Emeritus; SUNY Distinguished Service Professor Emeritus; State University of New York, Upstate Medical University, Syracuse, NY; Ninety-second President of American College of Surgeons. Dr. Numann is a trailblazing pioneer for women in the field of Surgery and has held numerous positions of leadership, most recently the Presidency of the American College of Surgeons (the second woman ever to have held this position in its 100 year history). She is the founder of the "Association of Women Surgeons,"an international organization of women who practice in surgical specialties. Dr. Numann graduated with an MD from SUNY Upstate Medical Center in 1965, completed surgery residency training at this same institution and subsequently joined the faculty at SUNY Upstate Medical Center in 1970. She remained there until her retirement in 2007. She loves to travel, cook and read (especially cookbooks), and has an appreciation for art (particularly Japanese art) and antiques. Walking through antique shows provides her usual physical activity. She has always admired Eleanor Roosevelt, who was one of the only visible career women during her childhood.

Susan E. Pories, MD, FACS, Breast Surgeon

Medical Director, Hoffman Breast Center, Mount Auburn Hospital and Beth Israel Deaconess Medical Center; Associate Professor of Surgery, Harvard Medical School; Past President, Association of Women Surgeons. Dr. Pories graduated from University of Vermont with an MD in 1984. She then trained as a general surgery resident at the same University. Following this she completed a surgical oncology fellowship at New England Deaconess Hospital (now Beth Israel Deaconess Hospital), Harvard Medical School. She also did a Medical Education Fellowship at Mount Auburn Hospital, Harvard Medical School, between 2005 and 2006. Dr. Pories is a breast surgeon at the Beth Israel Deaconess Medical Center and Mount Auburn Hospital. In addition to the above titles, she is the current President of the Association of Women Surgeons. Dr. Pories co-chairs the Harvard Medical School (HMS) Academy Writing for Scholarship Interest Group, she is Faculty Advisor to the HMS writers' group, and serves on the "Arts & Humanities @HMS" Planning Committee. She is the co-editor of *The Soul of a Doctor* and co-author of *Cancer: Biography of a Disease.*

Sylvia Marina Ramos (Pen Name: Sylvia Ramos Cruz), MD, MS, FACS, General Surgeon

Breast Specialty Care; Volunteer Faculty Appointment: Clinical Professor of Surgery, University of New Mexico School of Medicine. Dr. Ramos was born in Puerto Rico and grew up in New York City. She graduated with an MD from Albert Einstein College of Medicine in 1974. She also completed surgical training there, was on the faculty at Einstein and obtained a Master's Degree in health services management at NYU. She moved to New Mexico in 1990 and currently practices part-time, specializing in the diagnosis and management of breast diseases and lymphedema. After almost forty years in Surgery, she's still nourished by her interactions with patients. She is fortunate to have her daughter, Carolyn, and grandson, Santiago, near her in Albuquerque. She's an avid gardener and world traveler. As an activist for women's rights, which are human rights, she co-ordinates the campaign for ratification of the Equal Rights Amendment for the American Humanist Association. Dr. Ramos loves words for their sounds and how they help distill personal experience into elemental humanity. She feels fortunate to be a member of an inspiring poetry writing group and to participate in the vibrant Albuquerque writers' community. Throughout her life she has tried to stay true to her own words of wisdom, "Live up to your hopes, not down to your fears."

Susan Reid, BA, MD, FRCPSC, General Surgeon

Professor and Chair Department of Surgery, John A. Bauer Chair in Surgery Faculty of Health Sciences, McMaster University, Hamilton Ontario, Canada. Dr. Reid is the first woman to Chair a Department of Surgery in Canada. She graduated with a BA degree from York University in 1984, after which she completed her medical training at McMaster University in 1987. This was followed by Postgraduate Training and certification in General Surgery (1992) and Critical Care (1993) at the same University. Dr. Reid has been faculty at McMaster University and Hamilton Health Sciences since 1993. Extensively involved in Education, she has served as Program Director in General Surgery, Department Education Coordinator, Associate Chair of Education, Chair of the Education committee for the Canadian Association of General Surgeons and Presidents of the Canadian Association of General Surgeons. Her favorite things to do outside the hospital include spending time with her husband and children, running, cooking and spending time at the cottage in the summer months.

Taylor S. Riall, MD, PhD, FACS, Hepatobiliary and Pancreatic Surgeon

Associate Professor, John Sealy Distinguished Chair in Clinical Research, University of Texas Medical Branch (UTMB), Galveston, Texas. Dr. Riall graduated with a BA in Chemistry with Highest Honors from Rutgers University and then earned her MD at Johns Hopkins University School of Medicine in 1996. She stayed in Baltimore to complete surgical residency training at Johns Hopkins Hospital and studied pancreatic cancer as a research fellow. She was an Instructor at Johns Hopkins from 2004 until 2005, following which she moved to UTMB. There, she earned a PhD in Health Services and has been involved with population-based outcomes research with a focus on pancreatic cancer patients. Dr. Riall is an academic surgeon and performs mostly complex pancreatic and hepato-biliary surgery, as well as some general abdominal surgery. She specializes in pancreatic cancer surgery, and is a member of UTMB's pancreatic islet cell transplantation program. In her free time, she enjoys running, swimming, cycling and ballroom dancing. She loves spending time with Charlie, her husband.

Christine Rohde, MD, MPH, FACS, Plastic and Reconstructive Surgeon

Assistant Professor of Surgery, Columbia University Medical Center, New York Presbyterian Center. Dr. Rohde graduated from Harvard Medical School in 2000, and completed general surgery training at Brigham and Women's Hospital, Boston. She moved to New York to train in plastic surgery at Montefiore Medical Center/Albert Einstein College of Medicine, followed by a microsurgical fellowship at New York University Medical Center. While working full-time, she obtained a Masters in Public Health from Columbia University Mailman School of Public Health, graduating in May 2013. She is thankful for a wonderful husband and three beautiful children, who help keep her sane (and insane at the same time). Having trained in classical voice, she enjoys performing opera whenever possible. She also enjoys knitting and card-making for relaxation.

Minerva Romero Arenas, MD, MPH, General Surgery Resident

Sinai Hospital of Baltimore, Baltimore, Maryland. She is a General Surgery Resident at Sinai Hospital of Baltimore. She studied Cell Biology and French at Arizona State University as an undergraduate and received her MD and MPH from the University of Arizona College of Medicine and the Zuckerman College of Public Health in 2009. She has completed a research fellowship at the University of Texas MD Anderson Cancer Center in Texas. Her interests include surgical oncology and endocrinology, global health, health disparities, quality improvement, and genomics. She is passionate about recruiting the next generation of surgeons and is involved in mentoring. She enjoys fine arts, films, gastronomy and sports. She blows off stress with swimming and kickboxing, and treasures spending time with her family and loved ones.

Sharona Ross, MD, FACS, Minimally Invasive, Hepatobiliary, Pancreas and Foregut Surgeon

Florida Hospital Tampa, Director, Minimally Invasive Surgery and Surgical Endoscopy; Director, Advanced GI and HPB Surgical Fellowship Program; Founder and Director, Women in Surgery Initiative. Dr. Ross was born and raised in the nation of Israel. After two years of military service in the Israel Defense Forces, she moved to the U.S., where she graduated *Phi Beta Kappa* and *Summa Cum Ladue* from the American University in Washington, D. C., and later *Alpha Omega Alpha* from the George Washington University School of Medicine and Health Sciences in 2001. After completing her General Surgery residency at University of South Florida (USF), Tampa, Florida, Dr. Ross was awarded the prestigious HPB/Advanced Gastrointestinal Surgery and Minimally Invasive Surgery Fellowship at USF/Tampa General Hospital. She then completed an Endoscopic Gastroenterology Fellowship. In addition to the above-listed titles, she is the Program Director/Chair of the 2010, 2011, 2012, 2013 and upcoming Annual International Women in Surgery Career Symposium. Dr. Ross was one of the first surgeons in the United States to undertake Laparo-Endoscopic Single Site (LESS) surgery, and continues to develop new techniques and instrumentation to improve its safety and application. As a leader in American medicine, Dr. Ross continues to push the envelope in the advancement of Minimally Invasive Surgery.

Amy Rushing, MD, FACS, Trauma Surgeon

Wellspan York Hospital, York, Pennsylvania. Dr. Rushing is originally from Chester, Virginia, and attended medical school at Eastern Virginia Medical School (EVMS) in Norfolk, Virginia. She completed general surgery training at EVMS in 2009 and went on to train in surgical critical care at R Adams Cowley Shock Trauma Center, University of Maryland in Baltimore from 2009-2010. She completed her training in acute care surgery at The Johns Hopkins Hospital in 2011 and thereafter joined the faculty as assistant professor. She recently moved to York, Pennsylvania. Her husband, Greg, completed his training in cardiac surgery at Johns Hopkins in 2012. When away from the hospital, she enjoys cooking and travel as well as raising her precocious beagle named Halsted.

Carol Sawmiller, MD, FACS, General Surgeon

Clinical Assistant Professor of Surgery, Wright State University. Dr. Sawmiller earned her medical degree at The Ohio State University College of Medicine in 1994, where she served as Student Council President. Her general surgery residency training was done at Saint Mary's Hospital, an affiliate of Yale University. She spent one year as a post-doctoral research fellow in vascular surgery at Yale University, publishing multiple articles in surgical journals. Dr. Sawmiller served in the United States Navy after completing residency. She was the Ship's Surgeon onboard the aircraft carrier the *USS Carl Vinson* in 2001, one of a few women to hold this position. The ship provided primary support for the military response to the September 11 terrorist attacks. She deployed again in support of Operation Iraqi Freedom in 2003, establishing an evacuation hospital for casualties of the Iraq war. She achieved the rank of Lieutenant Commander prior to her honorable discharge. Dr. Sawmiller spent several years in private practice in Bremerton, Washington, and is currently part of a busy general and laparoscopic surgery practice, "South Dayton Surgeons, Inc.," in Dayton, Ohio. She is a Clinical Assistant Professor of Surgery at Wright State University. Dr. Sawmiller lives in Bellbrook, Ohio, with her husband and two children.

Gianna Scannell, MD, FACS, General Surgeon

Professor of Physiology, St. James School of Medicine, Anguilla. Dr. Scannell attended Medical School at University of Padova, Italy, and graduated in 1974. She moved to America shortly after completing residency training in General Surgery in Italy. She repeated that residency training at the University of California, Irvine (UCI), where she graduated in 1986. In 1988, she completed fellowship training in Trauma and Surgical Critical Care, also at UCI. She remained at UCI as an Assistant Professor in Trauma and Critical Care until 1995, when she became Associate Professor at the University of Florida, Jacksonville. Dr. Scannell then worked for several years as a private practice surgeon in rural Washington. She has recently moved to Anguilla (located in the Caribbean Sea) to be a professor and teach Advanced Clinical Correlation with the Basic Sciences at the St. James School of Medicine.

Carol E. H. Scott-Conner, MD, PhD, MBA, General Surgeon

Professor of Surgery, Former Chair of Surgery, Department of Surgery, University of Iowa Carver College of Medicine. Dr. Scott-Conner is professor of surgery and former Head of the Department of Surgery at the University of Iowa Carver College of Medicine, where she practices breast surgery. She attended New York University College of Medicine, graduated with an MD in 1976, and completed surgical residency there in 1981. She has been fortunate to maintain a very diverse academic general surgery practice, including surgical oncology, trauma and burns, until 2007, when she narrowed her practice to breast surgery. She lives in a rural part of Iowa City with her husband of thirty-nine years, Dr. Harry Conner. She loves to write and has authored or coauthored more than ten surgical textbooks. Her short stories regularly appear in small literary journals. A collection of her short stories was published as *A Few Small Moments*. She serves as editor-in-chief of *The Examined Life*, the literary journal of the University of Iowa, Carver College of Medicine. Other hobbies include watching nature and cycling.

Sheri Slezak, MD, FACS, Plastic and Reconstructive Surgeon

Professor and Chair, Division of Plastic Surgery, University of Maryland School of Medicine, Baltimore, Maryland. Dr. Slezak grew up in Seattle. She went to the University of Washington for undergraduate studies and then to Harvard Medical School. She graduated with an MD in 1980 and then completed training in general surgery at Columbia Presbyterian in New York City. Dr. Slezak did her plastic surgery fellowship at Johns Hopkins Hospital. She presently works at the University of Maryland. She has developed a national curriculum for plastic surgery and is a director of the American Board of Plastic Surgery. She enjoys work, but equally important is spending time with children, family and friends, travelling, attending book club, church and yoga.

Elizabeth Warner, MD, FACS, General Surgeon

Southwestern Vermont Medical Center, Vermont; Co-Chair, SVMC Breast Program Leadership. Dr. Warner lives in southern Vermont with her husband and two children. She graduated with an MD from Albany Medical College in 2000 and then completed general surgery training at Georgetown University Hospital. She loves her work as a community surgeon, and also enjoys tending to her garden, remodeling her historic home and caring for her chickens and pets. Writing and music have played important roles in her life. It is the balance between art and science, family and work, which sustains her as a doctor, mother and wife.

Kristy Weber, MD, Orthopedic Oncologist

Professor and Vice Chair of Faculty Affairs, University of Pennsylvania Department of Orthopedic Surgery; Director of Sarcoma Program, Abramson Cancer Center. Dr. Weber is an orthopedic oncologist. She deals with patients of all ages who have benign and malignant bone and soft tissue tumors and metastatic bone disease. She graduated from medical school at Johns Hopkins University in 1991. After completing Orthopedic residency training at University of Iowa, she did fellowship training in Orthopedic Oncology at Mayo Clinic, Rochester. Her first faculty position was at the University of Texas MD Anderson Cancer Center in Houston. She was then recruited to Johns Hopkins in 2003, where she continued her clinical work with patients who have bone and soft tissue tumors. She also ran a basic science laboratory studying bone metastasis and bone biology. In 2006, her research team won the Kappa Delta Award for outstanding orthopedic research. While at Johns Hopkins Hospital, she was chief of Orthopedic Oncology. She has served on the Boards of Directors of multiple national societies including the American Academy of Orthopedic Surgeons, Musculoskeletal Tumor Society, American Orthopedic Association and the Ruth Jackson Orthopedic Society. She was recruited by the University of Pennsylvania in 2013 to leadership positions in both the Department of Orthopedic Surgery and the Abramson Cancer Center.

Debrah Wirtzfeld, MD, MSc, FRCSC, FACS, Surgical Oncologist

Provincial Lead, Surgical Oncology, CancerCare Manitoba; Associate Professor of Surgery, Community Health Sciences and Biochemistry and Clinical Genetics, University of Manitoba. Dr. Wirtzfeld works in an academic practice in Winnipeg, Manitoba, Canada, and is the Provincial Head of Surgical Oncology, CancerCare Manitoba. As such, she has a provincial mandate for the standardization and optimization of surgical care for cancer patients in the province of Manitoba. She graduated from University of Calgary, Faculty of Medicine, with a medical degree in 1993, and stayed on at this institution for general surgery residency training. Her surgical oncology fellowship training was at Roswell Park Cancer Institute, Buffalo, New York. She deals with patients who have various types of cancer: melanoma, retroperitoneal/extremity sarcoma, advanced and inherited gastrointestinal malignancies. Previously, she was an Associate Professor at Memorial University of Newfoundland. While on sabbatical leave, she completed her Masters in Clinical Epidemiology. She is a previous President of the Canadian Association of University Surgeons and the President Elect of the Canadian Association of General Surgeons. Personally, she is mother to two amazing boys, Eric, ten, and Ryan, six. Her family also includes a cat and a gecko. She enjoys elliptical and circuit training, travel and building Lego.

Linda Wong, MD, FACS, General, Transplant and Hepatobiliary Surgeon

Director , Liver Transplant Program, Queens Medical Center, Hawaii; Professor of Surgery, University of Hawaii, John A. Burns School of Medicine; Professor, University of Hawaii, Cancer Center. Dr. Wong grew up in Honolulu and attended Punahou School, then received a BS from Stanford University and an MD degree from the University of California, Irvine, in 1986. She completed surgical residency at Cedars-Sinai Medical Center in Los Angeles and a transplant fellowship at California Pacific Medical Center in San Francisco. She then returned to Hawaii to join a practice with her father, Dr. Livingston Wong, who performed Hawaii's first kidney transplant in 1969. In 1993, she started Hawaii's first liver transplant program. She is currently a transplant, general and hepato-biliary surgeon as well as the director of the liver transplant program at the Queens Medical Center. In addition, she is Professor of Surgery at the University of Hawaii John A. Burns School of Medicine and Professor of the Cancer Center at the University of Hawaii. She is the leader of a translational research team studying liver cancer at the University of Hawaii. She has lectured extensively, has numerous publications, won several teaching awards, and is consistently on the list of *Honolulu Magazine's* Best Doctors.

Dr. Kathleen Yaremchuk, MD, MSA, Otolaryngology—Head and Neck Surgeon

Chair of Otolaryngology-Head and Neck Surgery, Henry Ford Hospital, Detroit, Michigan. Dr. Yaremchuk is board certified in Otolaryngology-Head and

Neck Surgery (OHNS) and Sleep Medicine. She is the Chair of OHNS and a member of the division of Sleep Medicine at Henry Ford Hospital. She completed her internship in General Surgery at Cook County Hospital in Chicago, Illinois, and her residency in OHNS at the University of Chicago, in 1982. She was the first woman elected to the positions of President of the Michigan Otolaryngogical Society and Vice President of the Middle Section of the Triological Society. She is a senior examiner for the American Board of Otolaryngology, and a member of the Board of Directors for the American Academy of Otolaryngology-Head and Neck Surgery. Dr. Yaremchuk is a recipient of the prestigious Jerome C. Goldstein award for Public Service from the American Academy of Otolaryngology-Head and Neck Surgery. She lives in Detroit, Michigan, where she enjoys travel to faraway places, entertaining friends and colleagues and taking time to smell the roses.

Martha A. Zeiger, MD, FACS, FACE, Endocrine Surgeon

Professor of Surgery, Oncology, Cellular and Molecular Medicine; Associate Vice Chair for Faculty Development; Associate Dean for Postdoctoral Affairs, The Johns Hopkins University School of Medicine. Dr. Zeiger graduated from Brown University before obtaining her medical degree at the University of Vermont College of Medicine in 1975. After serving in the United States Navy as a General Medical Officer in Hawaii, she completed her General Surgical residency at Maine Medical Center in Portland, Maine. Thereafter, she worked as a Commander and Attending Surgeon at the National Naval Medical Center in Bethesda, Maryland. She then completed fellowship training at NIH in Surgical Oncology, focusing on Endocrine Surgery under the tutelage of Drs. Steven Rosenberg and Jeffrey Norton from 1990-1993. After fellowship she joined the Department of Surgery at The Johns Hopkins Hospital, where she has built a busy endocrine surgery practice, established an endocrine surgery fellowship program and directed an NIH-funded molecular biology laboratory for over twenty years. Dr. Zeiger has held numerous leadership positions in national medical societies, including Vice President of the American Association of Endocrine Surgeons (AAES), and is currently on the Board of Directors of the American Thyroid Association. She founded and is Dean of Endocrine Surgery University, an annual course for all endocrine surgery fellows in North America. Hobbies include swimming, biking, kayaking, climbing and skiing.

Shannon M. Zielsdorf, MD, General Surgery Resident

Rush University Medical Center, John H. Stroger Cook County Hospital, Chicago, Illinois. Dr. Zielsdorf grew up in the small town of Bourbonnais, Illinois, as the youngest of three children. Her father was a podiatrist who operated on the foot and ankle; this is what initially sparked her interest in surgery. She attended the University of Illinois at Urbana-Champaign for her undergraduate studies, and subsequently graduated medical school (Rush University Medical College) in 2011. She is currently training to be a surgeon and hopes to enter a transplant surgery fellowship after residency. Her parents and both older siblings always stressed education and a hard work ethic; she attributes her success to their guidance and support. Her hobbies include playing in volleyball and softball leagues around Chicago, watching live music with friends, and spending as much time as possible with her young niece.

CPSIA information can be obtained
at www.ICGtesting.com
Printed in the USA
FFOW03n1823300315

12236FF